Gerald Eugen Mar

Pioneer of Radio

(1886 – 1961)

His Life & Achievements

by David Fry ~ G4JSZ

Gerald Marcuse during the Early Days at Caterham (1920's)

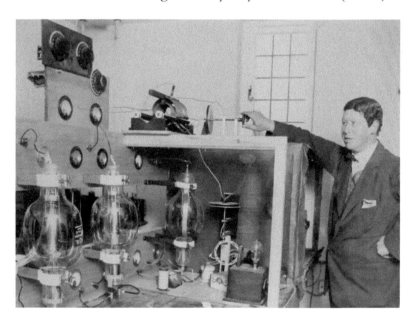

Gerald Marcuse Making Adjustments (November 1927)

In April 1924 the
President of the
American Radio Relay
League travelled to a
meeting in France which
was represented by the
main people involved in
radio. This resulted in
the formation of an
International Amateur
Radio Association.
Gerald Marcuse G2NM
is seated 4th from the left
in the top photograph.

Gerald Marcuse in his 'Radio Shack' at Tidewaters, Bosham (1960)

Contents

-oo-

David Marcuse (L) son of Gerald, with David Fry (R) the Author.

David Fry:

After graduating from High School in Toronto, Canada in 1966, David was licenced G8CDQ (1967) then G4JSZ (1980). He was appointed as a Technical Assistant at the BBC Engineering Department in 1968 at Evesham, Skelton (World Service Transmitters) & Droitwich in 1970. He returned to higher education, graduating in 1973 to teach Maths & IT at Droitwich High School. Here he established a vibrant radio club, coaching several students through the Radio Amateur's exam and is still in contact with some of them. He was appointed Head of IT at Shrewsbury Girl's High School from 1990-2006 then left to build a successful picture framing business. David's first book was based on a diary that Gerald Marcuse kept as an engineering student in Einbeck, Germany in 1903. He has two children, Matthew & Rebecca.

~oo~

6

Preface

Although it was bitterly cold outside with steady settling snow and well into the small hours of a Monday morning, Gerald Marcuse had been contacting other radio hams most of the previous evening and had just finished a call with an American operator. He was just about to close his station down when he heard a very faint signal calling him in morse code. He replied.

This marked an unexpected and astonishing historical event because it was to be the first ever contact between Britain and South America that had taken place by radio.

The date was January 19th, 1925, Stanley Baldwin was Prime Minister and the Titanic had set sail on its fated maiden voyage 14 years earlier. The morse code caller was McCaleb, the radio officer at the base station with the Alexander Hamilton Rice expedition about 1000 miles up the River Amazon in Brazil. The expedition had been partly funded by the Royal Geographical Society but as no word of it had been heard for the previous six months it was presumed lost.

Hamilton-Rice had been exploring the upper Amazon for over 18 years so he was very experienced indeed. The expedition had endured appalling conditions, the loss of an aircraft, much equipment and had lived with the threat of being taken by head-hunting Indians. He was attempting to locate a mysterious tribe known as the 'White Indians'. Radio communication having been established with Marcuse, the base station's location was identified and the expedition continued.

This was to be one of many 'firsts' achieved by Gerald Marcuse who turned out to be one of the world's greatest experimenters in early radio.

-oo-

Introduction

Receiving radio signals in this digital age may have lost the excitement that it once enjoyed but the entire success of the revolution in digital communications that we have today can be credited to the development and experimentation of radio communication in the early 1920's. Much of this was carried out by Radio Amateurs.

Today, how a device works and what is inside it is of no general interest to people because they are only concerned with what it will do and how they can get the best from it. There is nothing wrong with this!

Irrespective of whether the device is a digital receiver, a phone or other state-of-the-art electronic device, it is perceived as a 'black-box' that does the job. Thankfully, electronic equipment is very reliable today, but when a device fails it is unlikely we would repair it ourselves. More likely, it is thrown away because of the high cost of repair when compared with the more manageable cost of replacement with a new and up-to-date device. Enter the throw-away society.

From the early days of electronics right up to the mid-1990's most retail suppliers that specialised in the sale of electronic equipment had workshops (or links to them) to support customer after-sales service. This is not the case today because faulty equipment is usually sent to a remote location and repaired by replacing a circuit board or module inside the 'black box'. Today very few people work at component level so when the faulty component on a circuit board (costing just a few pence) is identified, the entire board costing many pounds is replaced subject to the equipment being economic to repair.

It is hard to imagine that the radio experimenters who were working at the cutting edge of technology in the early days had a detailed understanding of every discrete component, could identify a faulty one and replace it if necessary. The collaborative outcome of sharing this specialised knowledge with other amateurs meant they could drive innovation through their own experiments. Although there were few component suppliers, many amateurs obtained them directly from the Marconi Company.

Today, people recognise the name 'Marconi' mainly because it appeared on domestic radios in the early 1900's when it became synonymous with the word 'radio' and communications in general. Guglielmo Marconi (1st Marquis of Marconi) founded the Marconi Company in England in 1897.

The Marconi name (and remaining assets) was bought out by the Swedish company Ericsson in 2006 and the name is still used as a brand within Ericsson while other parts are owned by BAE Systems. Marconi's name is linked to his experimental station (2LO) which was used by the British Broadcasting Company in November 1922 when it began daily broadcasting from London. This Company became the British Broadcasting Corporation after it was granted a Royal Charter in 1927.

Gerald Eugen Marcuse (1886 – 1961) was not only a contemporary of Marconi and knew him personally, but he enjoyed similar fame during the early years of radio. Marcuse's amazing exploits earned him an international reputation as an experimenter and broadcaster. He had to battle with the legal authorities, especially with the inertia of the Post Office which was the legal body responsible for issuing amateur radio licences. Also, he was in conflict with the BBC because it was reluctant to accept the appropriate operating frequencies that should have been used for broadcasting overseas. Marcuse was using short waves while the BBC insisted on using much lower frequencies that simply didn't work as well.

During the past ten years I have researched Marcuse's life, have visited his homes and have studied the places he was connected with. I have enjoyed the full support of the Marcuse family which has been kept up-to-date with progress. This has involved many meetings and discussions as well as being given access to family archives and photographs. I have had the consent and cooperation of the Amberley Museum in Amberley, West Sussex to view, appraise and copy the paper-based Marcuse archives all of which I have digitised. On two occasions I have visited Einbeck, Germany where Marcuse studied in 1903 and I have been in regular contact with the Director of the Einbecker Museum who has shown an interest in making this biography available in German.

The Los Gatos Library in California (Marcuse was the first person to communicate, with radio, between Britain and California) has a permanent display of some of my findings.

In 2019 I attended and addressed a ceremony in Bosham, West Sussex that commemorated the restoration of a bench which had been presented to the Parish in 1962 in Marcuse's honour. David Marcuse (Gerald's son) addressed this well attended ceremony.

Gerald Marcuse (Callsign: G2NM) was a leading pioneer in radio experimentation who paved the way for the first BBC radio overseas service broadcasts. Together with Radio Amateurs in Britain and all over the world, these efforts helped to establish reliable communication on the airwaves.

Guglielmo Marconi is the person credited with transmitting the first radio signals across the Atlantic from Poldhu, Cornwall to St John's Newfoundland, in Canada on December 12th 1901. Marcuse was the first person to communicate between Britain and South America as well as to California, Australia and New Zealand.

Marcuse was the most prominent and successful British Amateur to pioneer the transmission of 'entertainment' from Britain to people all over the world in his 'Empire Broadcasts''. He was granted a special licence by the Post office to carry out 'test transmissions' for which he had assembled an astonishing array of equipment and aerials to make this possible. He was broadcasting live and recorded music as well as rebroadcasting BBC programmes, bird song and the chimes of Big Ben. He achieved many important 'firsts' in radio communication and he was one of the motivating forces behind persuading the British Post Office to legalise amateur experimentation through a licensing system. Where Marconi was very successful in focusing his own discoveries on the development of commercial products and the Marconi Company, Marcuse never lost sight of raw experimentation using the technology. He did this by pushing forward the boundaries and making it possible for others with a genuine interest in radio to acquire the skills. Also, he represented his country at international meetings where he helped to establish a set of guidelines and norms for radio amateurs to operate within.

Gerald Marcuse was the son of Eugen Marcuse who was a fluent German speaker so it was not surprising to learn that after his early schooling in 1903, Gerald attended an engineering school in Einbeck, Germany where he kept a detailed Diary. This is of great historical interest to Einbeck because it provides a unique snapshot of the life of a student at the engineering school in 1903. The building still exists today but it has been restored, extended and is now the Town Hall. From 1904 to around 1908 Marcuse continued his studies at Crystal Palace School of Engineering.

He was working for a company called Ruston Proctor in 1909 and was on his way to install a steam pump near Adana in modern day Turkey when he found himself a witness to the massacre of Armenian Christians. He had to endure incredible hardships during this business trip.

Marcuse was issued with his first amateur radio licence in 1913 and he held this for 49 years until his death in 1962. At a time when communication between countries was at best limited, he received hundreds of letters from amateurs and listeners all over the world. These confirm that his test signals had been heard as well as his programme broadcasts to the Empire. In the late 1920's and 30's his pioneering successes were publicised in numerous articles by the world's press and many of these are included in his Scrapbook held at the Amberley Museum, West Sussex. I have digitised and indexed all the letters and a list of these is included in the Appendices.

Marcuse's other notable achievements included serving with the Royal Observer Corps during World War 2, assisting with setting up a wireless scheme for both the Police and ambulance services and setting up the Bosham Fire Brigade.

Marcuse was President of the Radio Society of Great Britain (RSGB) in 1929 and in 1946 he was made an honorary member for his enormous contribution to pioneering radio. This biography will serve as an historical archive about an important pioneer in early radio and it sets out the achievements Marcuse achieved through his brilliant understanding of the technology of the day and his perception of what was needed and what was to come.

The Marcuse Family

Gerald Marcuse's father was a German migrant, his name was Eugen Marcuse and he had come to live in England and to settle in Croydon, Surrey.

Eugen was born in Greifenhagen, a small village in the Mansfeld-Südharz district of Saxony, Germany (about 100 Km north west of Leipzig.

Like his father, Gerald was fluent in German.

Eugen Marcuse (born 1850) had immigrated from Germany when he was a young man and he lived in London working for a seed and corn merchant. He was married on August 22nd 1883 to Louisa, who was the second daughter of Henry Roberts, a sea captain, at Benhilton Church in Sutton, Surrey. Louisa and her two sisters, Maud and Kate, were considered so attractive that they were known in the town where they first lived as 'the Belles of Sutton'! Henry hand-typed a very brief account of Gerald's life and this is kept at the Amberley Museum.

After Eugen and Louisa were married, they went to live at Cressington Grove, Sutton and in 1900 they moved to Dunedin, Harestone Valley, Caterham, Surrey. While he was living in Caterham, he founded the Caterham Cottage hospital and asked Princess Helena, the third daughter of Queen Victoria to be a Patron. The hospital was opened officially by the Princess in 1903.

Technical Centre where Marcuse studied in Einbeck (1903).

Family Tree

Marcuse family tree commencing with the 'Roberts' maternal line (the Paternal Marcuse, German line unknown)

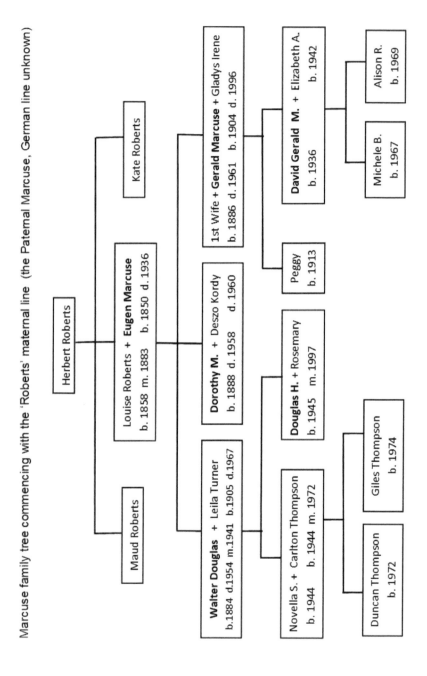

Herbert Roberts

Kate Roberts

Maud Roberts

Louise Roberts + **Eugen Marcuse**
b. 1858 m. 1883   b. 1850 d. 1936

1st Wife + **Gerald Marcuse** + Gladys Irene
b. 1886 d. 1961   b. 1904 d. 1996

Dorothy M. + Deszo Kordy
b. 1888 d. 1958   d. 1960

David Gerald M. + Elizabeth A.
b. 1936   b. 1942

Peggy
b. 1913

Michele B.
b. 1967

Alison R.
b. 1969

Walter Douglas + Leila Turner
b.1884 d.1954 m.1941 b.1905 d.1967

Douglas H. + Rosemary
b. 1945   m. 1997

Novella S. + Carlton Thompson
b. 1944   b. 1944 m. 1972

Duncan Thompson
b. 1972

Giles Thompson
b. 1974

Eugen went on to found the Caterham Soldier's Home which was opened by Lord Roberts of Kandahar in 1898 and he remained on the governing body of both institutions for several years.

Eventually Eugen started his own seed business in Mincing Lane (& Mark Lane) in London and he made a great success of this but the whole business was destroyed when London was bombed during the second World War.

Eugen and Louisa had three children, Walter, Gerald and Dorothy; Gerald, the middle child, was known as 'Gerry'.

Walter

Walter was born in 1884 when he finished schooling and he started work at the family seed business. His father sent him to Madagascar to investigate the possibility of growing butter beans (Phaseolus Capensis) and to export the bean crops back home. This bean is similar in shape to the English broad bean. After negotiating with the local inhabitants Walter set up butter bean plantations and started a successful import-export venture for the family business at home.

In 1864, whalers brought the bean to Madagascar from New Bedford, Massachusetts. They had established a trading station in St. Augustin's Bay and traded general goods and Lima beans (from California) with the natives.

The Marcuse family business was the first company to import the Madagascar butter bean into Britain. Walter wrote a book based on his experiences entitled, 'Through Western Madagascar, in Quest of the Golden Bean'; this was first published in 1914. There is one chapter about the bean but most of the book concerns his travels and adventures. He describes paying the people he employed on the plantations with gold sovereigns and this was in spite of the inhabitants having little concept of their true value. Female workers would bend the coins and clip them into their hair for decoration! On one occasion Walter was attacked for the gold bullion he was carrying and narrowly escaped being murdered.

At the outbreak of the first world war, Walter joined the Duke of Cambridge's Hussars, a cavalry division of the British Army, and after the war he left the family business to work for Shell's oil business in Mexico. He retired and went to live in Selsey near Chichester and died in 1954 aged 70 leaving his wife Leila and two children Novella and Douglas.

Dorothy

Dorothy (Dolly) was born in 1888 and married Deszo Kordy, they had no children and Dorothy died at the age of 70 in 1958. Very little is known about her but she must have been close to Gerald because she sent him letters and cards when he was away from home studying in Einbeck.

Gerald Marcuse's Education

Gerald was born in Sutton, Surrey on June 4th 1886 and in 1892 he attended Caterham Primary School. In 1899 he went to complete his secondary education in Caterham.

From January 10th to December 12th 1903, he studied at a technical school, (The Technikum) in Einbeck, Lower Saxony, Germany. He stayed there for the first part of the year and then moved to Hildesheim to do practical work. He kept a diary during the year and it is from this that we know a lot about what sort of person he was, what his interests were, and how his early impressions of life were formed. Four years after he attended the technical school, it closed. A full transcription of his diary has been published in English and German by David Fry but the original diary is held at the Amberley Museum.

The Engineering School (date founded unknown) suffered a checkered history from its original inception in Hildesheim, to it moving to Einbeck in 1871, and then to its final closure in 1907. Founded by Dr. Emil Kirchner it became a successful and popular school with circa 100 students in 1871. Kirchner was a social democrat and he held the broad aim of bettering his students from every social background by providing them with a sound education.

16

This political influence meant Kirchner held very egalitarian views about the basic rights of an individual. The Social Democrat Party held the belief that the authority of professors and doctors in the labour movement had to be stopped; workers had to be led by workers. Eugen Marcuse would have known about the school's reputation and would have wanted the best for his son even though he and his family were living in England. Kirchner became embroiled in a rather bitter conflict with the local Council that ultimately resulted in the city opening a municipal institute that was run by Dr. Stehle, a former employee of Dr. Kirchner. Meanwhile, Dr. Kirchner left Einbeck and opened another institution, a Polytechnikum in Langensalza, taking a large number of his students with him.

Unfortunately, the mixture of strongly held political views in Einbeck, along with political parties with very different beliefs, would result in the eventual demise of what had become a fine establishment of learning. It was nationalized in 1900, mainly because of cost, to became the 'Royal Engineering School of Einbeck'. Marcuse would study there for a little less than a year in 1903, four years before it closed.

The Technical Centre today, now the Town Hall.

The house where Marcuse lived in Einbeck, No. 5 Burgermeisterwall
(Front) 1903. Photo taken in July 2018.

Engineering School Student Reunion 1894

After leaving Einbeck he embarked on an engineering course at Crystal Palace School of Art, Science & Literature and he completed this in 1907. The school had a well-known School of Music and a School of Art where René Jules Lalique attended in the late 1870's. Henry Morgan, founder of the Morgan motor car company had studied engineering there but most of the other classes were for women.

After completing his course Marcuse left this engineering school with the equivalent of an engineering degree and the certificates he was awarded are still in the possession of the family.

The subjects Marcuse studied at the Crystal Palace School of Practical Engineering resulted in him receiving the following Certificates:

1. 1906

Term	Subject	Mark	Order of merit
Easter	Preparation of Drawings & Estimates	Passed	12
Easter	Steam & the Steam Engine	101/170 & 46/120	35
Summer	Pattern Making & Foundry Work	Passed	unplaced
Summer	Railways, Construction & Appliances	84/176 & 57/120	28
Winter	Fitting & Smith's Work	Passed	8
Winter	Materials & Manufacture	96/176 & 62/120	25

2. 1907

Summer	Electrical Engineering Term 1	89/155 & 92/120	6
Summer	Manufacture of Electrical Apparatus	Passed	10
Winter	Dynamo Construction	Passed	2
Winter	Electrical Engineering	83/169 & 48/120	5

Marcuse's studies at the Engineering school in Einbeck included some subjects that he would be taught at greater depth at the Crystal Palace School but he may well have learned about Railways for the first time at Crystal Palace. In Einbeck he studied drawings, steam, foundry work, materials and electrical work. At Crystal Palace, his 'Order of Merit' appears to be higher for Electrical work, including being 2nd in the group for Dynamo Construction and 5th for Electrical Engineering; these were subjects that would be very useful to him later on.

His marks for the second term in Electrical Engineering were 83/169 and 48/120 which corresponds to 49% and 40% respectively. The fact that he came 5th in the order of merit for fewer than half marks indicates that it must have been a difficult exam although it is not known what marks the other students had achieved. His marks for the first term in Electrical Engineering were 89/155 and 92/120 which corresponds to approximately 57% and 76%. He was doing well in the subjects which we would have expected him to do well in.

Marriage & Family

Marcuse married in 1913 and he and his wife lived at Little Coombe, Coombe Dingle north of Bristol. He was issued with his first Experimental Radio Licence in the same year and this was where he set up his second broadcasting station. They had a daughter Peggy, and the correspondence with one of his friends confirms that he talked very proudly about her.

In 1923, he left Bristol so that he could take over the family business from his father who wished to retire from his position on the London Corn Exchange. His brother Walter left the family business at this time so it likely that Gerald would have been filling the gap left by his brother. It is not known if Marcuse's wife and daughter went with him. Sadly, they divorced in 1925.

The son of a family friend, a Mr S. H. King, mentions in a letter that his parents lived about ten minutes' walk away from their house and his father used to visit Marcuse many times but never met his wife. In a letter dated 6th July 1984, he mentions that Marcuse's "enthusiasm and dedication to his pastime was already a big barrier between husband and wife. I believe this situation ended in some domestic tragedy in the late 1920's - possibly divorce - I am not certain."

On 10th December 1931 he married Irene at the Savoy Chapel, London. They went to live in Sonning which is where he set up his third broadcasting station. Their son David Marcuse was born in 1936. David married Elizabeth, and they had two daughters Michele and Alison. In June 1981, Michele completed a history of her grandfather's life for her GCSE History project at Cranbrook School.

The facts and dates were checked at the time by her grandmother Irene so Michele's project serves as an important reference for the time-line of Marcuse's achievements. The project is held with the Marcuse Archives at the Amberley Museum. David went on to be an engineer and successful company director and at the time of writing he and his wife were retired and lived near Stratford-on-Avon.

Business Trip to the Middle East

After Marcuse had completed his studies at the Crystal Palace School of Engineering, his first job, was to start working for Ruston Proctor & Company. This was a highly respected Lincoln firm that was a leading manufacturer of steam tractors and engines which it was exporting all over the world. Primarily, Rustons were steam engineers but they made railway locomotives, industrial equipment, mining machinery, threshing machines, corn mills, maize shellers and pumps for steam power. Proctor started in Lincoln in 1840 as millwrights and implement manufacturers and was known as 'Burton & Proctor'. Joseph Ruston, a former MP and philanthropist, became a partner in the company in 1857 so the company changed its name to Ruston, Proctor & Co. and it grew to become a major agricultural engineering firm and was known

21

locally as 'Rustons'. In 1918 the firm merged with the established Richard Hornsby & Sons company from Grantham, Lincolnshire and the business was named Ruston & Hornsby.

Marcuse became a very competent steam installation engineer during his apprenticeship and after this, he was employed by Rustons to carry out their main business of installing industrial suction gas engines. Marcuse travelled all over the world for them, including Odessa in Russia, the Middle East, Mexico and the United States. Some of these travels coincided with strife and civil unrest in highly dangerous circumstances. In April 1909, aged 23, Marcuse had to install two gas engines in Ayas close to Icel, a town which was in the Ottoman Empire but today, it is in modern-day Turkey.

He had to travel by steam ship to Mersine calling at Alexandria, via Malta and Tunis, but was delayed for several days due to the massacre being inflicted by the Ottomans on the Armenian Christians. Eventually he arrived at Adana in Turkey and he was horrified at what he saw. The massacres had been going on for many years and were witnessed and photographed by an American, William Lewis Sachtleben, as far back as March 29th 1866. Sachtleben at one time held a world record for long-distance bicycling. To this day, despite international pressure, the Turkish authorities have never acknowledged that the massacre even happened.

Witness to the Adana Massacre

The situation that Marcuse had inadvertently walked into is commonly called the 'Adana Massacre' which occurred in Adana Province from the late 1860's through to the early 1900's. It is believed that from 80,000 to 300,000 people were mutilated and killed in violent pogroms. There are various explanations of what took place but there are no straightforward answers.

Marcuse was very lucky to get out alive and unharmed after what he had witnessed notwithstanding the transport he was restricted to, that by today's standards was very slow and unreliable.

As he said during Interview (4) with G2ARC:

"There were no airplanes, all camels, springless wagons, horseback. Could not get from Syria to Baghdad, only on horseback or camel caravan. No aircraft or motorcars." Marcuse's trip to Adana was one of numerous such business trips which he made all over the world for Ruston-Proctor. Given that his venture into the respective countries was to install an engine, he would have been given every facility to travel safely and complete the installation; thankfully this was to be the case.

Marcuse's passport from 1909 authenticates his travels to the Middle-East as it shows the signatures and dates of the different British officials who signed it at different stages of his visit. It is clear from copies of the correspondence between the Managing Director of Rustons a Mr. Bournemann and Marcuse that his services as a competent engineer were highly valued. A full account of his experiences and what he endured is included in Appendix 2, page 88.

Caterham Home

When he was running his father's business in London he lived at Coombe Dingle, Caterham. Every morning he took the 9.16am train to London Bridge and then walked across the bridge to Mincing Lane. His

house was in an excellent position for radio (photo) experiments and it was from here that his most successful contacts were made. The house is still there but it has been renovated, extended and converted into a home for the elderly. A plaque has been fixed to the front wall to commemorate Marcuse's achievements in Empire Broadcasting which was dedicated in a ceremony after his death. The family kept a spaniel dog.

Marcuse continued with his Empire Broadcasting until his licence ran out which occurred when the BBC had more effective equipment in place to broadcast programmes using short waves, and of course at much higher power levels.

The photograph below shows Marcuse's house in Caterham as it is today; the plaque is visible from the front of the building. A careful look at the house before and after renovation and extension reveals the changes but some features of the original house are visible in the new building.

Interest in Radio

Marcuse developed an interest in radio communications during his mid-teens when he began experimenting with various forms of electrical apparatus. When he studied at Einbeck he described making a telephone with an electric bell and ten months later, following a visit to 'Electric Central', he comments in his diary that "this was exceedingly interesting". These remarks provide a clue to his initial interest in this side of engineering. It is evident that the success of the family business was decisive in supporting him with the means to buy the costly radio components and power equipment that he required for his radio experiments. Equipping and setting up the station for his Empire Broadcasts cost him £6000, this was a huge sum at that time. Fortunately, many companies who were manufacturing radio components provided these free to Marcuse so he could test them, and presumably talk about them. This obviously mitigating the cost and provided free advertising for the manufacturers. Several letters from these companies are included in the 'Letters' documents in Appendix 5. Marcuse showed extraordinary generosity to radio amateurs throughout the world by sending them components on request, in return they sent him reception reports which helped him to fine tune his equipment and make a better judgement about the timing of his broadcasts.

His interest in Amateur Radio (US: 'Ham Radio') prompted articles to appear with a twist on the 'Ham and Beans' theme following the exploits of his brother Walter!

Issue of Licence and Callsign

In 1914, when the First World War had started, Marcuse was 28 years old but he was not called up for active service because his work would have been considered a 'Reserved Occupation'. The British Government started conscription in 1916 but some men were exempt. If a man was exempt then he was issued with official papers and a badge to show this. The badge served to show that he was not allowed to do active service because his occupation served the country better by him continuing with that work at home. It would have been in the best interests of the country for certain engineers to continue in their occupations to support the war effort.

Although wireless was still in its infancy, there were hundreds of enthusiasts in Great Britain, on the continent and in the United States, many were licenced and many were not. At this stage it is not known whether Marcuse had actually applied for a licence. In the interviews with H.A.M. Clark in 1960, he is quoted as saying "...we didn't bother about licences (then)...". The Post office had already issued over 2000 experimental licences and 1600 of these were for using transmitting equipment. The Postmaster General first started issuing licences in 1905. The threat of amateur equipment being used for spying or falling into the wrong hands as well as on the grounds of general security resulted in the Secretary to the Post Office sending telegrams to all licensees in August 1914. This included those who 'held licences entitling them to use a power greater than 50 Watts'. The telegram ordered them to remove aerial wires and to dismantle their apparatus. In July 1915, the Postmaster General announced that all private wireless equipment would be taken into Post office custody, thus ending amateur experimentation for the duration of the war.

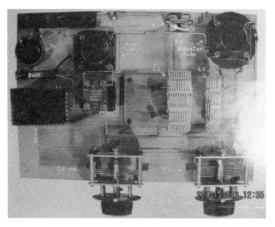

Marcuse's Receiver

Marcuse's Transmitter

After the war, in October 1919, a relaxation of the restrictions placed on wireless experimenters was announced and Marcuse, now 33 applied for, and was granted a licence; he was given the call sign '2NM' (later 'G2NM'). A document to this effect in the Amberley Museum gives the date of his licence as being issued on 19th November 1922. It lists who he was permitted to contact and the power was limited to 1Kw within a wavelength of 125 to 130 metres.

In 1922, along with about 20 other amateurs, 2NM transmitted speech and music daily on the 440m band for the benefit of other amateurs. Later in that year the French amateur, Leon Deloy, reported that he had heard 2NM and many others on his receiver.

On 5th June 1923, Marcuse gave a talk and demonstration to the children of Hill School, Caterham. He was photographed in the school hall with a large loudspeaker that stood on a table in the centre.

Radio Clubs & Societies

Due to a growing interest in experimentation, numerous wireless clubs were formed up and down the country. These included: Derby (the first), Liverpool, Northampton, Barrow, Newcastle-on-Tyne and Birmingham. 'The London Wireless Club' was formed in July 1913 but was re-named the 'Wireless Society of London' later in that year.

Some 20 years later in 1934, Marcuse became one of the founders of the Reading & District Amateur Radio Club which has continued to meet right up to the present time. This radio club has produced a brief pictorial history of Marcuse on their website, edited by Peter Smith, G4JNU with some aspects about Marcuse's early life missing.

The 'Wireless Society of London was re-named the 'Radio Society of Great Britain' (RSGB) in 1922 because it was felt that it represented the interests of British radio amateurs better. Later, the RSGB incorporated the 'British Wireless Relay League' and then formed a 'Transmitter and Relay Section' of the society. This had a membership of 97 but omitted Marcuse and other well-known amateurs. This was quite likely because many of the leading London amateurs had decided to set up a separate organisation which was to be named the 'Radio Transmitter's Society' (RTS) for which Marcuse became its Hon. Secretary.

At the same time as the RTS was formed, another society called the 'Amateur Radio Research Association' (ARRA) came into a brief formation whose membership included Marcuse. In 1924, the Transmitter and Relay Section of the RSGB and the RTS merged with Marcuse as its Hon. Secretary. The ARRA appeared to have dissolved into obscurity with most of its members joining the newly merged Transmitter and Relay Section of the RSGB.

After experimenting with radio and aerials at the highest level, on October 16th, 1924 Marcuse was appointed 'Manager of the British Isles' by Hiram Percy Maxim, the President of the American Radio Relay League (ARRL). He was made the official ARRL link between Britain and America.

Marcuse was President of the RSGB from 1929-30 so he followed the steps of Lord Fraser of Lonsdale in 1928. On June 25th 1946 Marcuse received a letter from the RSGB informing him that he had been unanimously been elected an Honorary Member of the Society. This stated:

"The Council are deeply appreciative of the great services you have rendered to Amateur Radio in general, and to the Society in particular". Arrangements were made to present him with a certificate at the next AGM of the Society.

American amateurs were the driving force behind the creation of an 'International Amateur Radio Union' (IARU) which was to become a significant body that would drive innovation, standardisation and enable amateurs to become part of a credible international group to influence governments at a time when many of them had not established rules for amateur radio communication.

Distant Contacts

Leon Deloy of Nice, F8AB, the French amateur, conducted the first Transatlantic contact on November 21st 1923 with Schnell and Reinartz in Boston using 100m equipment. This happened even though it was not yet legal for French amateurs to operate at this frequency because official consent was not authorized until 1924. Judging by the numerous letters present in the archives, both Schnell and Reinartz were in regular contact with Marcuse.

Jack Partridge (G2KF) took part in the first two-way UK-USA transatlantic short-wave amateur contact when he spoke to Ken Warner W1MO, at West Hartford, Connecticut on December 8th 1923. He acknowledged Deloy for his help in arranging to make it possible.

On December 16th 1923, the first amateur contact between Great Britain and Canada was made between E. J. Simmonds G2OD in Gerrard's Cross, Bucks. and A. W. Greig C1BQ in Halifax. The British Empire Radio Union (BERU) evolved following this first contact.

Marcuse was one of a group of 19 British, 14 French and 3 Dutch amateurs who was heard by over 100 American and Canadian amateurs during a series of tests transmissions held from December 1923 to January 1924. Among Marcuse's most significant long-distance communications were:

Country	Date	Type of Contact
California, USA	February 23rd 1924	Two-way
Brazil	January 19th 1925	Two-way
Japan	May 1925	Signals heard
New Zealand	July 25th 1925	Two-way

First Radio Contact Britain to California

This contact was made on 23rd February 1924 between Marcuse G2NM and C. C. Whysall, 6ZAR-6TV. Although it was acknowledged by Whysall that it was 'a record', they may not have realised that it was in fact the very first radio communication between Britain and California. Proof of the two-way contact is authenticated by Whysall's QSL card held by the Amberley Museum; the card is mounted on a board that states: "The first radio message ever received on the Pacific Coast direct from Great Britain".

The (QSL) card from Whysall that proves contact had been established:

fr 2NM is from 110 to 145 λ. No QRM Feb 23 1924.
I certainly hope our logs check on this recept-

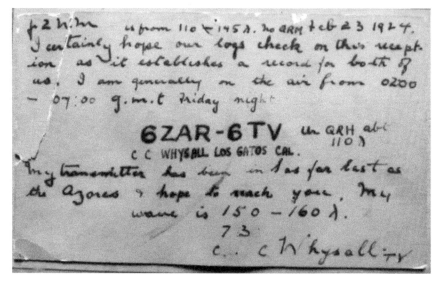

ion as it establishes a record for both of
us. I am generally on the air from 02:00
- 07:00 g.m.t. Friday night.

6ZAR - 6TV   Ur QRH abt 110 λ
C WHYSALL LOS GATOS CAL.

My transmitter has been in & as far East as
the Azores & hope to reach you. My wave is 150 to 160 λ

73

C. C. Whysall TV

On 26th January 2013 I made a request to the library in Los Gatos
which prompted one of the librarians to check through the QSL cards
belonging to American radio amateurs who were licenced during the
1920's. This revealed that there were at least twelve amateurs who were
active in the Los Gatos area at this time. I received the following
message from librarian, Lyn Dougherty, at the Los Gatos library:

"….Yesterday I went through about 300 QSL cards with Jason Farwell but we found none from G2NM. You might find one in the Gerald Marcuse's papers (possibly) U62AT, which would be from Lyndon Farwell. However, there is a list of other radio hams here operating in Los Gatos in the 1920's":

Lyndon Farwell, Burton R. Cole, Lawrence B. Hall, J. C. Horton, John R. Hub Bell, Alfred A. Hunt, Karl W. Kent, Miss U.E. LeFevre, Robert James Miller, Alton Penrose, Harvey Grant Taylor, Melvin D. Whiteman.

It appears that radio amateurs were very active in the Los Gatos area along with many hundreds of others around the United States.

Further checks in Los Gatos municipal archives revealed that Whysall, 6ZAR, lived at the corner of a road junction in 94 Hernandez Avenue, Los Gatos, Los Gatos, California, USA. The photograph shows the house at 94 Hernandez Avenue as it is today, certainly rebuilt, extended

and judging by the restricted access, it was in the process of further renovation at the time this photograph was taken.

Marcuse would have sent his QSL card to Los Gatos to verify the contact but no record of this has been found. The wavelength (QRH) of 110 metres is given which converts to a frequency of 2.725Mhz and the time of the contact may have been within the hours given on Whysall's card: 0200 – 0700 hours GMT.

Communications with North America

Guglielmo Marconi (left), often described as 'the Father of Radio', is credited with the first transatlantic broadcast. This historic event happened many years before on December 12ᵗʰ 1901 when signals (letter S's) were exchanged between Poldhu in Cornwall and St. John's, Newfoundland in Canada, a distance of about 2000 miles. Marconi founded what has been commonly termed 'The Marconi Company' in 1897 and he went on to establish radio stations and links with various organisations. His ground breaking work was recognised in 1909 when he shared the Nobel prize for Physics with Karl Ferdinand Braun.

The first radio signal transmitted across the Atlantic took place in 1901 which was some 23 years before the Marcuse-Whysall contact but it is not surprising that it took so long, because the First World War intervened. Licences were not issued during the war and existing licences would have been suspended, equipment would have been very difficult, if not almost impossible to acquire.

From the letters that Marcuse received which are held by the Amberley Museum, it appears that radio contact with American amateurs in the 1920's was a regular event.

A letter (Number 8, 1923-26 file) from Jack Partridge, G2KF, to Marcuse dated April 29ᵗʰ 1924, lists stations worked from December 8ᵗʰ 1923 to March 10ᵗʰ 1924 from G2KF using 1KW. It starts 'Dear NM' and ends 'Yours to a cinder, Jack Partridge KF'. He states that the most distant station contacted was 'ZU Montana'.

Marcuse's granddaughter, Michele Marcuse noted in her GCSE project that in 1923 that her grandfather had contacted a Canadian steamship called the 'Arctic' which was on a 6000-mile cruise off the coast of Canada. The crew were very pleased to receive the communication as they were many miles off land and it was a new experience and "exciting to know that you are the first ones to be contacted from as far away as Britain".

Another letter, one of a series, (Number 9 & 10, 1923-26), this time from Haverford College Radio Club, PA, U.S.A. discussed a proposed chess match between Britain and America. It contained a diagram of the inverted cone aerial they had in use. The letter, dated September 30th 1924, states that 'The game is assuming quite large proportions, and has already broken into the headlines in the local papers.' The correspondence sets out the organisation of a transatlantic-chess match between players in Oxford and Haverford. The game would be conducted from a wave band between 100-150 metres using a power of 500 watts from the American side. Several tests are proposed from which the waveband used by the best signal would be selected.

An undated letter (Number 11 & 12, 1923-26) from William S. Halstead, President of the Haverford College Radio Club comments on the wavebands to be used and the date and time of the chess match. It mentions that the game 'has developed into an important news item in this country'. Unfortunately for Marcuse and Harvard, the Post Office refused permission for the chess match to be broadcast but this would not be the last disappointment for Marcuse nor the last barrier to innovation that he would experience.

Annual Radio Banquet

On Saturday May 17th 1924 the Massachusetts Institute of Technology Radio Society and the Commonwealth Radio Society held a Banquet at the Walker Memorial Hall, Cambridge. Marcuse was invited and was listed in the programme (Scrapbook page 24) but was unable to attend. On the front cover there is a hand written note:
"Old thing: This is where you should have been on May 17th, The other old thing".

The Menu:
Tropical Fruit Interference, Thermo-Couples, Assorted-Leaks
Neutrodyne Supe with Dit-Dahs
Filament of Sole with Damped Waves
Spaghetti à la Marconi
Ham Roast with Rectified Currents
Honeycomb Tripe, Celluloid Sauce
Grounded Tubers Hetrodyne Beets
Fresh Radio-Freaks
Cabinet Pudding with Brandes Phones
Cold plate
Heaviside Layer Cake   CQ Cheese Litzendraht
Static Crackers Liquid Bakelite
(Please leave all 5-watt and other bottles at home)
The entertainment is listed as "QRM by Radio Orchestra"

Hamilton Rice Expeditions

In May 1924 an expedition led by an American, Dr. Alexander Hamilton Rice (photo: early 1900's), left France for the Upper reaches

of the Amazon. Dr. Rice had embarked on six previous exploratory missions and this would be his seventh and final one.

The purpose of the previous mission was, as before, to explore, map and discover the largely unknown territory around the source of the Amazon River; the party was composed of 12 white men and about 100 Indians. The radio operator was John W. Swanson, an experienced radio operator who was a United States Radio Inspector.

THE BOA VISTA STATION

MR. SWANSON RECEIVING AT BOA VISTA

SHORT-WAVE TRANSMITTING (Fig. 3) AND RECEIVING SET (Fig. 4)

Geographical Journal, June 1926 (Consent of Wiley Global Permissions)

First Radio Contact with South America

Up until the beginning of January 1925 no radio communication had ever been established between Great Britain and South America although it had been achieved between North and South America.

Very early in the morning of January 19th 1925, Marcuse had been in contact with a North American radio amateur and he was just about to close his station down for the night when he heard a very faint signal in morse code. This event marked another milestone in radio communications because the other operator, who had overheard Marcuse's previous conversation, was trying to contact him from South America.

The signal came from the Boa Vista region of Brazil which was about 1000 miles up the River Amazon where Dr. Alexander Hamilton Rice's exploratory expedition was camped. The British Royal Geographical Society (RGS) together with Department of Tropical Medicine of Harvard University had both sponsored this expedition and had not heard from it since it left six months earlier; in fact it was suspected that the expedition was lost.

From the recorded interview, Appendix 4, page 128 Marcuse stated:

"Dr. Rice's expedition – I contacted them one morning – WJS – it was on CW, on the upper Amazon and they were stranded up there, out of touch with the world. …McCaleb, an American amateur, he was the operator there, and I was able to give the Royal Geographical Society the progress of the special equipment they were using. The transmitter McCallin used on the Upper Amazon – or Rice Expedition – is now visible at the Royal Geographical Society in Kensington. It's there in a cabinet because I helped to put it in. That was WJS. It's there, the transmitter and receiver that McCaleb used on the Amazon."

McCaleb was the expedition's radio officer at the base station while Swanson was the radio officer at the forward position. Some of the original transmitting equipment used by Rice on that expedition is kept at the RGS but many components have been removed and the cabinet is now broken up amounting to the tragic loss of the full equipment. Although some parts are missing, the remaining pieces are now stored on a tray. In addition the RGS holds numerous slides which was the medium for the photographs taken during the expedition, these can be viewed but only copied by special arrangement with the RGS.

Following his contact with the Rice expedition, Marcuse contacted the RGS and he confirmed that the expedition was indeed safe even though the Rice expedition which had left New York on March 29th 1924 had not been heard from. The Expedition asked Marcuse to inform the RGS that they had reached the junction of the Rivers Urari and Uricatara and that their progress had been slow after experiencing difficult terrain. This was in spite of not being able to use their 'hydro-airplane' which had been damaged, nevertheless the aim of the expedition had been achieved. The 'hydro-airplane' was commanded by Walter Hinton who is credited as having made the first transatlantic air crossing but to achieve this he used more than one aircraft and made six stops.

Following this first contact between Britain and South America, Marcuse received international acclaim and numerous letters of congratulations along with newspaper reports confirming his success. On the 6th February 1925, the secretary of the RGS, Arthur R. Hinks wrote to Marcuse saying:

Dear Mr Marcuse,

To save errors in telephoning I am sending you the enclosed message by hand and shall be greatly obliged if you will transmit to Dr. Hamilton Rice. We very greatly appreciate your skilled and friendly assistance in this matter.

Yours very sincerely,   Arthur R. Hinks. (Scrapbook page 22)

Marcuse was asked to send the following message:

Hamilton Rice via 2NM and W.J.S.

Delighted receive today by courtesy Mr Marcuse first message ever transmitted by radio to this Society from expedition in field. Cordial congratulations on great progress recorded since letter November 10 just arrived. Reeves especially pleased Arnold's report usefulness astrolabe* attachment. Publishing news Journal March for information your friends England who anxiously await further reports and wish expedition complete success.

HINKS Geographical (Scrapbook page 19)

The astrolabe is an instrument that is effective in determining latitude on land or calm seas and was invented between 220 and 150 BC.

The reply that Marcuse was asked to deliver to the RGS read:

"The main party arrived at the junction of the Urari and Uricatara rivers, January 19. Latitude 3 deg. 52 North, 51 deg. 5 west. Progress slow owing to extremely difficult physical difficulties of country. Personnel of expedition numbers over 50. Good food, and relay transport working efficiently. Unable to use hydroplane at present ; due to low water. Object of expedition have been attained. All well. – RICE.

On May 8th 1925 the RGS Secretary, Arthur R. Hinks sent Marcuse a letter (Scrapbook page 26) thanking him for his efforts:

Royal Geographical Society,
Kensington Gore,
London, S.W.7
May 8th 1925

Dear Mr Marcuse,

I am pleased to see the letter from the radio operator for the Hamilton Rice Expedition and agree with him on the skill with which you worked. I have made a copy of the letter in order that we can have the technical facts on record. I do not quite understand how it is that we have not heard more from the expedition. It does not seem that the

38

New York papers have received many messages, and I suppose that you have not either or you would have let me know.

I shall hope to meet you some day and discuss the questions which you raise about equipment for further expeditions. At the moment my interests are in waves of 19,000 metres instead of 20 for the signals.

Yours very truly,   (Arthur R. Hinks) Secretary.

When Marcuse moved to Caterham in 1922, he chose an excellent location for amateur radio. At an altitude of around 180 metres above sea level 'Coombe Dingle', Queen's Park, Caterham south of London was ideally positioned for radio communications and Marcuse used his knowledge to create a superb radio station. He contracted a company to erect a tower in his garden that, at the time of the South American contact, was about 30 metres high. With little interference from the authorities, radio amateurs were able to 'adjust' their power to appropriate levels. It is likely he used a power of at least 100 watts to his aerial although later he received dispensation from the Post Office, the licensing authority at the time, to increase this to 1000 watts.

The important fact surrounding this first contact with South America was that Marcuse used short-wave frequencies at a time when the official view was lower frequencies were more successful. This is clearly illustrated by the comment that Hinks, the secretary of the RGS made in his letter to Marcuse, "At the moment my interests are in waves of 19,000 metres instead of 20 for the signals." It is surprising that even after Marcuse's outstanding success, there was a reluctance to accept that short waves were the way forward.

Marcuse's story was exclusively reported by the Evening Standard newspaper on January 19th 1925:

"At six o'clock this morning the Brazil man came through, I was finishing a conversation with an American amateur and proposed going to bed, as I had been 'working' with our new-found friends in Australia overnight, when I heard a faint call. Apparently, the man in South

America had heard me saying good-bye to a man in North America, so he called me before I closed down.

I was thrilled when I found an English Amateur had been the first to talk with South America. The next amazing thing was the fact that a thousand miles of dry land lay between us, constituting obstacles that the ocean did not hold.

The third wonder was the fact that my distant caller was a member of an isolated expedition buried in the wilds round about a flourishing civilisation, threatened by natives, fauna, and tropical diseases."

Last Summer Dr. Hamilton Rice, an American explorer who had been up the Amazon many times, set out from London and Southampton to penetrate into the legendary country of the 'white Indians'. It was known that the expedition carried a wireless set, but since they have got inland nothing has been heard of them.

Judge, then, my surprise when my caller said, "This is the Rice expedition, now camped at Boa Vista de Rio Branco, Brazil". I asked, "What Rice expedition?" and he answered, "The Rice expedition". Then I remembered the expedition, and have since looked up its records.

Like a typical Englishman, I suppose, I could think of nothing better to say than to ask him what the weather was like! "Balmy and warm in the day – temperature 90 degrees – but at night very cold", was the answer.

"I am very pleased to talk with you", continued the operator who gave me the name of McCaleb. "A slight wind is reaching us from the pampas", he added. He gave me details of the expedition, which he said had penetrated inland 200 miles from the nearest river.
To Call Again…. Then daylight came, for by now it was eight o'clock, and we parted across 7000 miles of space, his last words being, "I'll see you tomorrow at eight o'clock".

(Further information and correspondence included in Appendix 3.)

Signals heard in Japan

Marcuse received a letter from the Post Office, dated May 1925, stating that the Japanese Telegraph Authorities had heard his signals in Japan (Marcuse Letters & Recollections No. 100).

The letter to Marcuse was from A. J. Gill, for the Engineer-in-Chief, Col. T. F. Purvees, M.I.E.E., and the address was: Office of the Engineer-in-Chief, General Post office (West), London, E.C.1. The letter informs Marcuse that his signals 'using the call letters 2NM' had been heard by the Japanese Telegraph Authorities, "the hours during which the signals are heard are very limited and are between midnight and morning. The dates and times and wavelengths are not stated". He asks Marcuse to supply "precise information regarding the wavelength and power normally used during February and March. The information furnished will be regarded as confidential and used for technical purposes only, while if the limitations of your licence have been exceeded in the tests, steps will be taken, if possible, to amend the licence to regularise such tests".

The letter shows that Marcuse's contact provoked intense interest from the British authorities. The fact that his signals should be heard over such a long-distance contact would have established a milestone in communications and raised questions about the methods used at the time.

First Contact with Australia

On Monday July 20th 1925 Marcuse made contact with the United States battleship 'Seattle' using morse code when this ship was near New Zealand (but heading towards Australia) and approximately 400 miles from Sydney NSW. The two-way contact on 45 metres lasted about 2 hours but the signals being exchanged were so strong that they continued their conversation using telephony for an additional twenty minutes. This contact was confirmed in a report by the Marconi Wireless Telegraph Company Ltd on 22nd July 1925 and is held in the Amberley Museum. The wavelength he used was the 45m band using Marconi & Osram T.250 valves. This achievement was adapted in advertisements placed in 'Popular Wireless & Wireless Review' magazine by Marconi & Osram on August 15th 1925. One of these adverts is clipped in page 31 of Marcuse's Scrapbook. The advert includes a sketches of Marcuse's radio equipment and the USS Seattle.

A clipping (Page 36) from Marcuse's Scrapbook, dated December 21st 1925, from the Christian Science Monitor includes a very detailed article by Marcuse in which he gives an account of using short waves for long distance communication. The article is titled 'Short Waves Discussed by G. W. Marcuse' and is prefaced with comment, "...Mr Marcuse is regarded as the most successful British amateur in long-distance radio work with short waves..."

Marcuse discusses the problems of using different wavelengths at different times of the day and night. Remarkably, after contact with the American Commander on board the Seattle, he says that "...he (the Commander) would not believe that these signals emanated from a British amateur, and, do what I may, I could not convince him of the fact". Marcuse states that the USS Seattle was sent out for the sole purpose of carrying our short-wave experiments.

The Commander of the Seattle suspected that he was a victim of an elaborate hoax by some New Zealand amateur 'pulling his leg'. However, at some stage during the communications, Marcuse was visited by a 'representative' of an enterprising American newspaper service, who also seemed to have some doubt that this was possible. The representative brought with him four lengthy questions that only he knew about which were to be sent to the Commander of the Seattle. Every question was replied to without any repetition and then at last, the Commander was satisfied that Marcuse was an amateur from England speaking by wireless telephony.'

Marcuse goes on to say that he mentioned the incident because he felt sure that this was the first-time wireless telephony had ever been used from England to a vessel sailing within New Zealand waters. Marcuse goes on to discuss (without using the term) the skip distance of short-wave signals, the phenomena of signals bouncing off the 'ceiling or the Heaviside Layer' (ionosphere). He discusses French engineers belonging to the radio corps who attempted transmission on short waves in 1918, believing that the signals would not be audible to the Germans but would be audible in Palestine and Egypt. Then he examined ideas of distortion, fading and the effect on morse code and telephony using different frequencies. The article provides an insight into Marcuse's understanding of these ideas that were well ahead of the current thinking of the day.

In 1925 Marcuse began to broadcast concerts to American amateurs on the 45-metre band from the Savoy Hotel, London. This would have been a very novel idea at the time as well as being very good advertising for the Savoy! The content of the concerts included singing from his local church choir, music from his personal record collection, live concerts, piano playing, bird song from his garden and recordings from the sound of Big Ben.

Marcuse received many letters from other amateurs who heard his broadcasts and a lot of these gave very reliable signal reports that would have enabled him to make adjustments in his power and frequencies used. T. H. Harris, an amateur from Sydney, Australia, wrote to him on November 1st 1926 with signal reports and a list of other amateurs that he had heard including: G5SZ, G2KF, G5LF, F8EU, G2F(U or M), G5MA, G5NN, G5VL, G5HS, G2OJ, G6UZ, G2CC, G5SZ, G5NJ, G2IT, G2KF, F8EE. (Letter 1923-26, No. 100)

On October 23rd 1925 a meeting was organised by Popular Wireless Magazine which brought together the important players in British radio communication. This included Senatore Marconi himself, the managing director of the BBC, the chief engineer at the BBC and many others.

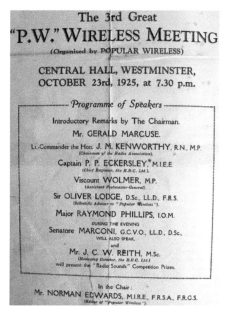

The 3rd Great

"P.W." WIRELESS MEETING
(Organised by POPULAR WIRELESS)

CENTRAL HALL, WESTMINSTER,
OCTOBER 23rd, 1925, at 7.30 p.m.

············ *Programme of Speakers* ············

Introductory Remarks by The Chairman.
Mr. GERALD MARCUSE.

Lt.-Commander the Hon. J. M. KENWORTHY, R.N., M.P.
(Chairman of the Radio Association).

Captain P. P. ECKERSLEY,* M.I.E.E.
(Chief Engineer, the B.B.C. Ltd.).

Viscount WOLMER, M.P.
(Assistant Postmaster-General).

Sir OLIVER LODGE, D.Sc., LL.D., F.R.S.
(Scientific Adviser to "Popular Wireless").

Major RAYMOND PHILLIPS, I.O.M.

DURING THE EVENING
Senatore MARCONI, G.C.V.O., LL.D., D.Sc.,
WILL ALSO SPEAK.
and

Mr. J. C. W. REITH, M.Sc.
(Managing Director, the B.B.C. Ltd.)
will present the "Radio Sounds" Competition Prizes.

In the Chair:
Mr. NORMAN EDWARDS, M.I.R.E., F.R.S.A., F.R.G.S.
(Editor of "Popular Wireless").

The Editor of Wireless World, Norman Edwards was in the Chair and he gave the introductory remarks.

Post Office Restrictions on Licences

British radio amateurs were at the forefront of communications during these early days but the stifling bureaucracy of the Post Office was often unhelpful to them. Official permission for variations in the licence and the limited frequencies which they were allowed to operate on acted as a brake on their experiments at a time when many radio amateurs knew more about the subject than those setting the rules, a case of the tail wagging the dog.

Eventually, the Post Office gave way under pressure from the amateurs and it started to issue permits for transatlantic tests. The permits not only restricted the power, but also the frequency and the times when amateurs could transmit. This was so restrictive that fewer than expected applied for licences. Marcuse applied for and was given a permit in December 1923 but the frequency was limited to communications on 90m only.

Marcuse had restrictions placed on him with regards to transmission time, input power and wavelength. He complied with all the restrictions and was granted a permit to continue broadcasting. The position of the Post Office appeared to be increasingly bureaucratic because it failed to keep up with technical developments. It did not seem to recognize the popularity of amateur radio that included high-profile figures; Marcuse would 'toe the line' by complying with the various restrictions placed on him. He preferred to win concessions and work within the law and he communicated this to other amateurs.

In April 1925, Marcuse attended the first congress of the International Amateur Radio Union (IARU) and as he was identified as the leading light in the British delegation, he was elected as International Vice-President. One of the main purposes of the meeting was to establish wavebands for International amateur use and to standardize the use of intermediate letters in amateur calls to indicate the country of origin.

In order to acquire a 'transoceanic permit' that would enable amateurs to communicate overseas, Marcuse wrote an 'open' letter to the editor of the Bulletin of the RSGB in September 1925 stating that, while admitting he had "considerable difficulties" with the Post Office, he chastised those amateurs who were clearly "not adhering to certain clauses of their license". This, in effect warned them that further infringements might result in recent hard-won concessions being revoked.

Eventually, the Post Office conceded to the use of higher output power and to an extension of the total transmission time but amateurs who required a 'Transocean Permit' had to apply through the T. & R. section of the RSGB which ensured that applications were vetted. Both the vetting and the restriction on the number of permits issued brought about a certain amount of frustration among younger enthusiasts who could not see the point in having to apply for a special permit to allow them to transmit across 'oceans', not least having to curtail the power used and the times when their transmissions were restricted. They could not have realized the considerable efforts that had been made by amateurs like Marcuse who followed the rules, at the same time as he fought for fewer restrictions, by making appropriate representations to the authorities and by letter writing.

Through these efforts Marcuse proved himself a true practitioner who loved experimentation and enjoyed the challenge of breaking into uncharted territory. His talents were recognized at an international level and his combined efforts helped him to achieve that rare status of a radio amateur who, while being involved at the highest level of organization and administration, never lost sight of the practical aspects of his interest through experimentation and operation.

The BBC & Radio Amateurs

The first BBC broadcast in Britain was made from London using the call-sign 2LO on November 14th 1922 at the Marconi House station in the Strand; however it was ten years later on 19th December 1932 that the BBC started broadcasting to the Empire. The late and highly respected John Phillips, a former Senior Maintenance Engineer at the BBC station in Wychbold, near Droitwich wrote:

"Experimental sound broadcasting began in the British Isles as far back as 1919 by the Marconi Company and other large electrical engineering manufacturers. The British Broadcasting Company came into being in 1922 and took over three 1.5 kilowatt transmitters; 2LO in London, 5IT in Birmingham and 2ZY in Manchester. "This is 2LO calling" was heard from the London transmitter. Regular daily broadcasting on medium waves commenced from these stations on 14th and 15th of November 1922. In July 1924 the first long-wave transmitter, 5XX, opened at Chelmsford, and 12 months later this was transferred to Daventry to carry an alternative programme that would become the forerunner of the National Programme.

Expansion of the B.B.C. continued and by 1925 over 20 medium-wave stations were in operation. These were all low-power services situated in large towns and cities but today these would be classed as local radio stations.

On the 1st January 1927 the British Broadcasting Company was dissolved and the British Broadcasting Corporation was constituted under a Royal Charter."

The newly constituted BBC launched the 'Empire Service' from Borough Hill, Daventry on short-wave and this was to be the predecessor of what is known as the 'World Service' today. There is no doubt that the BBC desperately wanted to broadcast programmes to the Empire but was 'locked in a cloud' by believing that this was only possible by using lower frequencies. The fact that Marcuse was able to broadcast successfully to the Empire using short waves was proof in itself that it could be done but there appeared to be a stubborn resistance within the BBC to experiment with and to use these higher frequencies.

After considerable efforts, Marcuse was eventually granted a licence to broadcast entertainment out of his own pocket. It is suggested that this came at a personal cost of £6000 to do this.

Marcuse Broadcasts to the World

The photograph shows the considerable efforts he made to cope with the power requirements of his equipment. At some stage his generator 'blew up' but he was given replacement parts at no cost by the maker. His father thought that he was wasting his money but he let his son get on with it and must have provided some financial support. Judging by the numerous newspaper articles he received, Marcuse had gained a large amount of world-wide publicity and he became a household name throughout the Empire. His short-wave broadcasts were received but BBC broadcasts were not being received. A lot of criticism came his way culminating in an official statement from the BBC:

"...deplores the present unfortunate exploitation as a publicity stunt, giving a wholly artificial importance to the admittedly unsatisfactory and irregular direct reception available merely to a limited number of experimenters".

It would appear that the BBC objected to amateur experimentation unless full coverage of a transmission to a target area was possible. The content of the letters Marcuse received was very supportive to him and the popular feeling of people around the world was in complete opposition to the BBC's view.

Today, the BBC website includes a Timeline: '100 years of the BBC', 1922, that begins, 'Following the closure of numerous amateur stations…'. There is no mention of the work of the amateurs who paved the way to the BBC being able to broadcast successfully and it remains as a denial of historical fact.

The Argus, Melbourne dated August 10th 1922 includes an article that was headlined 'BBC bans an Empire Relay' in which Marcuse complains of the 'Dog in the Manger' attitude of the BBC.

The 'West Australian', Perth article: 'Empire Broadcasting – Most Baffling Problem' is dated August 5th 1927. The article quotes extensively from a BBC statement in which the Corporation declares its commitment to the broadcasts but states that relaying programmes on short waves 'would arouse a temporary interest, but would inevitably be followed by keen disappointment and disillusionment'.

The Natal Advertiser, Durban, South Africa dated August 9th 1927, published an article entitled 'A Mystery Studio – Broadcasting to the Empire – London Man's Enterprise – Plenty of Offers of Help'. The article develops the theme of the Empire Broadcasts and goes on to mention that as Marcuse's offer to relay BBC broadcasts was rejected, he would be setting up his own studio.

The Courier, Brisbane, Queensland, August 10th 1927; reports on the forthcoming broadcasts and mentions the inclusion of a first-class orchestra from 'Dance Land'. It questions how much progress the BBC had made and states the experts from the BBC blamed the difficulty of its own programmes being heard was due to 'reception in the Dominions'.

Marcuse's Empire Broadcasts

'Empire Broadcasting' was all about transmitting programmes to British Empire countries in the 1920's and this included countries such as South Africa, India, Australia, New Zealand. Ex-pats, servicemen and people of British descent were anxious to hear news and receive programmes from home. From the hundreds of letters that Marcuse received from all over the world, even the sound of 'Big Ben' or the song of a blackbird, provided comfort for people in these countries who were a long way from home.

Marcuse first started transmitting in 1913 from his home in Purley, South London when he was 27 years old and this was at a time when many amateurs were sending test signals without licences. He had applied for a licence but this was not granted until after the First World War. In the interviews recorded in 1960, Marcuse commented about the early years of amateur radio by saying, "We did not bother about licences". In Britain it was a 'free for all', so that those who had the interest, the technical knowledge and the resources could set up a station and experiment.

In the early 1920's Marcuse's interest in radio began to take off. He was granted his first licence (G2NM) in 1920 after he had moved to Coombe Dingle, north-west of Bristol where he lived with his first wife. He mooted the idea of 'Empire Broadcasting' in 1922, but his application for a permit was refused by the Post Office because 'it might infringe copyright'. Marcuse stated he wanted to re-broadcast BBC programmes which were not heard abroad. The Argos, Melbourne newspaper clip (Scrapbook page 6), dated August 10th 1922 demonstrates the problems he had with the BBC which continued for many years:

```
G2NM        Marcuse, G

            "Dunedin", Caterham Valley, Surrey

            "Coombe Dingle"

Licence issued 19.11.22
                    76150/21        189889/23

Permit from 13.10.24 - 15.4.25

Power not to exceed 1 kw.

Stns permitted to work were

Bartle, H.F.    Blackheath

Nickless,J.E.   E.11

Burnham, W.W.   S.E.13

Crampton,W.J.   Weybridge
                        /NJT
Marconi Scientific Trust Co.   W.1

Parker,H.C.    E.17

Trans-oceanic sending tests Power not to exceed
        1 kw.  15.4.25

Moved to Sonning, August 1929

Permit to use 125 - 130
              115 - 130 (cw & Phone)

Organised Trans-oceanic tests from 13.10.26 to 15.4.27.

Private wire from "Coombe Dingle" to "Woodside" for
  exper.purposes, 27.4.27.

Temporary trans-oceanic permit licence all bands received 19.9.28.

Address changed from Coombe Dingle to Dunedin Feb.1929 (temp).
  and new permit issued 8.3.29 for fixed or portable work
  within 10 miles of "Dunedin".
```

Marcuse's first licence dated 19th November 1922.
The exact conditions of use were listed, including the stations
'Permitted to Work'.

BBC Refuses Permission to Re-Broadcast

At Caterham Marcuse conducted transatlantic tests regularly but his first transmissions were made on the 180, 400 and 1000 metre bands. The tests were made with a friend who lived about five miles away in Purley using 'Spark' gap communications and the most distant contact he made was about 20 miles away. The Post Office was in charge of all radio licensing and it started to restrict amateurs so that they could only conduct their tests on bands below 200m. The reason for this, as Marcuse put it: "these bands were no good, commercially". Ironically, within two years the opposite would prove true. Marcuse continues:

"It is suggested that copyright difficulties may be the reason for the BBC's refusal, but it cannot be that, for I intended to broadcast practically no copyright matter, and for the little I should have broadcast I am sure I could have obtained the owner's permission. The experiment would have been very valuable in showing the practicability of a regular all-Empire broadcasting station and that, I think is the real reason for the BBC's refusal. I intended to broadcast excerpts on short wavelengths of 23 and 33 metres for 12 months. I am sorry that the thing has temporarily fallen through, because I have spent a lot of money since Christmas in rebuilding my plant specially for the purpose.

The BBC's 'dog-in-the-manger' attitude will not deter me however, and I am working out other arrangements about which I can say nothing as yet. I can say, however, that I expect to be able to make an Empire broadcast despite the BBC."

Marcuse, together with a group of other enthusiasts, communicated with each other using morse code on Sunday mornings using spark transmission, a very early method. The apparatus consisted of a 'Gamage' spark coil that initially had a half-inch gap; later, it was fitted with rotary gaps. It was supplied by A. W. Gamage, a department store that began in 1878 and later went on to run a mail-order company.

Marcuse's 'Empire' broadcasts that were transmitted from Caterham included recordings from the Caterham Orchestra and these were broadcast in the afternoons. His contacts included an Australian (Rosa

Alba) who helped him broadcast an all-Australian concert. Broadcasts were transmitted 180, 400, 440 and 1000, metres but eventually the Post Office placed restrictions and insisted that all future broadcasts should be made on wavelengths below 200 metres.

Permission to Broadcast Granted – at last!

Eventually he was very successful in persuading the relevant bodies to allow him to transmit entertainment using his equipment. His broadcasts were all recorded in logbooks but nearly all of these were lost during his various house moves. In 1924, the 'The Student Prince', an operetta with music in four acts opened on Broadway. When this came to England, Marcuse was asked to broadcast it but the Post office would not grant him a line. When he moved to Caterham, he was granted two Post Office lines to the house of his friend Percy Valentine, at a cost of £3. 15s. 0d. Percy had a control room; a studio and his uncle was a conductor of the Lloyd's insurance Orchestra. One of the lines was used to send programme content, the other was used for communications between the two of them.

From an early age one of Marcuse's greatest loves was music. This interest grew when he was attended engineering school at Einbeck in Germany and alongside his engineering studies, he was learning to play the flute and he attended music concerts. Here, he must have developed an interest in classical music because he knew what would be appropriate to broadcast and what would be enjoyed by the public, so most of his broadcasts contained musical entertainment.

In 1925 Marcuse started broadcasting to amateurs in America from his home in Caterham and among the first to be rebroadcasted was the BBC transmission of a concert held at the Savoy Hotel in London. His broadcasts included piano recitals, his local church choir, (gramophone) records, concerts, the bells of Big Ben and bird songs, including a blackbird and thrush from his own garden. Many of the letters he received from all over the world confirmed good reception and in May 1925 he had a confirmed report that his signals were received as far away as Japan. The tone of the Post Office's letter changes from showing a genuine technical interest in the frequencies he operated on, to that of issuing a masked threat: if Marcuse provided information showing he had contravened his licence, they would take steps to amend it. This was part of a considerable, on-going controversy surrounding Marcuse's Empire Broadcasts but his efforts proved to be highly successful and very popular with people throughout the world. They filled a gap left by the BBC whose broadcast signals were being transmitted but were not being heard. There was even a suggestion that the BBC doubted that an 'Overseas Service' was needed. At the time, Marcuse and others were using wavelengths that long distance communication was indeed possible using short waves.

A newspaper clipping appears on October 19th 1927 titled, 'Angry with the BBC' (Scrapbook page 61). The article comments that the BBC had shut down 2FC, a station in Sydney that was re-broadcasting a special short-wave programme:

"Daily Express" Correspondent.
Melbourne, Wednesday, Oct. 19.

"The B.B.C.'s action in shutting down the re-broadcasting of the special shortwave programme transmitted from 2FC Sydney just as transmissions were reaching the peak of clarity and strength in London on Sunday night is strongly criticised by Melbourne amateurs and experts.

"The corporation seems to be doing its best to kill all attempts to establish Empire interchange programmes on shortwaves", declares Mr Hugh McCubbin. "The latest move places them in an untenable position after the treatment of Mr Marcuse, and the questionable action of refusing to re-broadcast Melbourne's special programme."
Similar indignant comment is made by other experimenters.

A letter to the (British) Times from Ian Fraser of Hengistbury Head, Hants, (Scrapbook page 68iii) dated August 12th 1927 goes further. It appears that Ian Fraser used his influence, 'I said I would give him every possible assistance in securing the necessary licence and permission'. (Marcuse's licence was granted from September 1st 1927.) The article ends with the comment that 'All those who have for some time felt that the BBC should not have allowed a foreign station to usurp their function will regard this as eminently satisfactory'

The BBC objected to Marcuse rebroadcasting their programmes claiming that they breached copyright which explains why Marcuse started producing programmes of his own.

Following the circulation of a survey to locations in the (then) British Empire, the returns all expressed the need for an 'Empire Broadcasting service' for those countries. People wanted to keep in touch with home and to be informed about what was going on.

The following news was reported in Wireless World on August 24th 1927 (Scrapbook page 51):

"Mr. Gerald Marcuse (2NM), the well-known Caterham amateur, who on September 1st will inaugurate telephony transmissions for the benefit of the Colonies on wavelengths of 23 and 30 metres. It is expected that the transmissions will take place on three nights a week, Mr. Marcuse providing his own programmes."

A clipping from an Australian newspaper (Scrapbook page 58) dated September 1927 states that Marcuse would be transmitting from the 'Columbia Graphophone Company', in London.

The Australian artists named are: Miss Daisy Kennedy, Mme. Evelyn Scotney, Mr John Amadio, Mr Fred Collier, Mr Harold Williams and Mr William Murdoch. It mentions that the Australian High Commissioner, Sir Granville Ryrie would be returning to London from a League of Nations Assembly in Geneva specially to broadcast a short address. Re-broadcasting arrangements are given.

An undated article from 'The Times of India' (Scrapbook page 75) is titled: 'Albert Hall Concert heard in Bombay'. It discusses the programme received by the secretary, Mr R. H. Atkins of the Bombay Presidency Radio Club commencing at 8pm GMT, equivalent to 1-3am Indian Standard Time. The programme contents are given:

Song:	Katie, Beautiful Katie
Song:	John Brown's Body
Short Speech:	Should old acquaintance.
Song:	We're here, we are, oh here We Are.
Song:	Keep the home Fires Burning.
Song:	It's a long way to Tipperary.
Band:	Bagpipe Band and bugle calls.
Hymn:	Oh God our Help in Ages Past.
Speech:	Short Speech and singing of 'For He's a Jolly Good Fellow'
Speech:	Speech by H.R.H. The Prince of Wales
Hymns:	Onward Christian Soldiers & Abide with me
Finally:	God Save the King

It goes on to say that two stations were transmitting, namely the 'new Chelmsford station of the BBC and the experimental station operated by Mr Gerald Marcuse', but it was not certain which of the two stations he had tuned into. The article comments on the Indian Broadcasting Company failing to relay the BBC broadcast because nothing had been heard due to the unsuitability of the wavelength for reception in India.

A meeting of the Colonial Conference held in London in 1927 agreed that an Empire Broadcasting service for people living in the colonies would be a positive step forward and would improve communication between them and their home country. At last this view was accepted by the BBC and their testing would soon start.

Marcuse applied to the Postmaster General for an extension to his transoceanic wireless transmitting licence and this was granted with the proviso that he relayed BBC programmes using the wavelengths of 23m and 33m using a power not exceeding 1KW. His aerial was a 'Zepp' antenna (a 'Long-wire' antenna originally used on Zeppelin airships) which was supported by a 100ft mast. This was a colossal structure by anyone's standards in those days but other restrictions were outlined in a letter sent to him by the Postmaster General.

The letter was addressed: General Post Office, London, EC1 and was dated August 9th 1927:

Sir,

With further reference to your letter of 21st June, asking for an extension of your transoceanic wireless transmitting licence so as to enable experiments to be carried out in transmitting telephony to parts of the British Empire, I am directed by the Postmaster general to convey his authority for transmission of speech and music for a period not exceeding six months from the 1st September next by means of wireless telephony with power for transmission not exceeding 1Kw and waves of 23 and 33 metres, on the understanding that continuous transmissions will not take place on more than three days a week (Mondays, Thursdays, Saturdays or Sundays) and will not exceed a duration of two hours on each occasion.

The following special conditions were attached to this authority:

(1) That items of current news value shall not be included in any programme;
(2) That not more than 50 gramophone records shall be utilized during the whole period of the experiments;
(3) that the transmissions shall not include an advertisement of the Gramophone Company or of any other body or person;
(4) that any transmission shall be discontinued on demand if it interferes with Government or commercial services; and
(5) that this authority shall be subject to withdrawal or modification at any time at the Postmaster General's discretion should occasion arise.

I am to call your attention to the statement in the Post Office letter of the 17th June last that the Postmaster General cannot hold out any hope that a licence to transmit regular programmes to the Dominions or Colonies would be granted to any other body than the British Broadcasting Corporation.

I am, Sir, Your obedient Servant, W. J Leech.

In spite of Marcuse receiving this official consent, the tone of the Post Office's letter was restrictive by stating that only the BBC would be granted a licence to broadcast regular programmes. Instead of adhering to the maximum limit of three days a week, he continued to broadcast almost daily. After proceeded with these 'tests' he received hundreds of supportive letters, most included reception reports from all over the world which reinforced his determination. After seeing that Marcuse's broadcasts were successful using short waves, the BBC capitulated and started transmissions of their own using a lower frequency. However, their signals could still not be heard very well while Marcuse's signals came through with clarity. Radio Amateurs in the colonies were rebroadcasting Marcuse's relay broadcasts themselves.

'Scrapbook' Confirms the Empire Broadcasts

Date	News Source	Location Tests Received	Page
1922	Unknown newspaper	Halifax, Nova Scotia, Canada	7
19-03-24	RSGB (P.R. Coursey)	USA & Canada	11
26-07-24	Unknown Newspaper	Melbourne, Australia	12
08-01-25	Christian Science Monitor	Boston, Mass., USA	16
14-12-25	Telegram	Ismailia, Egypt	35
10-07-27	Ceylon Observer	Colombo, Ceylon	40
28-09-27	Telegram	Capetown, S. Africa	66
12-11-27	Telegram	Bombay, India	71
23-04-28	Telegram	Sydney, Australia	82

In 1928 Marcuse broadcasted a relay of the Royal Albert Hall Armistice Concert and to achieve this he linked up popular artists and others including Ian Fraser who was a governor of the BBC. Fraser held the rank of Captain in the King's Shropshire Light infantry and had joined the army in France during World War 1 but at the Battle of the Somme he was made blind by a bullet. Later he became Chairman of St Dunstan's, an independent charity for blind servicemen, a post he held for 52 years and was awarded a knighthood for his work. Marcuse also invited the High Commissioner of Australia to speak during the broadcast. This was the very first programme to be sent to Australia from Britain.

Logbooks

Marcuse didn't think that he kept a logbook in the early days but he did keep them later although most were lost between moving houses. One of his logbooks (used in 1930) is held by the Amberley Museum in West Sussex (Amberley Index: MD 1/30). The first entry in this was made at 1830hrs on June 22nd 1930 and the final one was logged at 2230hrs on 17th November in the same year. Marcuse made regular broadcasts of music and entertainment throughout the year with occasional 'time-out' entries. The one on October 26th is recorded as:

"No Transmission – away on Caravan, Shooting"

The entries continued when he returned on November 2nd at 18.30:

1st	Time – Selection	Schubert
	Rhapsody No 2	Liszt
18.30	Sigurd Jorsalfar. (4 parts)	Grieg
	Brandenburg Concerto	Bach
	No 2. F Major	
	O Maiden – My Maiden	Lehar
	A Boy saw a Rose Bush	Lehar
	Lohengrin Prelude	Wagner
	Scheherazade	Rimsky – Korsakov
	On hearing the first	Delius
	Cuckoo in Spring	
	Good-night	

Another logbook (Amberley Index: MD 1/60) ran from 25-05-1961 to 06-04-1961. The entries show that he was operating on 160m & 80m with his old friends. He would usually start operating around 9.30am for an hour or so then sometimes continue through the day. He was active on the air right up to the day he died on 6th April 1961; his last contact was with G8TH at 10.07am when he stopped transmission as shown in the log at: QRT 1010. This was Marcuse's last entry.

Marcuse demonstrated that his pioneering transmissions did work and his test broadcasts could be heard but sadly he was 'shut down' after the BBC finally started broadcasting using shortwaves. The BBC's initial scepticism that these frequencies were of little use had become a remarkable volte-face, and nowhere in the BBC's history is the contribution made by radio amateurs acknowledged or even mentioned; clearly a shocking oversight.

A few years later in 1936 Marcuse made the first ever contact on the 5-metre band with America, another remarkable feat.

The First Callsign Book

The Amberley Museum holds a copy of what could be the very first callsign book in which all amateurs were listed. This was called a 'Wireless Directory' and it was issued by a company called Radio Press, Devereux Court, Strand, London, WC2. Radio Press used to issue a magazine called 'The Wireless Constructor' which would include articles on radio construction. These were the days when a soldering iron consisted of a handle, an iron rod with a lump of copper attached to the end. The copper would be heated with a Bunsen burner or heated in the fireplace on 'smoky coals'.

The introduction states how difficult it was to put together a comprehensive list of callsigns as the British Post office did not produce a publication of them. It offers a free copy of the second edition to any amateur whose callsign was missing from the first. The callsign book includes a complete listing of low and high-power stations including ship and amateur wireless calls. The listing starts with ACA (Aldershot) and a symbol indicates if this was a ship, land station or a battleship, the latter indicated by cross swords!

Amateur stations include the name of the owner of the callsign, the address, mode of transmission (Spark, Teleprinter, CW, Telephony), the wavelength and the power in watts. If details were unknown, they are omitted. The most popular wavebands appear to be 150-200m, 425m, 440m and 1000m. As this callsign book was issued in the early 1920's it needs to be remembered that there must have been many other amateurs operating who had no callsign. In the interview tapes, Marcuse recalls that "we didn't bother in those days". 2NM is listed between G. J. Hughes, 2NL and 2NN whose callsign appears but with the name & address both missing.

Call.	Name of Owner.	Address.	System of Transmission.	Wave-length in Metres.	Power in Watts.
2 NB	J. W. Barnaby	Sylvan House, Broad Road, Sale, Manchester.	C.W. and Telephony.	440	10
2 NC	J. Goodwin	Crown St., Duffield, Derby.			
2 ND	E. H. Pickford	6, Wilson Road, Sheffield.			
2 NF					
2 NG					
2 NH					
2 NI					
2 NJ					
2 NK					
2 NL	F. J. Hughes, A.M.I.E.E.	Ashdene, 129, Wells Rd., Bath	Spark		10
2 NM	G. Marcuse	Coombe Dingle, Queen's Park, Caterham., Surrey.			
2 NN					
2 NO	H. R. Adams	Crescent Cabinet Factory, Sutton Road, Walsall.	C.W., T.T. & Telephony	440	
2 NP	H. G. Treadwell	Middleton Cheney, Banbury	Spark, T.T. C.W. and Telephony		
2 NQ					
2 NR	J. Knowles Hassall	Mount Pleasant Works, Wooden Box, nr. Burton-on-Trent.	C.W. and Telephony	440	
2 NS	M. Burchill	30, Leighton Rd., Southville, Bristol.	C.W. and Telephony		
2 NT					
2 NU					
2 NV					
2 NW					
2 NX					
2 NY	J. N. C. Bradshaw	Ambrose House, Bilsboro,' near Preston		150–190 and 440	10
2 NZ	J. N. C. Bradshaw	Ambrose House, Bilsboro',	Portable Set	150–180	10

Clandestine Service during World War 2

At the outbreak of World War 2 all British radio amateurs were ordered to close down and all essential parts of their equipment were confiscated and placed in storage by the Post office. This was returned after the war in January 1946 but radio amateurs would play a very important part in communications in all services during the war.

Marcuse was issued with a special licence on 3rd July 1939 that authorised him to act as a maritime radio operator on board a British ship equipped with appropriate radio receiving and transmitting equipment. This was called a 'Restricted Certificate of Proficiency in Radiotelephony' and holders of this licence had to make a declaration that they would *preserve the secrecy of correspondence* as well as being limited to 'the power of the carrier wave in the aerial' not exceeding 50 watts.

Marcuse was a member of the Royal Observer Corps during the war and in 1937 he assisted with the formation of the 'Civilian Wireless Reserve' of the RAF. After this, his son David Marcuse stated that one day his father was 'visited' at the family home in Sonning-on-Thames and asked to move to Bosham for special duties. Clearly his talents as both an expert in radio communication and a fluent German speaker were recognised as being helpful to the war effort. This was Marcuse's fourth and final move but it is not known exactly when he moved.

A wartime meeting of VI group leaders at the Leatherhead regional office of the Radio Security Service. Old-timers will recognize many familiar faces, as very many of these amateurs served on the RSGB Council in the 'forties and 'fifties, including at least three former Presidents (Arthur Watts, G6UN; "Dud" Charman, G6CJ, and the late Gerald Marcuse, G2NM). Lord Sandhurst (centre, standing and smoking a pipe) and a number of "Box 25" officers are also in the group

Radio Security Service Get-Together (Rad-Com Dec 1980)

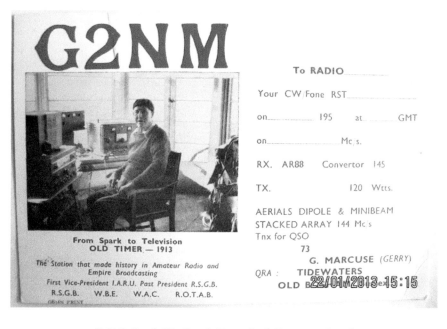

G2NM's QSL Card (Proof of Contact Card)

He was listed as a Group Leader in the Radio Security Service (RSS) and members of this unit were known as V1's. If any members of the group were of 'call-up' age, they used Royal Observer Corps (ROC) uniform and membership as a cover for their real job. An article in the

Radio Society of Great Britain's journal 'RADCOM', dated December 1980, includes a lot more detail about the work of the V1's and the contribution they made during the war.

The war started in 1939 when Marcuse was 53 years old and at some stage, he served under cover in ROC uniform in the Solent from a Motor Fishing Vessel (MFV). It is likely he was escorted by the Royal Navy, where he intercepted and recorded German radio signals that were passed on as part of the intelligence gathering during the war. He monitored Morse code messages and returns of his findings were sent on to the appropriate authorities. In the absence of official records for his service with the RSS, it is not generally known when Marcuse actually started his work on the Solent but from the correspondence it would appear that this could have been sometime after 1941.

In 1942, On behalf of the Chief Constable, the Clerk of the Peace for Berkshire congratulates Marcuse in a letter dated 26th June 1942 for his assistance with a 'Wireless Scheme' that he had advised on for use by the Police Authority. The Home Office had approved the scheme. A similar success was achieved by advising the Ambulance service about setting up mobile communications for ambulances to communicate with head office. Thus Marcuse was responsible for advising about the formation of communications in both the Police and Ambulance services.

On August 14th 2019, Marcuse's son David spoke to a group that had assembled to commemorate the restoration of the bench at Bosham and in his address he included the following:

"… my mother, the cat Mowki and I moved to Bosham on June 28th 1944 whilst my father was serving in the Solent for the Royal Observer Corps on an MFV, decoding morse code messages from Germany, translating them and sending them to Box 14, Hemel Hempstead…"

UNITED KINGDOM OF GREAT BRITAIN AND NORTHERN IRELAND.

Restricted Certificate of Proficiency in Radiotelephony granted by the Postmaster General.

This is to certify that under the provisions of the General Radio-communication Regulations annexed to the International Telecommunication Convention, 1932, Mr. *Eugen Gerald Marcuse*

has been examined in Radiotelephony and has passed in :—

(*a*) Knowledge of the adjustment and working of radiotelephone apparatus.

(*b*) Sending and receiving spoken messages correctly by telephone.

(*c*) Knowledge of the Regulations applying to the exchange of radio-telephone communications and of the part of the Radiocommunication Regulations relating to the safety of life.

It is also certified hereby that the holder has made a declaration that he will preserve the secrecy of correspondence.

Signature of examining officer _____

The holder of this Certificate is therefore authorised to act as radio-telephone operator on board a British ship equipped with a radiotelephone installation of which the power of the carrier wave in the aerial does not exceed 50 watts.

_____ for the Postmaster General, G.P.O., London.

3 JUL 1939 _____ Date.

Signature of holder _____

Date of Birth *14 June 1886* Place of Birth *Sutton, Surrey*

The authority granted by this Certificate may be withdrawn by the Postmaster General at any time at his discretion. The holder of the Certificate shall return the Certificate to the Postmaster General upon receiving from him notice of the withdrawal of the Certificate to the thereby. Until so withdrawn the authority granted by the Certificate shall continue in force so long as the provisions of the International Telecommunication Convention concluded in Madrid in 1932 remain in force.

This Certificate should be carefully preserved. In case of loss through avoidable causes, a duplicate will only be issued on payment of a fee of not less than 10s.

Any person other than the owner thereof becoming possessed of this Certificate should send it forthwith to the Inspector of Wireless Telegraphy, General Post Office, London, E.C.1.

K 741

Restricted Certificate Awarded for Clandestine Operations

Recognition from Bletchley Park

Marcuse's valuable contribution during the war was recognised when he received an undated letter from the Controller of the Radio Security Service thanking him for the 'many hours of work' he had spent and for the 'personal self-sacrifice he had contributed' [Scrapbook page 94]. A copy of this letter was sent to Bletchley Park (Photo below) by David Fry on February 17th 2015. The Oral History Officer confirmed by email that Marcuse was now listed in the 'Bletchley Park Roll of Honour' for special service to his country. The letter of thanks the controller sent to Marcuse is addressed, P.O. Box 25, Barnet, Herts. and includes the phone numbers at the top left.

It is with great pleasure that I forward to you the attached certificate in recognition of the valued and devoted service which you have voluntarily rendered to our Organisation during the War.

This certificate is signed by Sir Herbert Creedy who, during the War years when your work was of the utmost value, was the head of the Department to which we were responsible.

I would like to add my personal thanks for all you have done and for the many hours of hard work and personal self sacrifice you have contributed.

Colonel,
Controller,
Radio Security Service.

Bletchley Park (*Printed with permission from Bletchley Park*)

Letter from the Oral History Officer dated 18th Feb 2015, 12:38 Hrs

"Dear Mr Fry,

I did receive your earlier email and have now added Gerald Marcuse to the Roll of Honour.

You will need fill in the form for whichever of the armed forces he was a member. However, from what you told me in your previous email, it seems that Mr Marcuse may have done all his wartime service as a civilian member of the RSS, and I am afraid that no personnel records of this organisation are available.

Many of those who joined the RSS as teenagers were later called up into the Royal Signals to continue their work in uniform, but as Mr Marcuse was 53 when the war began, he would not have been liable to National Service.

Perhaps his family can confirm whether or not he did serve in the Army and, if so, it would be worth them requesting his service record."

(ends)

-oo-

Sometime around 1946 Marcuse was successful in setting up a Fire Brigade at Bosham following a disastrous fire in the village which partly destroyed someone's house. The fire brigade was equipped with volunteers, a fire tender, a siren and a phone line. In 1975 Bosham Parish Council honoured Marcuse by naming a new road in the village after him. It was called 'Marcuse Fields' because he established the fire station serving as a tribute to his memory. David Marcuse recalls:

"One day in about 1946 (I think) Mrs Gestetner had a fire at her thatched house and it took 1½ hours for the fire engines to arrive, meanwhile the fire had caused a lot of damage to the house. This fact aroused the keenness in my father to get a Bosham Fire Brigade assembled. Having acquired an appliance from Chichester and the loan of a barn from Farmer Brown (opposite Eddie Coward's shop) he set about finding volunteers, a siren, and a dedicated phone alarm. This was all achieved and they remained as volunteers until well after the Station had moved to Critchfield Road around 1954. It then became a paid job and eventually closed late 1960's but in the early days they had many calls and saved many properties, barns and hay fields."

From the 1950's right through to his death Marcuse never stopped experimenting with different frequencies and aerials at his Bosham home. Also, he was operating with mobile communications in his car as well as maintaining contact with his old friends in the Radio Amateur Old Timers' Association (RAOTA) and local amateurs.

The Marcuse Interviews held in 1960

Marcuse was 74 years old when the interviews were conducted and he died in 1961. Arguably, the interviews provide the best account of his achievements as they were spoken 'from the heart'. Although a little patchy in places, the transcription is complete and it shows that Marcuse retained a sharp mind with very good recall. They were most likely taken to prevent a vital account of early radio history being lost. The interviews are recorded fully in Appendix 4.

- oo -

Marcuse's Achievements, Awards & Recognition

From the first issue of his 'Experimental Licence' by the post office in 1913 to his death in 1962, Marcuse received numerous awards for his efforts. His help and advice to other amateurs, short-wave listeners and to component manufacturers is evidenced within the numerous letters that he received from all over the world. Other successes would have been seen in his log books which, apart from one, appear to have been lost. The following is not an exhaustive list but it includes the most significant achievements.

Year   Event

1913 The Post office issues Marcuse with his first Experimental Licence.

1922 Marcuse issued with his First Post Office Licence 19-11-1922 (76150/21 & 189889/23) for wavelengths below 200m: 2NM.

1923 A Certificate of Membership from the 'Wireless Society for London No. 696 issued to Marcuse in October 1923.

1923 G2NM conducts regular transatlantic tests.

1923 G2NM contacts USA & Canada.

1924 Marcuse appointed ARRL Operations Manager for the British Isles.

1924 G2NM contacts a Canadian steam ship 'Arctic' on a 6000 miles cruise off the Canadian Islands.

1924 First ever contact between Britain (G2NM) and California (6ZAR in Los Gatos) on February 23rd 1924.

1925 Marcuse contacts the American warship 'Seattle' lying in New Zealand waters using a wavelength of 45 metres and entertained it with songs by Caruso, violin selections by Heifetz and jazz music. Thus the first ever contact is made between Britain and New Zealand, 400 miles from Sydney, N.S.W.

1925   Marcuse commences broadcasting from the Savoy Hotel, London to American Amateurs.

1925   Marcuse received a letter from the Post Office, dated May 1925, stating that the Japanese Telegraph Authorities had heard his signals in Japan (Marcuse letters & Recollections No. 100).

1925   Pioneered the use of Telephony for Amateur Contacts overseas.

1925   The first ever contact between the Britain and South America following Marcuse's contact with the Hamilton-Rice expedition on the River Amazon.

1925   Marcuse is awarded certificate of Appointment as O.W.L.S. Station #45-C. This was a group sponsored by the ARRL that designated an amateur as an 'Official Wave Length Station'. Members had to retain a transmitting frequency that was 1% correct 'between themselves' although the group advertised an accuracy of 2% in order to join. The aim was to encourage accuracy and to standardise amateur frequencies.

1926   Marcuse organised Trans-Oceanic tests from 13th October 1926 to 15th April 1927.

1927   The Post office grants Marcuse a licence for Empire Broadcasting on 9th August 1927.

1928   The Post office grants Marcuse an extension to carry out experiments in wireless telephony to parts of the British Empire for a further period of three months from 1st June 1928 on the conditions set out in their letters to him "from this office of the 9th August 1927 and 15th February 1928".

1929   Marcuse is made President of the RSGB.

1936 Marcuse makes first ever contact with America on 5 metres.

1937 Marcuse assists in the formation of the 'Civilian Wireless Reserve' of the RAF.

1939 On 3rd July 1939, the Postmaster General grants Marcuse a 'Restricted Certificate of Proficiency in Radiotelephony'. This entitled the holder to operate as a radio-telephone operator on board a British ship. All holders had to make a declaration that they would 'preserve the secrecy of correspondence.'

1942 On behalf of the Chief Constable, the Clerk of the Peace for Berkshire congratulates Marcuse in a letter dated 26th June 1942 for his assistance with a 'Wireless Scheme' that he had advised on for use by the Police Authority. The Home Office had approved the scheme.

1943 Marcuse is awarded 'The Five Band Club' certificate No. 70. This was sponsored by The Short-wave magazine that based the criteria for the award on the recipient making substantial support for VHF activity.

1945 Marcuse is awarded a Certificate of **'Valued and Devoted Service'** to the Radio Security Service (RRS) during World War 2 (Scrapbook page 94). Sir Herbert Creedy, the Head of the Department, signed the certificate. The letter recognises 'the valued and devoted service which you have voluntarily rendered to our organisation during the war', and continues, 'I would like to add my personal thanks for all you have done and for the many hours of hard work and personal self-sacrifice you have contributed.'

1946 In a letter dated 25th June 1946, signed by John Clarricoats the General Secretary of the RSGB, Marcuse was elected an Honorary Member of the society for his great services to Amateur Radio in general. It was mentioned that the occasion would be marked by the presentation of a certificate at the forthcoming AGM.

1946 Marcuse is elected to the active membership of the First-Class Operator's Club. He was the current President of this exclusive group and having satisfied the criteria, his election was notified in The Short-wave Magazine. He was awarded Certificate Number 18, signed by himself and endorsed by the Secretary A.M.H. Fergus.

1949 Marcuse is awarded membership of the 'VHF Century Club'. This was sponsored by The Short-wave Magazine' and required members to show proof of having worked two-way on the VHF bands from 50Mhz upwards with one hundred different amateur stations.

1961 Irene Marcuse is made an honorary member of the Amateur Radio Mobile Society.

1961 Marcuse is re-issued with a Wireless Telegraphy Amateur Sound Licence costing £2 that he had held continuously since 1913 until his death in 1962. Several receipts for his licence renewal can to be found. (Scrapbook page 103).

1962 Silent key.

All the certificates, awards and acknowledgements above that have survived are held in the Amberley Museum. Marcuse's certificates he received from the Crystal Palace School are in the possession of the Marcuse family.

- oo -

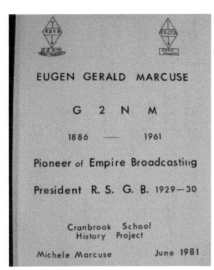

EUGEN GERALD MARCUSE

G 2 N M

1886 — 1961

Pioneer of Empire Broadcasting

President R. S. G. B. 1929—30

Cranbrook School
History Project

Michele Marcuse   June 1981

Michele Marcuse's Project

Michele completed a GCSE project based on her grandfather's life when she was 14 at Cranbrook School and it serves as a very useful and interesting account of his activities. What makes it especially important is that her work was based on interviews with her grandmother Irene who was very supportive to her husband and took a great interest in his work. After Gerald died in 1961 Irene, realising the historic value of his papers, collected them together along with the letters, photographs and log books. It is quite likely that the decision to relocate Gerald's material to the Amberley Museum was based on her initiative. Michele's hand-written project is located in the Amberley Museum along with the other material.

Papers Not Returned by the RSGB

Before the archives were consigned to Amberley, John Clarricoats (G6CL) borrowed some of the material for his book 'World at their Fingertips'. Also, the Science Museum had borrowed papers for an exhibition and it is likely that the BBC needed material for programme content. The evidence from several of Irene's letters suggests that not all of the borrowed material was returned. Irene chased up missing material that she had lent out but only received some of it back. A letter from R. F. Stevens (representing the RSGB) to Marcuse's widow, Irene Marwood dated 9th July 1969, states that 'we have not yet had the time to sort out and classify the books and pictures which have come to the Society from Mrs Clarricoats but we hope that this work will be started in the near future'.

A letter from the Science Museum to Irene dated 13th October 1972, requests permission to borrow 'suitable items' for a special exhibition for the RSGB jubilee. This suggests that the items would be exhibited 'in showcases already available in the room that houses our own radio station, GB2SM'. The letter is signed by Keith Geddes, Assistant Keeper, Radio Collection, Science Museum, London, SW 7.

Your ref. ScM 6472/3740/1.

Tideswaters,
Windmill Field,
Old Bosham,
Chichester.
Oct. 26th.,1972.

Dear Mr. Geddes,
Thank you for your letter of Oct. 13th.. I have delayed answerring it as I hoped to have a replyto a letter I wrote to Mr. Newnham on Oct. 16th. about points which you raise, but, as yet I have not heard from him.

Regarding your questions:-
1. Gerry did conduct some radio correspondence from his business address which was blitzed during the war and everything was destroyed. So it is possible some of the early correspondence dissappeared then. A;so there were two moves, one from Caterham to Sonning and another from Sonning to Bosham during whichpapers, which at that time may not have been considered important, could have been thrown away.

2. As far as I know he did not otherwise dispose of any papers during his lifetime.

3. When John Clarricoats was preparing his book he took all the papers away for inspection. I am sure the correspondence you refer to with the GPO and the Australian photographwere included in this parcel. Indeed the fact that they appear in the book (photo opposite p.116, letter p. 131)is a proof of this. I did not examine the parcel in detail when it was returned to me but when I unpacked it, prior to the recent visit of the local Radio Society, I discovered the letters and the photograph were missing. I wonder whether these items were retained by John for some reason and on his death, perhaps,they found their way into the archives of the RSGB. It is on this point that I have written to Mr. Newnham (as Radio Society Historian) asking him to make a search for them, and I await his reply. When I hear from him I will certainly let you know.

4. A propos your exhibition, I should be happy for you to borrow the papers for inspection and to lend you such items as you think suitable for your display.
Yours sincerely,

G.I.Marwood.

K.E.Geddes Esq.,
Assistant Keeper, Radio Collection,
Science Museum,
London SW 7.

73

What is clear is that Keith Geddes and Geoff Voller visited Irene to view and discuss the papers she held. In the letter he asks about the whereabouts of 'numerous papers no longer in her possession that her late husband must have had. These would include considerable official correspondence with the Post Office, the BBC and the RSGB, along with log books and the circuit diagrams of his equipment'. Mrs Marwood sent a letter to the Assistant Keeper of the Radio Collection at the Science Museum, October 26th 1972. The letter offers proof that material that was borrowed from Mrs Marwood 'went missing'.

Irene replies in detail by letter on 26th October 1972 suggesting the following reasons for the loss:

1) Marcuse conducted correspondence from his business address that was blitzed during the war resulting in total loss of material held there.
2) The two moves made by the family from Caterham to Sonning and from Sonning to Bosham resulted in papers considered unimportant at that time, 'could have been thrown away'.
3) When John Clarricoats was preparing his book (The World at their Fingertips) he took away all the papers (in Irene's possession) for inspection. She mentions that specific items appearing in that book were not returned to her (photo opposite page 116 and a letter on page 131). She goes on to suggest that: "items were retained by John for some reason and on his death, perhaps they found their way into the archives of the RSGB". Irene states that she had written to Mr Newnham, the RSGB Historian, asking him to search for them.

Irene's letters to Mr Newnham (dated 16th October 1972) lists the missing items. Having not heard about the missing items for over three years, Irene wrote to R.F. Stevens again on 4th December 1971 requesting the return of the missing items.

A letter from the RSGB to Irene dated 11th December 1972 stated that Mrs Clarricoats did not have any of her late husband's papers, but that 'these were either destroyed or removed' before she moved house. This letter was signed by R.F. Stevens and he explains that the printers returned photographs to him and that he had sent them to John Clarricoats. (Stevens was responsible for the production of Clarricoats's book)

A friend of Irene called May, wrote a letter to her on 7th February 1973 stating that she had found some large envelopes at the RSGB headquarters that contained 'the missing papers' as well as "several photos which we thought you might like to have, as well as Marcuse's Log Book of Broadcasts".

The detailed nature and tone of the correspondence indicates that some material might still be buried in the RSGB archives or lie elsewhere in the possession of persons or organisations.

Silent Key

Gerald Marcuse died on April 6th 1961 at his home 'Tidewaters' in Bosham. The funeral was well attended by family and friends as well as

amateur radio operators; the latter included Victor Simms (RSGB) and Frank Briggs (Radio Amateurs Old Timers Association). His ashes are interred at the Holy Trinity Churchyard in Bosham. A very special sundial marks the position with the words: "To the Glory of God and in memory of a loving Husband and Father."

On the top is a map of the world which is positioned to show some of his famous contacts.

The words are well-chosen and acknowledge his ground breaking exploits.

A Life Well Spent, Filled with Great Achievements

Marcuse's many interests included sailing and shooting along with all his public involvements with the Fire & Ambulance Services. He spent many Summers "afloat in bliss' on his boat Eirene II with his loving wife and son but never lost sight of his true interest in radio transmission. He even built a transmitting set into his car for mobile use.

Marcuse shown in his radio shack during his later years.

The area around Tidewaters was a nursery run by a local inhabitant who died leaving no one to maintain and look after it. Consequently, the land was put up for sale and it was purchased by a builder for a housing

estate. After completion, Chichester Council asked the public to submit suggestions for appropriate names for the estate. A lady who had bought one of the houses and who was aware of Gerald's great achievements submitted the name "Marcuse Fields" and this was selected.

Funds were raised to purchase and place a bench outside the Church in Gerald's honour complete with a plaque which also acknowledged his achievements.

Celebrating the Bench Restoration at Bosham

This event held on August 14th 2019 was very well attended by locals, enthusiasts and the RSBG. After a brief gathering around the restored bench, everyone withdrew for lunch and addresses by David Marcuse and David Fry.

Address by David Marcuse

"Thank you all so much for making the effort to come here this morning and especially those who have travelled some distance. My Father and Mother would have been delighted to see you all here and were always ready for a party and what I am about to say has been very difficult to précis.

My mother, the cat Mowki and I moved to Bosham on June 28th 1944 whilst my Father was serving in the Solent for the Royal Observer Corps on a Motorised Fishing Vessel, decoding morse code messages from Germany, translating them, and sending them to Box 14, Hemel Hempstead.

My father was fluent in German as he was the grandson of a German national and had attended engineering college in Einbeck, Germany in 1903. He graduated from there using his fluency in the German language, which he never lost.

Towards the end of 1944 he returned home to Tidewaters, Bosham and it was then that he revived his lifelong hobby of short-wave radio. He also began to get involved with the village becoming a County Councillor in Chichester representing Bosham. With his HAM radio interest he needed somewhere for a shack and my mother generously gave him part of the dining room which inevitably extended through the whole room.

Masts were erected in the front garden with aerials and wires all over the place. As a result of his regular contacts with America, Australia and other far off places, people were always keen to come and visit so the easiest thing for him to do was to extend his 'radio shack' further into the 'boat house' and that was where the Chichester & District Amateur Radio Club, I believe was born.

Apart from radio, being a County Councillor, a Yachtsman and of course a father to me, he had other interests develop. One day in about 1946 (I think) Mrs Gestetner had a fire at her thatched house and it took 1½ hrs for the fire engines to arrive. Meanwhile the fire had caused a lot of damage to the house. This aroused the enthusiasm in my father to get a Bosham Fire Brigade assembled. He acquired an appliance from Chichester and the loan of a barn from Farmer Brown (opposite Eddie Coward's shop) and he set about finding volunteers, a siren, and a dedicated phone alarm.

This was all achieved and the posts remained voluntary until well after the Station moved to Critchfield Road around 1954. It then became a paid job and eventually closed in the late 1960's. In the early days they had many calls and saved many properties, barns and hay fields.

My Mother was always an enthusiastic supporter of my father. She was a keen member of the Church, the WI and joined with my father starting the table tennis club in the Village Hall. My Mother also was a very active helper in the back room at the Chichester Festival theatre in their early days. As a family, we have always been keen sailors from the early days of The Bosham Sailing Club and I was one of the early members from 1947 and still remain so today.

April 1961 was a very sad time when my Father died from a long illness but we wanted a memory of life and activity both in the village and worldwide on radio and we were given permission to erect this seat which was unveiled in April 1962 by the Chairman of the Parish Council Frank Parham and some radio dignitaries. Latterly the Council very generously offered to name the new road Marcuse Fields in his Memory. However 'tempus fugit' and after nearly 60 years the seat became unsafe and was taken away. The best solution proved to be to make a new replacement and this was made possible thanks to the Parish Council and I am delighted it is unveiled today."

Liz & David Marcuse Seated on the Restored Bench

Seat Dedication Ceremony
(Courtesy of Elaine Richards, G4LFM)

Standing (left) Elaine Richards, Seated front, left to right: Helen Lister, Liz Marcuse, David Marcuse, David Fry (G4JSZ)

Marcuse's Last Logbook

Police Gratitude

Office of the Clerk of the Peace for Berkshire.

TELEPHONE No. 3081 (8 lines).

N/JL.

SHIRE HALL,
READING.
26th June, 1942.

ALL COMMUNICATIONS TO
BE ADDRESSED TO
"THE CLERK OF THE
PEACE."

Dear Sir,

        The Chief Constable informed the Police Authority
of the very considerable assistance which you have given to him
voluntarily in connection with the Wireless Scheme which has now
been approved by the Home Office.   I am, therefore, directed to
convey to you the thanks of the Police Authority, and to say that
your assistance in this connection has been very much appreciated.

                Yours faithfully,

                H. c. Morland

                Clerk to the Standing Joint Committee.

G. Marcuse, Esq.,
The Ranch,
West Drive,
Sonning,
Nr. Reading.

Early Commercial Receivers

RECEIVERS.
3 Valve "All Range" Receiver.

This type of Receiving Set is constructed to meet the demand for a universal receiver for
all Wireless Signals on all wavelengths from 100 to 30,000 metres.

The Set is of neat and attractive design and is mounted in a polished oak case measuring
approximately 12×8×5 inches high.

The ebonite panel is fitted with 2 variable condensers, 2 filament regulators, series parallel
switch for short wavelengths and all necessary ter-
minals for tuning coils and condensers.

The strength of signals is such that a " loud
speaking telephone " can be used without further
amplification.

Price (less accessories):—

3 Valve Receiver	... ...	£15
Coil-holder for 2 coils	...	£1 17 6
Set of Coils	... ...	£5 17 6

22/01/2013 12:36

Elected Honorary Member of the RSGB

THE INCORPORATED

RADIO SOCIETY OF GREAT BRITAIN

PUBLISHERS OF
THE R.S.G.B. BULLETIN.
THE AMATEUR RADIO HANDBOOK.
THE RADIO HANDBOOK SUPPLEMENT.

NEW RUSKIN HOUSE,
LITTLE RUSSELL STREET,
LONDON, W.C.I.
TELEPHONE: HOLBORN 7373.

JC/MG

25th June, 1946

G.Marcuse,
Tide Waters,
BOSHAM
Sussex

Dear Mr. Marcuse,

It is with very great personal pleasure that I write to you on the instructions of the Council to inform you that you have been unanimously elected an Honorary Member of the Society.

The Council are deeply appreciative of the great services you have rendered to Amateur Radio in general, and to the Society in particular, and they have asked me to convey to you their warm thanks for your continued interest in our work.

Arrangements will be made to present you with a suitable certificate at the forthcoming Annual General Meeting of the Society.

Yours very sincerely,

John Clearcoat

General Secretary

The Post Office Prevents Completion of Concert

Your reference........................
71086/27.
P.O. reference........................
All communications should be addressed to
THE SECRETARY,
General Post Office.

GENERAL POST OFFICE,

LONDON, E.C. 1.

16 September 1927.

Sir,

    With reference to your letter (undated) in which you ask that permission be given to complete the transmission of the programme which you were authorised to broadcast to Australia from your experimental wireless station on Sunday last the 11th instant, I am directed by the Postmaster General to say that you are aware of the reasons why the broadcast was ultimately agreed to, and, as the High Commissioner's speech was duly broadcast as was also that of Captain Ian Fraser M.P., he does not consider that there is sufficient reason for completing the concert. He regrets, therefore, that he cannot accede to your request.

           I am, Sir,

             Your obedient Servant,

             W.J. Lund.

Gerald Marcuse, Esq.

No Official Public Recognition

When all Marcuse's considerable successes are taken into account, it is very remarkable that other than public acclaim and thanks, he received no official recognition for his ground-breaking work. However when Marcuse was alive, this was discussed by people who were in a position to achieve it. Austin Forsyth OBE, (G6FO), who was Editor of Short-wave Magazine, wrote a considerable editorial for the January 1954 edition in which he argued that Marcuse's name should be put forward for the next Honours List.

A copy of his editorial and a letter dated 30th December 1953, addressed to: Old Mill House, Maids Moreton, Buckingham was sent to Douglas Ritchie (BBC Publicity) and to Sir Noel Ashbridge, Chief Engineer of the BBC, asking for a statement for publication in the February Edition. He also sent a copy to the editor of the Daily telegraph suggesting he may like to print the substance of the editorial as a letter to the Editor.

He told Marcuse that he was considering writing to the Lord Lieutenant of Sussex, drawing his attention to the fact that Marcuse had no public recognition of his pioneering work in radio and would propose that Marcuse's name should be put forward for the next Honours List, adding that he would not do it until he had heard that Marcuse had no objection.

A proof version of the Editorial signed by Austin Forsyth and the letter are held in the Amberley Museum, Letters 1935 & onwards. Forsyth highlights the regrettable omission by Sir Noel Ashbridge during a talk entitled 'Service on Short Waves', by failing to make any mention about the pioneering work done by Marcuse on short waves before the BBC. The article continues:

"What Sir Noel most regrettably omitted to mention, and what is far more important than many of the points he did discuss, was that all the experimental proofs as regards short-wave propagation were furnished – not by the BBC, or Marconi's or any other agency – but by the amateur transmitters of the day, and the amateurs alone. Further than this, the first experimental short-wave broadcasting station in this country was established, not by Marconi's or the BBC but by Gerald Marcuse, G2NM, then of Caterham, Surrey who was specially licensed by the GPO to transmit an experimental programme service to the Empire on 32 metres. Incidentally, he was also permitted to do this at his own expense. It was as a direct result of the success of these Empire

Broadcasts from G2NM that the BBC went ahead with their experiments.

In view of the ground covered by Sir Noel Ashbridge in his talk, his eminence as a radio engineer, and the respect due to any pronouncement he may make in the field of radio engineering, it is much more regrettable that he failed, by so much as a single phrase, to give any credit at all where the record proves it to be abundantly due."

The talk was in commemoration of the 21st anniversary of the BBC Overseas Service and it was billed in the Radio Times as being for, among others, "fans and hams". It remains open to speculation then, did Marcuse object to receiving Public Honours? There is no evidence in the archives held at Amberley that this was the case.

The main obstacle might have been Marcuse's constant battles with the BBC which would have made the prospect of official recognition untenable in the eyes of the BBC hierarchy. If the latter, it remains a tragic omission that Marcuse's outstanding achievements in radio and broadcasting remain unrecognised and this continues to this day.

THE SHORT-WAVE Magazine

EDITORIAL

Omission
In the B.B.C.'s Home Service at 9.15 p.m. on December 18, Sir Noel Ashbridge—the Corporation's distinguished Chief Engineer and until recently their Director of Technical Services—was featured to give a talk entitled " Service on Short Waves," in commemoration of the 21st anniversary of the B.B.C. Overseas Service. The talk was billed in the RADIO TIMES as being for, among others, " fans and hams " (sic). In the course of his talk, Sir Noel reviewed briefly developments from the early days before 1914 to the present time—DX on 600-metre spark, the significance of the thermionic valve, the opening of vast new areas of ether space, the Marconi/Franklin experiments on short waves, the B.B.C.'s first short wave station at Chelmsford, culminating in their regular overseas service, established on December 19, 1932.

Quite a comprehensive review, covering a lot of ground in a short time, in the space of which it was obviously not possible to mention everything. But to have heard this talk you would—if you did not happen to know otherwise—have been left with the clear impression that it was the B.B.C. that carried through all the experimental work to make " Service on Short Waves " possible.

What Sir Noel most regrettably omitted to mention, and what is far more important than many of the points he did discuss, was that all the experimental proofs as regards short wave propagation were furnished—not by the B.B.C., or Marconi's or any other such agency—but by the amateur transmitters of the day, and the amateurs alone. Further than this, the first experimental short wave broadcasting station in this country was established, not by Marconi's or the B.B.C., but by Gerald Marcuse, G2NM, then of Caterham, Surrey, who was specially licensed by the G.P.O. to transmit an experimental programme service to the Empire on 32 metres. Incidentally, he was also permitted to do this at his own expense. It was as the direct result of the success of these Empire broadcasts from G2NM that the B.B.C. went ahead with their experiments.

In view of the ground covered by Sir Noel Ashbridge in his talk, his eminence as a radio engineer, and the respect due to any pronouncement he may make in the field of radio engineering, it is much more than regrettable that he failed, by so much as a single phrase, to give any credit at all where the record proves it to be abundantly due.

It was the amateurs alone who first explored the short waves—this they did to such effect that they are now in process of losing the very territories they did so much to discover. Thus the wheel has turned against us—it must be accepted as part of the price of progre[ss] at least let the record be kept straight.

Appendix 1: Amberley Museum Documents

Marcuse Letters 1923 – 1926

MD2/23:   1 only
MD2/24:   1 - 10
MD2/25:   1 - 19
MD2/26:   1 - 19
Marcuse Letters 1927:   MD2/27:   1 – 58
Marcuse Letters 1928:   MD2/28:   1 – 86
Marcuse Letters 1930:   MD2/30:   1 – 30
Marcuse Letters 1931:   MD2/31:   1 – 36
Marcuse Letters 1935:   MD2/35:   1
Marcuse Letters 1938:   MD2/38:   1
Marcuse Letters 1953:   MD2/53:   1

Scrapbook

MD1/13 – 61 (The paper Index is titled: MD1/13/61 but the actual index goes up to MD/1 – 117. (A paper index is present but the actual pages have not yet been indexed,

Marcuse Letters

The Amberley Museum has organised the letters in seven files. In this book the actual letters are described briefly to give an outline of the contents. All pages are listed, including extra pages from the same letter.

Recollections were not Indexed by the Library in Amberley at the time of checking. All the documents scanned for the purpose of this biography have been re-indexed by the author.

o~o

Appendix 2: Adana Massacre & Correspondence

The Armenians were devoted Christians but they were living within what was then, the Ottoman Empire headed by the Sultan. They were relatively wealthy people but in the Ottoman Empire there were a lot of Muslim fundamentalists who were determined to install Islamic law. The head of state was Sultan Abdul Hamid II who treated the Armenians as second-class citizens. When the Sultan was dismissed in a bloodless revolution by a pro-secular group of Turks, the Armenians were looking forward to equal rights but it was not long before a military revolt resulted in Istanbul, the capital being seized and a period of extreme violence ensued in which the Christians (Armenians) and their property were attacked.

The killing of Armenians and the destruction of property were ordered by the Sultan and this included all machinery, engines and tractors. The revolt lasted about two weeks but the violence against the Christians continued for over four weeks until the government established order. In July 1909, some of those implicated in the massacre were brought to justice resulting in 124 Muslims and 7 Armenians being executed for their part.

It would appear that Marcuse's experiences fitted the Armenian account of what actually happened and in the words of Elizabeth S. Webb, a missionary attached to the school: "It was a terrible situation, women and girls practically alone in the building, a murderous bloodthirsty mob outside, with knife and bullet for the Armenians and the torch for their homes."

The following are transcripts of the letters of *correspondence* between the Managing Director of Ruston Proctor and Marcuse shortly after he started his journey to (what is today) southern Turkey to install a Steam Pump.

9ᵗʰ **May 1909**. (*Marcuse*) According to your instructions, I left Manchester by S.S. Roman Prince for Mersine. After a rough passage, we arrived at Alexandria, having called at Malta and Tunis. At Alexandria I called on our agents and, to my great dismay, learnt that the Turks were killing the Christians by the thousand. After spending five days with the agents who were exceedingly kind to me, whilst the ship was unloading, we proceeded up the Syrian coast and eventually arrived at Mersine on May 3rd.

Mersine was all upside down, and on arriving there we were met by an English warship. An officer came aboard and warned me to be very careful on landing, as Mersine was threatened by the Kurds and Bashebasooks who had come down from the mountains - intent on killing the Armenians and the Christians. However, I found our agent, D. A. Lykiardopoulo, safe and well. I booked a room at the hotel, which was packed with refugees - many of them terribly wounded.

Of course, my first duty was to interview my Consul, Major Doughty Wiley, who was at Adana. However, I had to wait five days before the police would allow me to go to Adana. I took the morning train at 7 o'clock and arrived at Adana via Tarsus at 10, passing on the way some horrible and gruesome signs of the recent events; such as bodies terribly mutilated and houses gutted.

On arriving at Adana, the sight that met my eyes is hardly imaginable, and I cannot compare it with anything I have yet heard of. Women and children were killed in cold blood, and mostly tortured in the most gruesome way. More than half the town is burnt down and 20,000 have been killed. The whole of the commercial port of the town is in ruins. Adana before the massacre had 110,000 inhabitants, and now you hardly see 1000. Most of the survivors have taken refuge on a piece of ground outside the town."

I found Major Doughty Wiley badly wounded in the arm and strongly guarded. I spent an hour with him and was instructed not to leave Mersine without his permission. He promised to provide me with an escort when it was safe to travel.

The man who has bought the GK gas engine and plant has wired to say that everything is now quiet at Ayas and that he is waiting for me. I shall travel to Ayas by steamer to Alexandretta and then by sailing boat - a journey of approx. ten hours.

The GK engine is for an ice-making machine. The ice is to be used principally for the fishing boats. The GO engine is to be used for Cotton ginning, and the mill is now being built for Hamidie. Because the cotton-gins only work for several months in the year, the power will also be used for a flour mill.

(Marcuse was given instructions not to leave Mersine without the

permission of Major Doughty Wiley, the Consul at Adana. When it was safe to travel and permission was granted, he was provided with an escort and he left by steam ship to Alexandretta, now Iskenderum and then by sailing boat to Ayas.)

A few days later while staying in a hotel at Ayas, on 15th May, Marcuse wrote:

15th May 1909. I returned to Mersine on the 9th, travelling by the evening train. Yesterday, the 14th, I received a telegram from Major Wiley, saying that I should proceed to Ayas with the provided escort. Luckily there was a steamer leaving this morning to fetch cotton seed and he brought me to Ayas. Ayas is situated in the Gulf of Scanderun, near the mouth of the River Pyramus. It has about fifty houses.

I found the owner of the GK gas engine and he showed me an old building where the engine is to be installed. Nothing was prepared, but I have got the ground dug out already and prepared for the foundation which I hope to lay tomorrow.

Ayas has not seen much trouble - only a few houses were burnt and some 30 killed. The governor of the village has threatened to have all the gendarmes hanged if anyone dares to lay a hand on me - so I feel quite safe! I expect to be here about a month, as there is some lifting to put up.

I am living on the premises as the proprietor of the hotel had to 'fly for his life' again. They have rigged me up a bed and table in a barn, but for vermin, it is quite comfortable. Since there are no other Europeans here, I am having to learn Turkish - but am picking it up quickly.

As soon as we can establish a footing here with suction engines, we shall see no end of orders. Although the people here are 2000 years behind, they are beginning to realise the necessity of machinery - especially for the production of ice.

Hornsbys have sold a few suction gas engines around Mersine and Adana, but most of the ones I have seen have been put down very badly and are giving trouble. Crossleys have sold two suction gas engines and plants at Adana, but they are sending a man to be with them. Yours faithfully...

21st May 1909. (*Marcuse*) I am progressing with the work as well as can be expected in view of the difficulties in this primitive country. For example, I have had to show the bricklayer how to trim all the stone that we have used for the foundations. They are finished now and I have unpacked the engine and accessories. I hope to get the engine on the foundation tomorrow. I hope to finish here by the time of the GO gas engine arrives. I will be installing it at Hamidie, about 8 hours ride from here.

25th May 1909. (*Marcuse*) I am still making progress under difficulty. I had to demolish half of the roof and then erect new supports. Time was lost searching for parts that had been thrown away - all were found, thankfully. The people here are very thick-headed and I wonder however I shall teach them how to work the gas engine and plant! The engine is now installed and the producer is nearly completed. I expect to be here for a further 10 days.

The trouble in the interior is by no means settled yet, although they are hanging all the ringleaders. They fetched seven from here yesterday, and hung them at Adana.

The gas producer was in a terrible condition when I unpacked it. Many bolts were broken and parts bent. Since there are no spares, I shall have to make do - but you can be quite assured that I will make a 1st class job of it, because it means a lot for our future orders in this country. The owner of this plant is sure to order another. No end of farmers and rich Turks have been to see this engine, and all impressed. The owner of the GO is always here! Yours faithfully…

Marcuse received the following reply from the managing director of Ruston Proctor:

9ᵗʰ June 1909. *(Managing Director of Rustons)* Dear Marcuse, thank you for your letters from Ayas. They were most interesting, and as I know Mersine, Tarsus, Adana and Alexandretta very well, my mind wandered back to those places, which it was my good or ill fortune to visit in the interests of business.

I must compliment to you on the way you stick to your mission. It shows that you have grit in you. You certainly are roughing it. I could compare notes with you, for nobody knows what I have gone through in that part of the world. It was my duty once, to fish a portable engine and thrashing machine out of the sea - and then put them to work! At another time I had to rebuild a thrasher that had been wrongly assembled. However, those experiences have no doubt helped to fit me for the position I hold at present. The little Turkish I know has almost faded, but if you will call on me when you return, I shall salute you in true Turkish fashion. Yours sincerely…

Marcuse writes back:

30ᵗʰ May 1909. I have finished this engine, except for the piping from the scrubber to the tanks, which I am awaiting from the agent at Mersine. I have had a terrible struggle, having no tackle - not even a pulley block. For rollers I had to use old piping, which flattened under the weight. I have to put up with many other hardships, but I am getting used to them. For instance, I am living in a barn infested with rats, snakes, fleas, bugs, etc.

13th June 1909. (*Marcuse*) I have come to Mersine to collect the piping for the scrubber. Loss of time finding this item shows how important it is to make sure that everything is shipped to a country like this, as not even a nut or screw is to be found out here.

Because it was still impossible to travel overland, I had to wait a week for a sailing boat. It took three days to reach Mersine in this open boat. Unfortunately I became very ill with dysentery, chiefly due to bad food and exposure. I was laid up for 10 days. The GO engine arrived here in good condition. I will take about 10 days to get it up to Hamidie.

20th June 1909. (*Marcuse*) The GO left two days ago in two sailing boats for Ayas. From there it will go by Bullock Wagons to Hamadie, so I cannot start work there for another week or so. I am just beginning to feel better after my dysentery attack. Our agent says that he has heard no more about the two Crossley engines supposed to be coming to Adana - so it may have been just a rumour. I have succeeded in obtaining piping for the scrubber, and I shall return to Ayas with it. I expect the job will be completed in one day.

The managing director of Ruston Proctor wrote:

27th August 1909. Dear Marcuse, thank you for your letter of 20th June, and others earlier. Your lines are most interesting reading, and I can transfer my mind to that country, where I myself have encountered many hardships. Whilst I sympathise with you, I am almost glad that you have had such a rough experience - it will be of such valuable assistance in your future life. There is nothing like having to go through the mill to appreciate what it really means. I was glad to hear that you got over your rough attack of dysentery. Your trip in the open sailing boat was an exciting experience, and no doubt it had its charms.

I was very disappointed to hear, on my return from holiday, that you are still out there. When will your mission end? Just imagine what this installation will cost, adding there to your expenses, wages and board. You know it is simply fabulous, and I doubt if the agent will refund us for his share of all these expenses. For the sake of two gas plants, to have you in Asia Minor for the next two months is both ridiculous and expensive, and it will absorb every bit of profit. With Best wishes for your safe return. Yours sincerely,

Meanwhile, Marcuse continued writing:-

4th July 1909. I returned to Ayas overland, namely from Mersine to Adana by train, and from Adana to Ayas on horseback. I have now had the GK running, and it runs very well. The bed and flywheel of the GK are still here, and we are having great difficulty arranging transportation. I may as well inform you that the owner of the GO has been arrested for being involved in the recent massacres, and is to be tried by court-martial - so you see, I am delayed again! I have had trouble finding mechanics, owing to them having all been killed, and those that escaped went to foreign parts. However, I found an intelligent waiter at a sort of hotel, and I told him, and he really proved a very good fellow.

Marcuse sent the following testimonial letter from the owner of the GK Engine & Plant.

11th July 1909. I am quite satisfied with the 32 bhp suction gas engine and plant. It has now been running a good time, and has run 12 hours a day without a hitch. Its simplicity and good workmanship enable us here, where a good mechanic is to be found, to run it with facility. I declare that the gas engine and plant has run very well for 10 days with one mill. Signed…

13th July 1909. (*Marcuse*) I have now returned to Mersine. I stayed with the GK and ran it for 10 days in order to teach the Greek mechanic how to run. I shall leave here for Hamidie in two days' time, to start work on the GO. The new owner was arrested for killing Armenians in his factory but he was found not guilty and is to be released. Will travel together to Hamidie.

19th July 1909. (*Marcuse*) I am sorry to inform you that, as the owner of the GO is still in prison, I cannot start working on it. It seems absurd that I have now been away from Lincoln nearly 4 months and only erected one engine and plant. Of course, it has been the massacres that have hindered me. I have now been waiting three weeks for the owner of the GO to be released. The owner of the GK is having great trouble with his mechanics, as they will not stay at Ayas. I have promised to find him a good mechanic and I am travelling to Ayas this afternoon.

25th July 1909. (*Marcuse*) I received a telegram from the owner of the GO to say that he was released from prison. I travelled to Hamidie through the night because it is impossible to travel during the day due to the great heat. A Frenchman here has installed a 30bhp compound steam engine supplied by Ransome Sims & Jefferies - and a 50 bhp Hornsby oil engine. Hornsby & Crossley have sold a lot of oil and gas engines in this country.

I have started on the foundation for the GO but, as I have only one man to help, progress is slow. I secured a bricklayer from Ayas. The GK is running very well. The engine bed and flywheel are still at Ayas. The transportation of 3½ tons and 5½ tons is no small matter! I plan to use the wheels from a Marshall thrasher, bolt them together, and draw it along with the Oxen. Before I leave here, I shall have an order for next year for a thrashing set, and an engine of 120bhp, either steam or gas.

The managing director of Ruston Proctor replies:

14th August 1909. Thank you for your letters of 25th July and earlier. We note the progress you are making with the GO plant, and are pleased to learn that the GGN plant is running very well, and gives entire satisfaction. We note what you say respecting the erection of a GN suction gas installation. However, we beg to say that we cannot allow you to erect any more suction gas plants for our agent Mr Lykiardopoulo, as we consider that the tuition you have given to his men should now enable them to erect and start suction gas plants & producers. Before proceeding home you must telegraph us to say that you have finished and then await our further instructions. We note what you say respecting an order for a thrashing set and a steam or a gas engine of 120bhp, and we sincerely hope that this business will come off.

Marcuse writes from Hamidie:

6th August 1909. Progress is still very slow - mainly due to lack of labourers, because all the working people were killed here. Also, neither the engine bed nor the flywheel for the GO have arrived yet.
I shall finish the foundations in two days, and will then commence to erect the gas plant.

11th August 1909. (*Marcuse*) The foundations are finished and I have now been waiting five days for the engine bed. We are taking a traction engine to Ayas tomorrow to fetch the bed and flywheel. I think our agent has the GN Engine and plant and I shall wait to hear if you want me to install it. There are ten non-Ruston thrashing sets here, five of them Marshalls. Please send me another book of writing paper, as I have nearly finished this one.

27th August 1909. (*Marcuse*) You have asked about the cost of housing, food, etc., out here. At Mersine seven shillings a day is not too much. We cannot compare Ayas with Adana or Mersine, because living here is more expensive in the larger towns which have lots of Europeans staying there. At Ayas my full living costs were no more than 4 Turkish pounds per month.
My costs are low because I have been living with the owners. If one looks at hotel costs (without food costs), they are:- Adana or Mersine, £8/month; Ayas or Hamidie, £6/month.
I am greatly relieved to tell you that at last, after a terrible journey, we have brought the engine bed to Hamidie. The owner was called to a tribunal at Adana as one of the ringleaders of the massacre. So of course, all the work fell on me. The roads were very bad, with dust lying a foot deep. We used oxen instead of the traction engine, as there was a difference of £10 in the cost. It took 10 oxen in most places to pull the wagon, and it took us four days from Ayas to here.

7ᵗʰ September 1909. (*Marcuse*) I have come to Mersine to buy piping for the water circulation - also to get a little of my strength back as Hamadie is such a terrible climate and the food is almost inedible. The GO is now finished, bar the flywheel and water circulation. I shall stay here for a week, then return to Hamadie to finish.

Yesterday, at Adana, I saw a 200 bhp Marshall steam engine being unloaded. It would be a good thing for us if you could send a traveller well-up in drop-valve engines, as there are several wanted here. Trepani will soon place an order for a 1000 bhp engine, and I know a man at Tarsus wants one at 150 bhp - but, as our agent says, I do not know enough about these engines, so he cannot push the orders. After the GK and the GO have been running sometime, there are sure to be some more orders - as I know several people who are waiting to see how they run before ordering.

28ᵗʰ September 1909. (*Marcuse*) I have been running the GO Engine for a week. Two other buyers came to see it running. I convinced them of the good qualities of our engines and they both said they would buy one. One man wants a GP 100 bhp, and the other wants a GO 130 bhp. Then I went to see three other customers - all of them want 100 bhp engines. So you see, although this country is in a bad state, we did fairly well. There are three things wanted here:-

1. Security and reliable protection
2. Irrigation.
3. Railways.
A scheme for the latter is already in hand. In March 1910 they are starting to build a railway from Erigili to Baghdad.
I have been sorry to hear how badly the people here have spoken of our thrashing machines; chiefly due to them being fitted with plain bearings. If we altered to ring oilers, I feel sure they would take up our machines again. At present they will only have Marshals thrashers and Fowlers traction engines and portables. I will leave for home in a few days' time, but will wait to hear if you have any further instructions for me. I plan to travel home via Smyrna, and expect to be in England by mid-October.

This was the last recorded correspondence.

Ruston-Proctor then sent Marcuse instructions concerning his next job. In spite of the fact that he had been working for several months in terrible conditions in the Middle East, he was instructed to get a boat to New York and travel to Mexico and install a large number of engines. Unfortunately, Marcuse arrived just as the Mexican civil war started. Mexican revolutionaries had already killed a large number of government employees and members of the army. Marcuse had arrived in the middle of the Mexican Civil War!

o~o

Appendix 3: The Hamilton Rice Expedition

Dr. Alexander Hamilton Rice was born in Boston, Massachusetts in 1875; he died aged 80 in Newport Rhode Island in 1956 after making a huge contribution to the exploration of South America.

Dr. Rice (seen in the photograph) was a multi-talented explorer and an expert in rivers; he was proficient in geology and geography and he was a professor of geography at Harvard University for over 20 years from 1929. He was the founder of the 'Harvard Institute of Geographical Exploration'.

He started his exploration in 1907 when he began mapping unknown rivers in the Amazon Basin and by 1925, he had succeeded in exploring over half a million square miles of it. During his final expedition in 1925 he used aerial photography which was a first in exploration. It appears that the main aim of the 1925 expedition was to make contact with a mysterious and little-known native tribe known as the 'White Indians'. Dr. Rice was able to make contact with these people but discovered that their circumstances were very difficult indeed, some suffering from malnutrition. A full understanding of Dr. Rice's expeditions would involve a separate study of its own, Harvard university holds a considerable archive about Dr. Rice's expeditions.

A little over four weeks after the first radio contact had been made, John Swanson, the radio operator accompanying Dr. Rice's expedition wrote to Marcuse from their field location and in the absence of the address where he was located, he gave his position in Longitude and Latitude. The original letter is held in the Amberley Museum archives but some edges are worn thus making a complete and accurate transcription difficult.

The letter was sent on February 21st and received on May 1st, a period of a little more than five weeks, remarkable in itself after the huge logistics involved in getting the letter on board a ship, outlined by Swanson in this letter.

The letter (Scrapbook page 23) reads:

Field Operator Station,
Rice Expedition, Callsign "LR"
Longitude 62° 26' W.
Latitude 3° 7' N.
February 21st 1925.

Mr Marcuse, Station G2NM,
The Radio Society of Great Britain,
London, England.
Dear Mr Marcuse:-

This letter may be fitting by stated as being ready to embark on an adventurous journey as in order to reach its destination it must be carried by airplane many miles over dense tropical wilderness, rapids and waterfalls to a post called Boa Esperanza, thence it takes a three-day journey by horseback to Boa Vista , a little hamlet of about 1500 people, mostly ranchmen whose cattle roam about the many miles of clear open Prairie. From Boa Vista the letter will find its way to Manaos by way of canoe and launches. From Manaos it is due for a rest in a mail bag aboard one of the Booth Lines that will carry it to England. I wish to offer my felicitations and express my appreciation on behalf of the expedition for your wonderful work in handling our messages destined to England. Good communication not unlike good conversation takes two and I must say you didn't fall down at your end but demonstrated that you not only have a first-class station but understand thoroughly its operation.

As you have probably noted above, I am with the advance party and (will) erect a station when opportunity allows at the various camps to communicate with the base station "WJS" reporting advance, ordering supplies etc, etc. The first message received tonight was from Mr Hinks of the Royal Geographical Society and it delighted me so much that I thought I should sit down and write you immediately about it.

The delay in the delivery of the message addressed to Dr. Rice was caused by the field station being out of commission from February 2nd to February 20th during which period the exploration party was advancing up river. Some idea of the difficult nature of the country that we have just come through can be had when I say that some days working from daylight until dark, we could look back and see the campsite of the previous night, less than one half a mile away. Three times the canoe in which my radio apparatus was loaded came near being swamped in the whirlpools and rapids and on two occasions my radio equipment was thoroughly water-soaked only to be placed in the sun to dry and the journey continued.

The station here consists of a 25-watt VT transmitter utilizing R.C.A. UV203A 50-Watt tubes – a small generator delivers 500V. to the plate instead of the stated 1000V. Just now the difficulties of travel and a little hard luck has reduced the installation to but one valve making the input to the antenna about 13 watts. Working on a wavelength of 70 metres I have excellent communication with Mr. McCaleb at "WJS" and have sent a message via a station at Atlanta, Georgia (HDO). My signals have also been reported 2SA at New York by many of the amateurs there. Considering I'm using a one wire T antenna, 40 feet in length and 50 feet in height, adequate counterpoise etc., right in dense primeval forest – this short-wave stuff is truly remarkable. I was optimistic enough to give you a call 6 G.M.T. this morning. Your signals come in here very strong on detector alone, using a counterpoise as receiving antenna (our antenna to "beat" the static).

The base station "WJS" at Boa Vista is a 100-watt station, V50-watt tubes parallel, 1000 VDC on Plates and a very efficient antenna system. Mr. McCaleb, my fellow ham, has done excellent work there and the station has been heard practically the World over.

A complete detailed report will be made by me as soon after the completion of the expedition as possible. I shall be glad to mail you a copy of it.

I sincerely hope that if you can get around New York way that you will look me up, I would be delighted to meet and congratulate you in person.

Please address communication to me: Radio Rice Expedition, c/o U.S. Supervisor of Radio, Customs House, New York, N.Y.
I must return to duty there by June 1st.

Again with heartiest congratulations, I am respectfully, John W. Swanson. Sent February 21st Received May 1st 1925.

(U.S. Radio Inspector on leave to take charge of radio Rice Expedition.) The first contact between Great Britain and South America marked a significant milestone in communications, not least under the conditions in which this was made. The RGS archives include a significant number of slides that record the event although the 'cabinet' that Marcuse set up appears to have been completely dismantled with components missing. The tray of remaining pieces includes some of those which were originally used as seen photographed in the RGS journal: The Geographical Journal, Vol. 67, No. 6, June 1926, pages 536-552. As the cabinet is missing and with many missing items it leaves a lot of unanswered questions. The RGS has catalogued their archives as: AHR/1, 2, 3, & 4. Dr. Rice's material from the Marcuse contact is AHR/2:

Hamilton Rice Expedition July 25th 1924 – June 1st 1925
Notes and lists of positions sent to RGS for preparation of map. About
200 oblique photos were taken with a Fairchild Aerial Camera, 20"
focus.

o~o

Appendix 4: The Marcuse Interviews

Below are the Interviews with Marcuse that were conducted by Harry
Clark (H.A.M.), G6OT, Leslie Rose, Jim (G2ARC, Ina Procter and his
son David, and Frank King G2FR. These were held in November 1960
and were based on a number of subjects including Empire
Broadcasting. The original version exists on a tape reel held by the
Marcuse family from which a full transcript was taken many years ago.
The transcripts taken from the tape are on a typed document which is
held by the Amberley Museum and they are printed below.

Interview 1: Marcuse with Harry Clark

Harry: "It would be natural to start at the beginning."

Gerry: "1913 I started"

Harry: "Did you have a licence then?"
Gerry: "I only applied for it – we did not bother about licences and
I never had a pre-war licence like Michael. It was Hamblin Clapp

Harry: "Did you contact him?"

Gerry: "Yes, 2KZ"

Harry: "Did you contact him on spark?"

Gerry: "Yes, and another fellow who never had a licence – in
Purley. Can't remember his name. Used to have a lot of fun on Sunday
morning."

Harry: "Where did Hamblin Clapp live?"

Gerry: "In Purley where I lived."

Harry: "Across the street?"

Gerry: "About a mile. We had very good contact, and then of course we started on spark in 1919 at Bristol with Alan, Hippersley and Wilcox the person's son from Warminster – of course they are all dead now."

Harry: "What type of spark coil did you use?"

Gerry: "Just an ordinary Gamage spark coil with a half inch spark, and then we started making rotary gaps. Alan, 2HG of course, was a very good engineer. The other night I told Irene that there was the 'Student Prince', they tried very hard to get me to broadcast, but the Post Office would not grant me a line. I paid £3 15s 0d for the two lines at Percy Valentine's house. He had the control room and studio and they had a music room there – wonderful place. His uncle was a conductor of the Lloyds Insurance Orchestra, so occasionally we used to have an orchestra. Mullard came down and gave a talk. This was the Empire Broadcasting at Caterham. We had Percy Valentine – and he had a studio. Had a full orchestra there – the Caterham orchestra. We used to broadcast in the afternoon."

Harry: "Then you had an Australian broadcaster?"

Gerry: "Yes, an Australian, Rosa Alba, then I had an all-Australian (concert). Harold Williams and all that crowd at the Columbia Studios. We have one of the singers living in Bosham now. Evelyn Scotney."

Harry: "These early spark days, how far did you get with that?"

Gerry: "Warminster – what was that - 20 miles."

Harry: "... and you were supposed to be on some wavelength?"

Gerry: "Yes, 180."

Harry: "Was that after 440?"

Gerry: "Before. (We) were on 1000 but Croydon was grumbling on Sunday morning that we were endangering life; then we went to 400 but the Post Office said we want that for broadcasting so 'off you go' and then said 'you can have all the metres below 200' – they are no good commercially. A classic remark."

Harry: "You were on 440?"

Gerry: "... and 1000. I was on them all."

Harry: "I have a very old log book – in the moves they got lost."

Harry: "Pity."

Gerry: "We did the chess match between Harvard University and Oxford – all night. That was 1924, at Caterham. It is a pity these fellows gave up so many years. Alan went off the air for about 15 years, so did Ralph (G2MJ). I am about the only one who has been continuous. I have kept going. They all went off the air. Fred went off for about 15 or 20 years. So did G2WJ and G2HQ. No, of course you cannot dispute that, Harry."

Harry: "No, it's in print. Did you start to do Empire Broadcasting before the BBC said they couldn't?"

Gerry: "Yes. It really started with Bermuda. 'BER' – a fellow there was a very enthusiastic amateur. Still alive. Called himself 'BER'. He used to receive me on 32.5 and rebroadcast in the islands. Then I had a letter from a lady. She wrote, 'I am enchanted with your voice which I hear every Sunday morning and I have three lovely daughters and a flourishing business. If you would like to come over you can have the pick of the daughters and the business.' Unfortunately I cannot find that letter. That is absolute gospel.

Then this fellow – this is interesting, but I cannot think who it is – he came over to England and got tied up with a BBC singer – a

104

leading singer – about 1928, can't think of her name. He got tied up with her and she had a husband and he was threatening this fellow that if he did not go back to Bermuda, he would shoot him.

So this chap, BER, came to me and said his father would not 'cough up', would I advance him the money to get back to Bermuda and he would send it back. So I paid his fare back to Bermuda. He brought this girl down. All done up in cotton wool – had bronchitis – to Caterham, a leading singer of the day, can't think of her name, and he got tied up with her and she had a husband. I paid his fare back and never heard from him since. They tell me he is still alive and still interested in Bermuda."

Harry: "And it's really his reports, or this other woman's reports that started it off?

Gerry: "Lots of them. Then I applied to the Post Office. Said I was willing to foot the bill, build the transmitter and transmit the programmes, and they gave me a limit of so many hours a week, and then 2FC – Sydney – wrote to me, had they (they had) permission to rebroadcast. Same as Ceylon and broadcasting organisations in the world and they used to rebroadcast my transmissions."

Harry: "What sort of power did you start on?"

Gerry: "About 1500 or 1200 watts. Originally, I had one of the first Goyder lock crystals in the country – that was about 500 and then I went up to 1½ kw and that's what I stuck at. Then the BBC got jealous and worried and started on 20 metres and everybody used to tell me that they couldn't hear them, but could hear me. So then the Post Office told me to clear off; they were going to start Empire broadcasting on the frequencies I used as it was so successful and they had to close me down."

Harry: "But you ran for two or three years?"

Gerry: "Two years."

Harry: "Every Sunday afternoon?"

Gerry: "No, every morning at 7am and then I always used to rebroadcast the Armistice Service at 11am and Big Ben – everybody clamoured for Big Ben and nobody would give me a recording. I had to wait until 12 (midnight) – it was the only time in those days they did it. Everybody wanted Big Ben. We used to broadcast the thrushes in the morning from Caterham."

Harry: "That was chiefly gramophone records I expect?

Gerry: "Yes, and live broadcasts from the BBC. Had a receiver at the bottom of the garden – remote control and I used to switch that on to receive them."

Harry: "Your licence permitted you to rebroadcast?"

Gerry: "It didn't, but I did. I did not care in those days. It cost me several thousand pounds but I achieved my object (ive). My father said I was wasting my time and money because there was no revenue and he only believed in revenue."

Harry: "Yes. There was no money."

Gerry: "No money – all output. I used to get various artistes down from London. Sent up the car and fetched them."

Harry: "Marconi was more helpful than the BBC?"

Gerry: "Yes, Marconi was a great help. I still have their microphone."

Harry: " A Reiss microphone?"

Gerry: "Yes. Mullards were very good – Captain Mullard helped me a lot when my generator blew up. Had it rewound for me. They supplied all the valves. The valves I got were free." It would have been a fantastic cost without them."

Harry: " You were high up at Caterham?"

Gerry: "700 feet up and 100-foot mast."

Harry: "Who put the mast up?"

Gerry: "Cooper Scrutton, still going. Do most of the ships rigging. Bullers built the mast – old Nick 2KP (T)."

Harry: "And you were working 32.5, that was in the 30-metre amateur band?"

Gerry: "We had that band in those days."

Harry: "Did you have any trouble with interference from the amateurs?"

Gerry: "No, so few of them. Not like today, and you very seldom heard of foreigners."

Harry: "Had you worked all those places, Australia and so on, by then?"

Gerry: "Yes, that's what gave me the urge."

Harry: "The dates between which you were running this regular broadcast service – started in 1927 didn't it?"

Gerry: "Somewhere about then."

Harry: "Finished by the time you went to Sonning?"

Gerry: "Oh yes. Only did a little bit at Sonning on 20 metres, just kept the old call (sign) going. Did a bit on Sunday afternoon. No, Caterham was the dream home for transmission. A wonderful site you see."

Harry: "When you were in the 30 metre (band) as amateurs, was that chiefly on CW or were you working phone?"

Gerry: "CW and phone. Mostly CW in those days. I had the first contact with Singapore, India and the various other countries."

Harry: "It was Singapore wasn't it, that caused all the frustration with the Admiralty?"

Gerry: "No, Stone cutters, Hong Kong. So in the end we built the transmitter and sent it out and when my words came out, they wouldn't believe it. Only a little thing, I used to work them on it, they would not believe it. They had their great racks there and still did not get through. Then the 'Yarmouth' went out on these trials and I worked all the way to Hong Kong every night on special tests. That's when Admiral Somerville was in charge, he had great vision. Nobody in the services was taking any interest in the short waves. (They) said that they were so prone to fading and disappearing. They did not believe in them. Old... what's his name – he confirmed it when I saw him at Portishead, said to me 'My station will keep communications with the world long after you have finished with short waves'. Now Rugby is bristling in short waves. He's now Chief Engineer, you saw him."

Harry: "Yes, at the Bristol Convention."

Gerry: "Oh yes, we had wonderful times. Of course you had no interference, the receivers were poor and homemade and we had not quite got to the superheterodyne.
Harry: "The 1 – V – 1's and things."

Gerry: "Then we started on HF with a V24 and a VQ and then Igranic brought out a kit, a super kit and I built several and I remember a doctor from Hampstead wrote to me and said, 'I understand you have an Igranic superheterodyne working? I am willing to buy it and I will pay you whatever price you like'. I sold it to him, then I built a Bowyer-Lowe superheterodyne and Charlie Wimble, one of the chaps from the market bought that from me. He insisted on buying it, he could not get one to work and I built quite a lot for chaps. Old Kenneth Alford, now there's an old timer, came in at the very early stage but he used a Goyder Lock and could never get the lock. I could hear him either side, I heard from him the other day."

Harry: "Did you?"

Gerry: "Yes – the oldest timer I remember. He used to come over to Caterham but he never did any good with transmission. There was 2OD, 2KF and 5RV – O'Ryan.

Harry: "6LJ?"

Gerry: "No, he didn't do very much. He was on it but was not one of the Transatlantic boys.

Harry: "Ralph, 2WJ?"

Gerry: "Yes, Ralph and 2SH – Old Shoggie."

Harry: "Ralph got in trouble for feeding news to the press, didn't he?"

Gerry: "Did he? Old 2LZ, he was the one I had the biggest trouble with for telling the world not to take any notice of 5DH – the Dollis Hill Post Office Station. That was the biggest headache I had. The days I spent up at the Post Office, round the table with him. It was only over-enthusiasm, but he will get into trouble again one of these days. I got him (taken) off in the end." He is using M.M. – Mobile Marine. There are no British mobile marines, so they all go back to him."

Harry: "He is not Mobile?"

Gerry: "No, not mobile there are no mobile marines, only on 2 metres. They would not give me one, there was one Captain on a coal barge."

Harry: "That was the Newcastle line."

Gerry: "That's right. These people are all very stupid – these mobile chaps. Of course the Post Office have very little faith. There is no doubt about the amateur today, they regard them as an unnecessary evil and the RSGB does not have the influence with the Post Office that we used to have because we were doing the stuff. There is nothing in it today. Brute force and ignorance."

Harry: "There is still good liaison with The Post Office. Good."

Gerry: "They are fighting a lot of the newer things – RTTY, slow speed television, facsimile – lots of things like that and if it had not been for them, there would never have been any amateur television on 460 mc/s. We even had to get aircraft flying for tests to prove it was not causing interference."

Harry: "What is this teletype?"

Gerry: "Well, instead of using Morse, it uses a high speed 5-unit code, the sort of thing that teleprint goes on – those signals with the funny noises that you hear. That is Teletype. It is tied up very much with buying radio ex-service equipment, no amateur could build one. They are trying to standardise things in the world because the Americans have one sort and the British have another.
This transatlantic phone cable is very wonderful."

Harry: "It has beaten radio."

Gerry: "No interference. You never hear a really clear radio commentary, it always gets that echo and fading."

Harry: "One of the Grand Bank trawlers caught one early this year. They had it up and repaired in 36 hours."

Gerry: "Off Newfoundland. I think the biggest progress today, Harry, of scientific development, is the Eurovision. I think the picture of King Baudoin – perfect transmission all the way through, and the finest one from Paris."

Harry: "I saw that, you were at Calais."

Gerry: "Yes"

Harry: "Supposed to last half an hour and went on after midnight."

Gerry: "All those outside broadcasts, films and transmissions, they are all very good quality. Commentators say you get the benefits, you can see it better than we can." Well, now they have the magnetic tape it will be easier. What the amateurs are trying to do now is to get a television picture across the Atlantic.

Harry: "Have you seen Jeremy's?"

Gerry: "Yes, it is very fine. Both Ralph and Jeremy have two-way television and are now running links like Eurovision. They have four transmitters, one after the other across the country and I reckon it will only be another year or so before Jeremy and Ralph will be getting television pictures across into Europe.

Harry: "They are enthusiasts."

Gerry: "There are a dozen or two. Jeremy's transmission – and Ralph has his own camera, one of our tubes on a Pye camera. A very remarkable achievement of Jeremy's. Just as enthusiastic. Every minute of the day and night and his wife does not mind. She is very tolerant. One of the finest things I ever remember was – most interesting – some fellow one-day said 'you're an old timer'. I said 'yes' and he said 'is your wife still living with you."

Harry: "He might well ask."

Gerry: "Yes – want to look at my dining room. Not many wives would have stayed with him. How that girl has suffered, she is a heroine."

Harry: "What time did you start?"

Gerry: "Used to broadcast before breakfast."

Harry: "Where was that?"

Gerry: "Australia – fifteen item programme."

Harry: "Just nice evening listening time; you did this before you went to the office?"
Gerry: "Yes."

Harry: "The office did not matter!"

Gerry: "No, you see Harry, in those days conditions in the city were so.... I would say, look here, this outfit is going to cost me a couple of thousand pounds. Well, we would make it; in those days you could make money in the city.

Harry: "Yes."

Gerry: "Don't forget, I used to trade in everything, pepper, cocoa, any mortal thing, clothes, rice. If you made a loss then you put that against the previous year, or future year. Today you cannot do it."

Harry: "How did the 'Star' get hold of that story, did you tell them?"

Gerry: "No, probably sent by a radio correspondent somewhere round the office. 'What are you going to do tomorrow night?' Something like that."

Harry: "And who was receiving that?"

Gerry: "Oh, someone in Australia."

Harry: "What was that cutting?"

Gerry: "Out of the 'Star' the London evening paper."

Harry: "They have a correspondent in Australia, I suppose?

Gerry: "I suppose so. It was headline news in those days."

Harry: "32 metres days?"

Gerry: "Yes
Harry: "From Caterham?"

Gerry: "Yes, 1927. Now how many hams today were transmitting in September 1927.

Gerry: "Harry, I was!"

Harry: "Yes, but how many

Gerry: "I don't know, it would be interesting to know, wouldn't it? I should not think it was more than a few dozen. I doubt if it is 50, as you say, very few of us have held a licence continuously. Yet I think people like Ralph held their licence, but they are not on the air. I could not find old Fred, before the war I was working every Sunday."

Harry: "After the war we had a great search to find them.
Gerry: "Yes"

Harry: "Heard any more of Barbara Dunn?"

Gerry: "No, nor Nellie Corry. (*Harry was talking about Nellie Corry*) She is back again, went to New Zealand. Several of them worked out there."

Harry: "What else have you got in that book?"
Gerry: "Any amount of things."

Harry: "A wonderful book."

Gerry: "It would take us all day, I had a very good secretary, Hoskins, and he dealt with it all, a very good chap. He is now running a paper business in Portslade."

Harry: "This was all after you had one most of your travelling?"

Gerry: "Yes, my travelling I did as a boy, David's age. It was wonderful then, no motorcars or aeroplanes, all camels and spring-less wagons. No radio, I'd have given anything for a radio then, I only had a camera. Got some photographs of my travels."

Harry: "I have not seen them."

Gerry: "I must get them out."

Harry: "It would be interesting to see what some of those places were like in those days."

Gerry: "Yes. Yet Baghdad today is a commercial city with television; when I was there it was just a shantytown. They were then surveying the land for the railway which is now the Bagdad Railway."

Gerry: "Were they – at that time?"

Harry: "Yes, just surveying. They had a little bit of railway run by a British company between Adana and Messina, about a couple of hours run, that's all. A little steam locomotive. Yes, all English signals and stations. At Tarsus, halfway between Adana and Messina was an American college and hospital.

Interview 2: Marcuse Frank King & Harry Clarke

Frank: "I want you to tell Gerry – or you and Gerry decide – on the year of your first contact."

Harry: "A bit difficult to remember that isn't it."

Gerry: "Yes, about 1920/21."

Harry: "I should make it 1923 to be on the safe side, at Caterham."

Gerry: "We were on 1000 metres when the Post office told us to shut up, so we went to 440 metres and the BBC told us to shut up on that, so we went to 220 and the Post Office said you can have all the frequencies below 200 because they are no good commercially. We showed them how to work. The chief engineer at Rugby said his old 20,000 metre transmitter would be going long after we had finished with short wave and he reminded me of the fact not many years ago at the Bristol Convention. Changed his tune now!"

I remember the first transmitter I built for short waves. It was the old 45 metres. 2FK, 2BOZ, G5AD and as 5AD, the first transmitter I built for 45 metres was built with the valve clamp strapped to two beer bottles.

The valve and its coils: two-quart beer bottles, the grid coil was on one bottle, the anode coil was strapped to the other bottle and the valve which was an LS5, with its base decupled. That was a two-plate, two-grid transmitter that was later on improved after listening to Goyder Lock by placing an eyeglass that had been ground down; I bought it for 1d in the Cattle Market at Islington.

This was ground down to the frequency required and this crystal was placed in the grid coil and the whole thing tuned till it locked with the crystal. I was able to work Australia two-ways. After that I made a phone transmitter of 45 metres that was built round the B4 dull-emitter. Wonderful valves they were.

After that the transmitter that followed was two DET1's, which were presented to me by GEC, dull-emitters, push-pull in the old Mesny circuit. The only thing was, I used an aerial about 180ft long of copper tape and it used to whistle and bang in the wind like the devil. This Mesny circuit being three coils, the grid coil inside the anode coil and the aerial coil outside the anode coil.

The trouble with a Mesny Circuit was unless you had an expanding aerial coil, you over-coupled every time so you transmitted on two different frequencies on the same valve. I used a counterpoise on that. Going lower in frequency to 20 metres I used a double strapped top aerial and three-strapped bottom counterpoise.

One of the earliest excitements and interesting letters I had from the GPO – they wrote and said they had a letter from the Japanese

Authority to say that my signals had been received consistently out there on several night and they would be glad to know what frequencies I was using – what power and if I was exceeding my licence terms, they would be very pleased to grant me a licence to carry on with these experiments.

Of course we had all the experiments with the cruiser 'Yarmouth' when she went out to Stonecutters and I did some regular test with the Admiralty. Admiral Somerville was then in charge and he was very interested in amateur radio, also Stonecutters because they could not make out how we could get such signals to Stonecutters on such small valves, so we actually built them a transmitter and a receiver and they had wonderful results with it.

That was in the early days. I used to keep on night schedule with stonecutters every night around 32-45 metres. It never failed, there was no QRM, no interference, it was all to yourself.

Harry: "I remember when 5KU and I came down to Caterham. A query you had about biasing a double-ended valve with a Franklin shield on it. On a wooden chassis, it was an American whitewood chassis. You had some bias problem about it and 5KU solved it for you.

Gerry: "We put in those HT accumulators at about 220V. It was a big thing, about a foot long, 95F. We had a couple of modulators to suit, choke coupling using Heising coupling. Great big pancake coil and sub-control. We had two Post Office lines to my pal's house and he did the studio work while I ran the transmitter.

Do you remember when 5CP, 6KJ, 2RK and myself all got together? Someone was playing a piano at 6KJ's, someone singing at my place, 5CP picked it up and transmitted by the other chap – forgotten who it was. Three different stations transmitting three different signals and compounded transmitting into one transmitter; that was in 1925 – I remember the date exactly.

If you tried to do it today you would get shot at dawn!

Coming up to more recent years, about eleven years ago now, I went to Rangoon to do some flying for the Burma Oil Company. I took out all the equipment to build a transmitter out there and, on the way, we crashed at Karachi and I got the transmitter going in the little shack that

I was given to sleep while the aeroplane was being repaired – I was able to contact England the same night.

Out in Rangoon I was XF2FK. I had over 4000 contacts in 210 days on the air. The Americans used to line up for me. I used to hear them making arrangements, I, 2, 3, 4, 5, 6, 7 and so on to contact me. I used to work as many as 60 to 70 an hour on CW using a bug key. I had two 807's on push-pull driven by one of those RCA VFO units. Wound up by a handle, very good. On 20 metres I used a full wave aerial fed with co-axial at $\frac{1}{4}$ wave along and for 10 metres I had a tubular dipole. No beans in those days. I could have put beams up but it was not necessary because Rangoon is a particularly good place for transmitting and receiving.

Harry: "Plumber's delight' was not thought of!"

Gerry: "Well, yes, they were because XF2KN had one with the rotating apparatus as well – a plumber's delight, but it was not necessary if you had an efficient transmitter. I made 168 contacts with 8DL in those days and he used to phone through to my home and see how things were for me and punch it back over the air. Later on – Gillian was in Cyprus – I used to talk to her on 10 metres.

Harry: "The Post Office frowned on it."

Gerry: "But turned a blind eye – they told me so themselves.

Harry: "Do you remember the first 'Hamfest' that was made in Wardour Street?

Gerry: "5KU, you and I made a film of various Ham stations and when we switched the projector on after the dinner at Pinoli's, we blew all the fuses in the restaurant. Bob Pollack, 5KU went and borrowed a couple of ladies hairpins and put them in the fuse box – real 'Ham fashion'. The first Hamfest was held at my place in North London and 61 Hams came from all over England. We did not speak a word of wireless – played poker, pontoon and drank beer and whisky all night. I remember those Hamfests at Pinoli's, they were good days and then we got on to a more prosperous type of dinner at the Cecil, which is no more, the Waldorf. Admiral Sir Henry Jackson and Dr. Eccles and all those various big shots used to come, but the early Hamfests beat the lot.

Harry: "Remember the first Hamfest Party, the blind fellow was the President?"

Gerry: "Ian Fraser. I used to spend many happy hours in Regents Park with Ian Fraser, very happy days they were. You will never repeat them. I still say today that the biggest curse of Ham Radio today is the contests. Everyone comes on for the contest, you never hear them again."

Harry: "What about when old Henderlick started selling crystals?

Gerry: "Wonderful – used to buy square bits of glass for various frequencies – they called them crystals. Ernie Dedman started making crystals, still is – 2NH and they cost the earth now. Used to cost 1d or 1/-d. It has completely changed.

Harry: "It's a long walk Gerry from a debased LS5 on two beer bottles to the old Tiger 300."

Gerry: "You have to buy everything now. They won't even give you discount. In the old days they were only too anxious to let you have a bit of stuff.

Harry: "When did you first meet Ralph Royle?"

Gerry: "No, I can't remember, was it 1920?"

Harry: "What was his callsign?"

Gerry: "2WJ. He was a schoolboy then. One of the transatlantic boys and short of a couple of chokes – 5KU's. But Ralph, it must have been 23 or 24."

Harry: "Do you remember 2XO – Maidavale?"

Gerry: "No."

Harry: "He was killed by a bomb outside his house - last war. Of course, Basil Davis is still going and 2BZ, he is a real old timer."

Gerry: "I know, because when I used to use my callsign, 2BOZ used to ring me up and say: 'are you using my callsign', because 2BZ was not allowed to go on the air, he was on an artificial aerial. He is still going on 2 metres only. He was one of the 1000 metre boys.

Harry: "Where does he live now?"

Gerry: "Same place, Park Lane.

Harry: "He is still there, on top of the flat? He used to be in the picture house."

Gerry: "No, he sold that. Do you remember Basil Davis's mother started a picture house with an old gas engine? Opposite that little alleyway where Lee's garage was, opposite the Trocadero. The old gas engine was in the corner and that was where, with his mother, they built the Croydon Theatre and the Marble Arch Pavilion, that was their venture.

Harry: "He was 2BZ and his brother had a callsign too."

(...the conversation continues but it is unclear who is talking...)

"Who was that old timer?"

"QQ"

"No, who was the bloke, 5KN, Cullen. Still going up in the Lake District now."

"Used to be on Putney Hill. I went there two or three times to see him. He was the Cullen of the grocery shops. Old Horace, like you, used to buy anything"

119

"Another old boy was 2LZ."

"Peter Eckersley – that's the one!"

"Active again now."

"Peter Eckersley, he got burnt out."

"2OO. Of course a lot of the old timers gave it up, did not carry on, but some of them came up again."

"2BY, talked to him on the phone the other day. I said, 'have you finished radio?' and he said 'never let it be said that 2BY has closed down.' He is building again, himself."

"2LZ – he is going strong now, back in the DX, and 2DQ." A lot of the old timers are resurrecting. 2MI – Milne, he is (still) going."

"Old 2CL doesn't go on the air much."
"Yes, every Sunday at 9.30 – RSGB news service."

"From the Science Museum?"

"No, that's 2BRS."

"Talking about the Science Museum, been in there once or twice. You go in and see the RSGB, which is exclusively for amateurs. All the equipment in there is commercially built. That's a thing I cannot understand. Why don't they have an amateur station there – transmitter and receiver. The whole thing is commercial."

"Where is the old RSGB transmitter?"

"Scrapped."

"5ML, Coventry – Fred Miles, he is only interested in 2 metres. I saw him at the Bristol Convention, he still lives at Kenilworth Road, between Warwick and Coventry."

"Go on Frank."

Frank: "I think the most wonderful bit that you could say about amateur radio on the transmitting side in the old days – and receiving – my first wave receiver for 45 and 23 metres was built on a glass panel and two valves, Reinartz. As regards transmitting, you had to build your own variable condenser and make your own resistances, everything! A wonderful feeling of satisfaction you got when you saw the thing work. The first time I gave a test call, 'de 5AD, five Yanks answered me, I was so excited I could not answer them."

"Don't forget that our grid leaks were a glass of water. Yes, and we used to put the variable condensers in a bowl of cater oil for insulation – never drank the castor oil, in case we had to run away whilst operating. Wonderful satisfaction."

"You made everything on the table."
Frank: "I'll tell you something else I made in those days – the first bug key ever used in London and that was built using a spring out of a woman's corset, and I won't tell you which woman because I can't remember! But I pinched it whilst she was in bed. That had a steel button on it, the other end was clamped between two bits of wood and sprung on a 'V' shaped piece of steel in the middle. I used to send the dots and made my own dashes. I took that to the first Hamfest at Pinoli's and put it with a buzzer on a loudspeaker. Everyone was trying to work it, but they couldn't!"

"You are quite right Frank, that was the greatest thrill, to build something for hours on end and then put it in the air."

"And then old Gerry Marcuse – 2NM – he sold me a generator to run off DC mains and at the second or third Hamfest at Pinoli's, they made a recording of this generator and all you could hear was, '5AD ... brrr ... 5AD ... brrr."

"That was not old Gerry's generator which did it, it was your rotten smoothing."

"I remember Gerry charged me eight quid for the generator – he bought it for 10/."

"Frank, don't forget that the smoothing condensers and chokes were very difficult to get."

"I know, and another thing was I had to smooth everything in the negative side, that was the difficulty."

"I can show you a couple of condensers out there – still got them. One cost £50, two microfarads, 4000 volts."

"That's a lot of volts."

"I had two out there, one 2 microfarad, and one 1 microfarad. I used to put this generator down in the garage on a wooden plank and switch on from upstairs and the thing used to nearly jump off the plank when I switched it on. It was a Mackie. I know I kept it a long time for the money."

"I don't think I ever got a chance to sell much at a profit in those days."

"I'll tell you; a chap came to see me once – to see the transmitter – Lord Carlow. He came round and said 'I have been listening to you on the air and I think your transmission is wonderful', and I said 'Well, it's more than I think of it". He asked me if I would go down to dinner one evening and he had a flat at Kensington. So I went to dinner and I did not know there was going to be a party and I had my gardening clothes on, and sitting down to dinner – about 9 people round the table – he was sitting up at the end next to his mother with his foot on the switch with about forty lackeys to fetch the food in and the first course was soup. The next one was fish and starts with his mother and goes round the opposite way and I was sitting on the other side of him. His mother was on his right and I was on his left and, of course, the fish goes round the other way. Now this is perfectly true, the maid came round with this silver dish of fish right round to me. I was jawing away to Lord Carlow about radio and one thing and another and his mother was talking to the other people; I calmly took up the servers and took this fish off the dish and I looked round and there was nothing left! The maid looked at lord Carlow with her eyebrows raised and he said, 'Oh it's quite all right, I did not want any tonight'. That's perfectly true."

"Talking about dinner parties, remember old Ken Secretan – 'Sec never sleeps'. Well, he once put on an extraordinary party, used to live in Castlenau at Barnes."

"Yes, used his place as a relay station for the boat race."

"Well, he had sumptuous do's. Candelabra and chandeliers – and dressed up people and I went round there with 2OD, and my word what a party, and the last time I saw him was at the Oratory School at Reading, the BBC monitoring service or Home Office station. That was a wonderful era. "Sec never sleeps!" Sumptuous dinner, but enough fish to go round!"

Interview 3: Marcuse, Jim, Ina Procter & son David

"It's a long way back to 1927 when I thrilled the listeners in Australia with Empire Broadcasting, and here we are with a nice whisky and gin, and the company of Jim, Ina, Irene and in front of a log fire with David in the background listening to 'This is My Life'."

"My life since 1919 has been radio and the biggest kick I get out of my old age is talking to my old friends up and down the country. Thinking back, I say now, and repeat it, that the finest thrill of my life is amateur radio and talking to my friends up and down the world. There are many new ones who have joined us and I am sure they are all as thrilled as I am. With present day apparatus it is easy. When I started, we had to make everything ourselves, but now you buy the finest communication receivers, rotary beams, transmitters and everything else – no need to bother yourself – write it all on a piece of paper and send it in and 'Bob's your uncle'!"

"We have just installed a rotary beam with a rotating mechanism and you get north, south, east and west, and you can talk to the world; it is quite a thrill still, but not the thrill it was in 1924, 1925, 1926 and 1927 when we had to make everything ourselves.

"We had great assistance from the manufacturers, in particular the Mullard Valve Radio Company who supplied us with the necessary valves. The Transatlantic boys, 2KF, 2OD and 5RV – there were about half a dozen of us on the air then, all striving to maintain communication with 12,000 miles - down under."

"We did it with all home-made gear and now you hear people calling 'CQ' from the Pacific, Australia, New Zealand, South America and the whole world. When they are calling, they say what their gear is; it is always commercial. Nobody builds their own set today, whereas in the good old days of 1924, 1925, 1926 and 1927 we made everything ourselves. You could not buy anything and we were lucky if we got a valve that would stand up to what were then called high frequencies."

"We originally started on 180 metres spark, then we went to 1000 metres, CW and phone. We were chased off this wave by the Post Office and went to 440 metres. We were then chased off by the BBC and then the Post Office wrote me a letter when I was a big noise in the RSGB and said that I could have all the wavelengths below 200 metres which were no use commercially. We showed them what to do and now the whole world is on short wave."

"I have a letter somewhere from the Chief Engineer at Rugby. He said:

"My old 6000 metre transmitter will be going long after you fellows on 200 metres and below have finished."

"The reverse is the case. The best frequency is about 8 Mc/s, but of course ITV have got down to centimetric stuff, but they have not got the ranges that we have. They don't want the range, but I think the finest contribution today to the scientific world of radio is the Eurovision (Song Contest)."

"I think to sit in one's room in the armchair with a drink and a smoke, and look at Eurovision from Czechoslovakia or wherever it is, is the finest thing that has ever happened and for me in my old age it certainly is a great thrill and a great consolation, and I think we – all the old timers and early enthusiasts – have contributed and helped towards these ends."

"I am sure we shall, eventually, not only have colour television but Transatlantic programmes on TV, although they may not be all we desire, but I still say the Eurovision is the finest contribution to radio that has ever been made."

"And with that I will wish you all a very Happy New Year, God bless you and have many years of happy listening and looking."

"This is 2NM – the old timer – signing off. And wishing you all the best."

"Cheerio!"

Interview 4: Marcuse continued with Jim

Jim: "Were you in direct competition with BBC?"

Gerry: "Never, never in competition with the BBC. I proved to them that Empire Broadcasting was possible. They would not believe it. When I proved to them that it was possible, they started up their own stations, but they chose the wrong frequency and people used to write to me saying that my signals were better than the BBC's and they could receive them, but whereas the BBC were on 20 metres, I was on 32.5."

"I beat them to it and the whole world was re-broadcasting my efforts from Caterham and don't forget I was 700 ft. up with a 100-foot aerial and put in a good signal especially to the Antipodes. They were re-broadcasting my transmissions in India, in Ceylon, in Singapore and in Australia and New Zealand."

"The Americans sent out their USS Seattle – one of their battleships – to New Zealand to check my signals and they received my telephony

125

signals in New Zealand waters on board ship. Our old friend Schnell was on board and he gave me daily reports."

"The biggest joke of the lot was one morning (I always used to start at 6 am for the broadcast – the best period for the Antipodes) a fellow knocked at the door – threw stones at the window – and he was an American reporter. He said 'Can I come in? I said 'Why?' He said 'They don't believe what you are doing is correct in America and they have asked me to verify it'. I said 'Come along in'. He had five questions written out which he asked the American battleship Seattle and he asked them these five; they replied to every one so off he went back to town delighted!"

"The only trouble was the power supply, but eventually we managed to get a DC supply for 4000 volts with a generator. Then they changed over to AC. We were on 480 volts DC at Caterham where I lived, and when they changed to AC they re-equipped me and we went over to AC."

"We now have rectified current but the rectifiers in those days would not pass the 1 amp I needed, but the generator did so on that power we managed to demonstrate to the world."

Jim: "What was your first licence or permit?"

Gerry: "The Post Office gave me a licence – a special licence – an experimental licence."

Jim: "That was before the BBC?"

Gerry: "Oh yes – before 2LO. The GPO – my friends Wissenden and Brown gave me the licence for which I paid £5."

Jim: "And they did not restrict you to any frequencies at the beginning?"

Gerry: "Yes, to frequencies below 200 metres. No restrictions except that I was only allowed to transmit during certain hours. Two hours at a time. Otherwise there were no restrictions."

Jim: "How did you make your programmes interesting to listen to for other people?"

Gerry: "Well, we did a bit of re-broadcasting of 2LO. We had gramophone records and people came down to sing. I had two Post Office lines to my friend who had a Music Room that we converted into a studio and built a control room. He was an electronic engineer and I had the transmitter and he had the microphones and control, so we just carried on.

We used to broadcast the birdsong in the morning from England – the thrush and the blackbird – that everybody was interested in, local Church services and so on. When we were short of programme material we just went over to 2LO and it started up. Before we just had to use gramophone records, it was all we had, and local talent.

The microphone was lent to me by the Marconi Company, a Reisz transverse current type. We built all the amplifiers and of very good quality. Choke control, of course, with a sub-control and main controls, about 1500 watts, and it really did its stuff. A Zeppelin aerial and there you are – we managed."

Jim: "The first jump from the spark coil was to the valves?"

Gerry: "Yes, the spark coil was 1919 and then we started up the valves – when would that be – 1921, they were becoming surplus then. We managed to find a few valves and we made a modulation transformer out of pancakes and an iron core and gradually built up the equipment. Of course, it is now all plate and screen modulation but in those days we used Heising or choke modulation. Very good quality."

Jim: "Tell us about the Rice Hamilton Expedition on the Upper Amazon."

Gerry: "Dr. Rice's expedition – I contacted them one morning – WJS – it was on CW on the upper Amazon and they were stranded up there, out of touch with the world. I contacted them one morning. McCallin, an American amateur, he was the operator there, and I was able to give the Royal Geographical Society the progress of the special equipment they were using. The transmitter McCallin used on the Upper Amazon – or Rice Expedition – is now visible at the Royal Geographical Society in Kensington. It's there in a cabinet because I helped to put it in. That was WJS. It's there, the transmitter and receiver that McCallin used on the Amazon."

Jim: "What kind of receivers were they (using) in the early days?"

Gerry: "The detector and LP, and then we managed to coax an HF stage but it wanted some doing and then eventually they came to the supersonic receiver. TRF – that was the first job. The one detector valve and an amplifier and HF in front, and I have got one here now. One of the originals. I remember when we first made the moving coil loudspeakers – that was a bit of fun.

Jim: "It's very difficult to compare present day with the past."

Gerry: "Very, very difficult, and nobody who has not lived through the past could possibly realise or appreciate what we went through in the early days. No, no they take it all for granted today. They've got television, hi-fi, all those various – what is it – stereophonic."

Jim: "That was in the original days of radio. What was the signal you used for your first contact across the ocean?"

Gerry: "CW, like today, only no speech on it. Had not got down to modulating it."

Jim: "What year was it - 1924?"

Gerry: "Of course it was 1919 when I talked to Alan Fawcett on spark. He was a surgeon lieutenant on a destroyer and made a model of the ship. Very clever engineer."

Jim: "What was the distance you could get with a spark?"

Gerry: "Twenty miles."

Jim: "In those days was it when the band was open you got across?

Gerry: "No question of the band being open. We used to work Australia every evening at 6pm on 80 metres. Just probing the air. It was absolutely quiet in those days, no difficulty."

Jim: "What length of aerial did you have?"

Gerry: "A sausage aerial, like the navy, about 100 feet up. My equipment when I started cost me 30/-. I made everything. Copper wire sausage aerial."

Jim: "And was that better than one length of wire the same length?"

Gerry: "Yes, it had capacity. Two counterpoises to balance it, all joined together. There was a stretch and then joined them all together. We went on to Wyndham and Zepp. No beams before the last war. Beams, plumber's delights, came in about 1940.

Jim: "How many Watts did you use?"

Gerry: "250 Watts."

Jim: "Was it a home-made set?"

Gerry: "Yes, condenser, receiver, everything. Could not buy anything, except the odd valve. Mullard gave me the valves. Captain Mullard, a flier, was a very good fellow."

Jim: "You really felt you had achieved something. All your own effort?"

Gerry: "Admiral Somerville at Admiralty used to get me when he wanted a certain test. Would I carry it out."

Jim: "How did you get your high tension?"

Gerry: "With DC generators, and a battery for the filaments. I had a 4000-volt generator made by Mortley Sprague of Tunbridge Wells. The generator put out 4000 volts at 1 amp. Then they changed to AC and replaced all my equipment."

Jim: "Then they brought in the indirectly heated cathode?"

Gerry: "Yes, then they came and I put in a rectifier"

Jim: "Was Fred on the air in those days?"

Gerry: "2LZ, 2LD, 5BV Hugh Ryan. There are only a few left now. 2WJ (Ralph) and 2LZ, 2KF (Partridge). 2LD is dead."

Jim: "2MY in Lancashire – in the Preston area, did you know him?"
Gerry: "Burn, in Manchester."

Jim"   "Did you ever go in for coherers?"

Gerry: "I had one. Crystals came in soon. Buzzer down in the coal cellar to tune up your crystal! Hit it on the nose with the buzzer. The other one was the magnetic detector with a drum of soft iron wire between electromagnets."

Jim: "Was your first licence experimental?"

Gerry: "Yes. I had to write a thesis but I knew more about it than the Post Office in those days. They could not refuse me one. It was wonderful. You had the field to yourself. The Post Office said frequencies below 200 metres were no good commercially and we could muck about with them. On 1000 metres we interfered with Croydon aircraft, then we were driven to 440 and the BBC drove us down to 200 – muck about with that they said."

(Interview interrupted for drinks)

Jim:　　"I'd like you to tell them something of your early days in Russia."

Gerry:　　"I was a service engineer. I went to Odessa as a diesel engineer (for Rustons). I took out the first batch of diesel engines made in this country. In 1909 I was out in Turkey, Asia Minor. We made our first diesel engine. Mr Diesel was a German, he built a big vertical 100 HP diesel engine but we went in for two cylinders, horizontal. His was vertical and I took out a batch of these semi-diesels originally. Started with a blow lamp and carried on with the diesel, and then we went over to full diesel."

"I will tell you where there is a very fine Ruston plant and that is Alderney. They have four engines direct coupled to alternators. Going backwards, 1912 – I was in Mexico then, got back just before the First World War from Russia. My father went to Vienna as my sister was going to marry a Viennese – a very nice fellow – brilliant violinist and a wine and spirit merchant – but she came to the conclusion that she did not want to live in Vienna, so she did not marry him. My father made me go there and meet them. When I got there, I told him what was going on in the Odessa office and he said I was better out of it. It cost the firm £16,000 in the end because they had been diddling them. I came back to England. Well, I went and told the Managing Director what I thought of his boss in Odessa, but he did not agree, so I said right, I would go to Australia, but my dear mother said 'I have only got three of you, why go all that way?'"

"We had three factories in Bristol my father got involved in because they owed him money, and he said 'You go up there and sort that mess out', so I did and we eventually cleared out with a very good profit."

"Then I was at a loose end and he persuaded me to come back to the London office and I said this is no good to me, I am not a merchant, I

131

am an engineer. So I took up radio seriously as a Ham and built a station for Empire broadcasting. My father was an import and export merchant in London. I left engineering much to my disgust."

Jim: "These early diesel engines, what kind of fuel did they use?"

Gerry: "Similar to that they use today, only thick. Had to melt it. Had a clamp round the exhaust to melt it. Same injectors as now. We used to do a lot of suction gas plants. Now you would not believe it, but I went out with some suction plants to Asian Minor to install them and we imported anthracite from Belgium for these suctions.

        "Now in Central America, before the oil gushes there, we used to run these engines on green wood charcoal which was always full of tar and we had an awful job to get the tar out of them. Then they had the ordinary oil engine with the vaporiser and blow lamp and then came on to diesel. I suppose we had not got the machines to make the cylinder heads. It is combustion explosion and we had not got the engineers or material."

Jim: "Were you able to sell them and impress the people there with the engines?"

Gerry: "Oh yes, we sold a lot. I installed a lot, mainly for wheat cleaning at Odessa."

Jim: "Do you think Russia, in the days you were there – 1912 – was any different from what it is now?"

Gerry: "Oh yes, it was a wonderful country. Hospitable and easy going, good living and cheap. They always had a fear of the police and being sent to Siberia."

Jim: "Is Siberia as bad as we think it is?"

Gerry: "They have the salt mines there now. Pretty awful."

Jim: "Can you speak Russian?"

Gerry: "A little bit. I learnt enough to get round because I travelled extensively."

Jim: "How long were you there?"

Gerry: "Several years. Got back in England in time for the first war. Things went very badly in Russia. Revolution and killed the old Czar and his family."

Jim: "Was Royalty in Russia as grand as it is here?"

Gerry: "Much more."

Jim: "Did you see anything of the Pageantry?"

Gerry: "Plenty of it. It was open. They looked upon it just the same as here. The people were just as keen. Loyal, very good Church people, very wonderful choirs in the Churches, very good services, lovely country. Food was very good, entertainment was good, singing good in the Churches."

Jim: "I remember my mother saying my grandfather went to a banquet when the Czar came over here in London."

Gerry: "Germans were out there."

Jim: "You must have been very sorry to give up that life of travel?"

Gerry: "I was. One day I said to my father – I am going for a real holiday. I am going across America and Canada and I got £500 and I spent it."

Jim: "You could in those days."

Gerry: "I met all the radio hams over and back."

Jim: "You went by sea?"

Gerry: "Oh yes, by sea, across to America."

Jim: "When you went to Russia did you go to France and overland?"

Gerry: "No, Hook of Holland – Berlin."

Jim: "You have been very fortunate."

Gerry: "Yes."

Jim: "The travelling you have done."

Gerry: "I spent a long time in Mexico."

(Interview (possibly) interrupted)

Gerry: "My first motorbike had a service carburettor. Don't forget I had a driving licence for 55 years."

Jim: "That's a lifetime."

Gerry: "It is for a lot of people. I do the driving though."

Jim: "I know, now?"
Gerry: "It's not necessary. I can drive all right. Irene likes driving. Last year when we took David's car she went in one and I went in the other."

Jim: "That was three years ago."

Gerry: "Was it?"

Jim: "Was that the Triumph?"

Gerry: "No, with a Morris 1000."

Jim: "Do you remember what revs those Ruston engines did?"

Gerry: "About 180 – slow speed, horizontal. That's medium speed for now, isn't it David?"

Jim: "I think you must be very pleased that David has followed in your footsteps."

"How did they run so slow?"

Gerry: "They had a big bore and a long stroke."

"Horizontal engines?"

Gerry: "Yes – 400 revs. Is about as slow as you get."

Jim: "I bet David's Blackstones don't run any faster than 180, not the horizontals."

"The pumps wouldn't deliver the fuel at that speed."

"Oh, yes they will. They work off the camshaft. They will do it all right."

"650 for horizontals."
Gerry   "We used to run the big ends out and the cylinders out the back and one thing and another."

Gerry: "There were no aeroplanes, all camels springless wagons, horseback. Could not get from Syria to Baghdad only on horseback or camel caravan. No aircraft or motorcars."

Jim: "Wouldn't it be wonderful to have cine films of all your trips right from the beginning?"

Gerry: "Wasn't anything."

Jim: "Did you take out your engines in sections?"

Gerry: "906, yes, built them there. Local labour. You had to train them. There were no engineers, I went out on my own."

Jim: "What were the Russians like as engineers in those days?"

Gerry: "No good at all. I had picked 25 men and when I had finished with them, they could not screw a nut on without crossing the thread." Now they have fields of tractors that want servicing but they cannot service them. That's their trouble."

Jim: "They are not mechanically minded?"

Gerry: "No, very good pilots though, so are the Chinese and the Japs."
Jim: "Air or sea pilots?"

Gerry: "Air pilot. The Russian make a wonderful pilot but not engineer."

Jim: "Those low revs amaze me."

Gerry: "You can get the power alright."

Jim: "The pistons must have been like buckets going up and down the cylinders."

Gerry: "When you go to Yarmouth, Isle of Wight, take a trip to Carisbrooke Water Works. That is where I put in a new plant – years ago – we had a Heywood & Tyler's pump and they asked me to start it up and test it, so I did. It blew the reflux valve off at the reservoirs – flooded the whole of Newport.

There was a Nunnery there and these Nuns came out shouting and gesticulating in French that their yard was flooded. When the floods were in Newport the other day, I asked Eldred, 3LOK to try and find out if there was anyone in Newport who remembered when I flooded it, but I never had a reply."

Jim: "When was that, approximately?"

Gerry: "1908/9"

Jim: "Why were you pumping it out?"

Gerry: "Filling up the reservoir at the top of the hill from the wells
for the new pump, but the reflux valve would not take it. Their mains
were not big enough."

Jim: "What engines were they?"

Gerry: "130 horsepower."
Jim: "Diesel?"

Gerry: "No, suction gas – anthracite and the flywheel, weighed
about 3 tons."

Jim: "How did you make the gas?"

Gerry: "Out of a gas producer – a retort – with running water."

Jim: "CO and H_2O?"

Gerry: "Yes."

Jim: "Gerry, you ought to write book!"
Gerry: "I ought to write a lot of things. They would not believe it,
people would not believe it. A lot of you cannot imagine travelling
without aircraft or motorcars. Our friends in Bahrain used to come
over from Baghdad to Syria – shipped their car to England. They could
not understand it when I told them I had done it by camel or springless
wagons. Drove all night and pulled up at sunrise because of the heat.
Put the horses up. Slept in the wagons."

Interview 5: Marcuse continued with Leslie Rose, 1961

Gerry: "Leslie, you being a Holy Father, how would you like to tour the Holy Land with a camel and mule?"

Leslie: "I'd like it very much!"

Gerry: "I can say it was a filthy dirty place when I was there. You say it was a nice clean, rich place before the Romans came and stripped all the gold off the roofs. Where has all that gold gone? Well, it was a wonderful country. The people were hospitable in those days and you were never short of anything. Of course, it was very barbaric and dirty."

"To go down to the Dead Sea was a great thrill. Nobody, unless they have seen it, can believe that the Dead Sea is below sea level. Salt water, and you can lay in it and not sink. No fish or anything living in it. And there were the Dead Sea Scrolls. Go down to Egypt. I did a lot of work round Egypt on irrigation and pumping and the poor old Egyptians are now looking for Pharaohs. Why they don't let the dead rest I don't know. Why must they dig them up?"

Leslie: "Because if they don't dig them up themselves, foreigners come and dig them up – the Americans, Germans and English."

Gerry: "And all want the bits and pieces for their own museums."

Leslie: "Yes, so they decided to dig them up and have their own museum at Cairo."

Gerry: "How did they build the pyramids, there were no ropes, pulleys or blocks?"

Leslie: "Plenty of ropes."

Gerry: "Plenty of labour – manpower and time was no object."

Leslie: "Nor was labour."

Gerry: "When I was out there, if you wanted anything lifted, you got 100 men around it who said 'Yes sir' and up it went."

Leslie: "What were you putting in there?"

Gerry: "Putting in gas and oil engines for pumping water – Ruston's engines. Pumping water, cotton ginning and ice plants. All keen on having ice with their drinks. Used to bring snow over from Alexandretta in barges – frozen packed snow that they buried because they liked their drinks cold, and flour milling."

"At one place called Ayas where they had and old Inn there, the old chap who it belonged to wanted a flour mill and an ice plant and we landed this by sea, but the other went by country to Humijaab (?). We dragged it over the desert with some thrashing machine wheels roped together and twenty oxen and there we were for days on end, and I rode in the saddle for a week or two."

Jim: "You must have a hard behind!"

Gerry: "Over the desert, wonderful. No motorcars or lorries, no traction engines, just sheer hard brute force and we got the engine up to Humijaab (?) and we put it in!"

~ oo ~

Appendix 5: The Marcuse Letters

The letters form a fascinating history of Marcuse's life and experiences and the content varies from official to personal. The correspondence is held at the Amberley Museum in files and these contain hundreds items of correspondence. They represent a very comprehensive overview of Marcuse's achievements but as already stated there is evidence that letters and photographs were lost or were lent out to people and/or organisations and some of these may not have been returned.

1923 – 1926 (1 to 105)

1. The stamped envelope for letter dated 26th September 1923

2. Letter to J. E. Bowman of Newcastle on Tyne, thanking him for a reception report and suggesting that they arrange a further test.

3. Letter from an amateur in Halifax, Canada, dated Feb 27, 1924 inviting Marcuse to visit Halifax (in May). A very *chatty*, friendly letter that refers to recent contacts.

4. (i) Letter from Louis E. Weber dated March 5th 1924 confirming the first contact by his son (Charles Weber) in Abington, PA, U.S.A. and England.

5. Ditto 4, part (ii).

6. Letter dated April 26th 1924 to the ARRL requesting discussion about the simplification of British licence prefixes by the use of a single letter.

7. Two business notes to Marcuse dated 10th & 15th May 1924.

8. Letter from Jack Partridge (G2KF) to Marcuse dated 29th April 1924 stating stations worked from Dec 8th 1923 to March 10th 1924 from G2KF using 1Kw. It starts 'Dear NM' and ends 'Yours to a cinder, Jack Partridge KF'. He states that the most distant station worked was 'ZU Montana'.

9. Letter from Haverford College Radio Club, PA, U.S.A. with a diagram of the inverted cone aerial in use. The letter is dated 30th September 1924 and states that 'The game is assuming quite large proportions, and has already broken into the headlines in the local papers.' The correspondence sets out the organisation of a transatlantic-chess match between players in Oxford and Haverford. The game would be conducted from a wave band between 100-150 metres using a power of 500 watts from the

American side. Several tests are proposed from which the waveband used by the best signal would be selected.

10. Reverse of (9)

11. Undated letter from William S. Halstead, President of the Haverford College Radio Club. It comments on the wavebands to be used and the date and time of the chess match. It mentions that the game 'has developed into an important news item in this country'.

12. Reverse of letter (11).

13. Letter dated 20th October 1924 from the Czechoslovakian Radio Club in Prague ('RadioKlub Ceskoslovensky'). The letter is responding to Marcuse's letter inviting Czechoslovakian radio amateurs to participate in the transatlantic tests that were scheduled to take place. In his reply, the Hon. Secretary comments that: 'Czechoslovakian amateurs will be probably restricted to experimenting with receiving only, because laws and regulations here, at present, do not permit private experimental transmitting'. He adds that Marcuse's letter strengthened the position of Czech amateurs in their dealings with their ministry of posts and telegraphs.

14. A letter dated November 4th (1924) from H G (Abe) Munro, a member of the All-Blacks rugby team 1924-1925 who was in Dublin. He follows up a previous correspondence by asking if Marcuse would send a message to the 'Varsity Dunedin, New Zealand', 'Knee nearly O.K. about 3 weeks yet'.

15. Letter from E. B. Crocker, Sydney, NSW dated November 30th 1924 in which he sends a QSL card confirming reception of Marcuse's signals saying: 'It seems almost too wonderful to be so. It is a very easy matter to log you radio amateurs, but we have to get up at 3.30am Sydney time to try for England.'

16. Letter dated 30th November 1924 from Harold Turner, Melbourne confirming reception of one of Marcuse's transmissions on November 29th attempting to contact 3JU (South Yarra, Melbourne).

17. Reverse of letter (16).

18. Letter dated 3rd December 1924 from A.H. Curtis, the General Manager of Igranic Electric Co. Ltd., Bedford, in which he congratulates Marcuse for establishing communication with New Zealand and confirms that he was sending him a gift of the latest type of low frequency transformer. This had a 'flat and horizontal' amplification voltage curve from about 1000 cycles upwards.

19. Letter dated 4th December 1924 (sender unknown as part of page missing) from Sydney, Australia requesting a QSL card to confirm sender's receipt of Marcuse's transmission of 30th Nov 90-100 metres.

20. *Insert 'Marcuse Letters 1925, 1-19'.*

21. Letter from (? Benzio) dated 18th January 1925, Cachar, India thanking Marcuse for his cable confirming that he would be recommencing tests on 85metres on Wednesdays. Benzio apologises for being unable to reply as 'my power is only about 30 watts'. He says that he would convey Marcuse's greetings to other fans in India 'which I am sorry to say are very few yet'.

22. Letter from Charles W. Harris, London dated February 6th 1925 asking Marcuse to send a message to Bill Sloan, Toronto. He mentions that 'Mr Sloan, in spite of being crippled to a great extent, is a very enthusiastic radio amateur'.

23. Letter from C.E. Trott (5AS), Sardis, B.C., Canada dated February 20th 1925. He comments on Marcuse's visit to Vancouver where he took some photographs.

24. Letter from G. F. Morrow, G6UV, Berkhamsted dated 13th February 1925 confirming details of five late night contacts from Feb 13th – 14th.

25. Reverse of letter (24) recording a further set of communications.

26. Letter from Sidney L.W. Norwood, in Yorkshire dated 8th April 1925 requesting information on the identity of two French amateurs that he had listened to using a receiver that he had built. He enclosed details of Marcuse's signal strength and other amateurs he had heard (2ZY, 5GB).

27. Letter from Phyllis Payne from London, dated 1st April 1925, addressed to Marcuse. She thanks him for a 'Radiogram' that Marcuse had received from Mosul on 29th March that he forwarded to her in Cobham. She goes on to ask Marcuse if he would send a reply to an RAF Pilot Officer residing at No. 6 Squadron R.A.F. Mosul: 'Delighted: All love Phyllis'.

28. Reverse side of (27)

29. Three-page letter from J. F, Hall based at No 6 Squadron, R.A.F., Mosul, Iraq dated 25th April 1925. The content concerns pre-arranged schedules and discusses the effectiveness of using the 90, 45 and 39 metre wave bands concluding that the lower wave bands are more effective. He had asked 2LZ to buy him a 20-60m wavemeter and includes a diagram of his own design. He complains about the mains supply being unreliable, 'Any time I fail to answer a schedule you'll know I'm either on duty, or no mains. Cheers!!! JFH'.

30. Second page of (29)

31. Third page of (29)

32. Letter from G S Hight (4BQ) in Rome, Georgia, USA, dated 13th June 1925, headed 'Hight Sales Company'. He thanks Marcuse for sending a card and for entertaining the Hight family in England,

inviting Marcuse, his wife and daughter to visit him in the United States. He says that 'Am still too busy to fool with radio very much, but I hope this fall that we can have regular communications, and in that was keep in closer touch with each other'. He asks for a picture of Marcuse's daughter: 'I would certainly like to see that daughter of yours again, so don't fail to send me a Kodak picture of her'.

33. A four-page letter from Jack Orbell (Z1AX & Z3AA), Te Aroha, NZ, dated 29th June 1925. He mentions that 'I am using your Mullard O.M. and she's a beauty – better than my M-O valve'. He goes on to say that he intends to make a 1000-volt generator. Amateurs mentioned include, 4AG, G2SZ, G2LZ, FX1. He states that he 'also heard a Froggie calling CQ and signing YZ on 40m giving his QRA as M. Lebroast, Fort Issy, Seine'. He goes on to suggest over fifteen other amateur stations that Marcuse might hear.

34. – 36. Second, third and fourth pages of (33)

37. Two-page letter from A.E. Duckett of Birmingham dated 5th July 1925 confirming Marcuse's contacts with 5SI (on 45m) and 7DC. He states that he was using a 'Single Valve Armstrong Super' which I made up for short wave work'.

38. Second page of (37).

39. Card from Bazab (Bab Khan, likely written in upon receipt), Peshawar, India dated 25th September 1925. A reply is requested and there is mention of a previous, unanswered request 'Please forget all the angers and reply'. The reply address is not clear, but could be a police house; a crest of the crown appears at the top right.

40. Reverse of card (39).

41. Two-page letter from J. Spillard of 'Signals', Ramleh, Palestine, dated 5th October 1925. He mentions that: '...I have been ordered

to stop working on 45m and experiment on 20-25m, have however put in for permission to arrange test with you on 45m). He states that: 'My instruments are entirely home constructed and I have no RAF sets', and continues: 'Many thanks for photographs of your sets etc which I greatly appreciate. They make mine look like a crystal receiver in comparison'.

42. Second page of (41).

43. Letter from the Superintendent of Buildings & Power at Massachusetts Institute of Technology, USA, dated 14th October 1925. (He) states that he had just sailed from Southampton and was disappointed not to have met up. The transmitter at MIT, 1XM, used 50-watt output and worked on 40m.

44. Reverse of (43) missing

45. Letter from Les M. Mellase, Wanganui, NZ, dated 30th October 1925 mentioning: 'I had just previously posted to you a reply re some of your phone work with the 'Seattle', together with some newspaper clippings'. It includes the contact details of several New Zealand amateurs.

46. Reverse of (45)

47. Letter from Lt. N.R. Swales, Abbottabad, India dated 25th November 1925 confirming reception on 45m would be ideal for broadcasting speech and music into India. He adds: 'I am hopeful of being able to supply English music via loud speaker to one of the Messes here or to the Club (the social hub of Abbottabad) sometime this winter'.

48. Reverse of (47)

49. Letter from W.L. Carter (A-2WL) of the Wireless Institute of Australia, dated December 1925 (most of date missing) but received on 25th January 1926. The letter confirms that details of tests to be conducted by a vessel 'Yarmouth' would be furnished to 'several reliable amateurs in this State. I note the stipulation and

assure you, the schedule will not be given undue publicity by us'. It goes on to comment that he was sorry Marcuse had not contacted A-2WI yet and confirmed it was on 90m, at 10pm S.M.T.

50. Letter from J. Patterson, via Periakulam, South India, dated 21st December 1925. He encloses a circuit of his low power transmitter obtained from 'the Zenith Reinartz people' and asks for a circuit suitable for the 45m band, CW only. He mentions that he had ordered two low-power transmitting valves from a company called 'Autoveyers Ltd' telling them to send whatever Marcuse recommended them to send.

51. Second page of (50)

52. Circuit Diagram of Patterson's Transmitter

53. Letter from Constance Hall, Salisbury dated 10th January 1925 thanking Marcuse for arranging for a radiogram to be sent to her from her husband. She asks if Marcuse could send another message back to her husband.

54. Second page of (53).

55. *Insert:* '*Marcuse Letters 1926,   1 - 19*'.

56. Letter (2nd) from J. Spillard from Ramleh, Palestine dated 17th January 1926 (received 1st February 1926). He thanks Marcuse for some photographs and explains that he has been unable to contact him due to 'statics during electrical storms'. He had listened to Marcuse's contact with Newfoundland (8AR). He goes on to complain about his aerial system being surrounded by objects, including buildings and ironwork.

57. Second page of (56).

58. Letter from J.G. Mezger (F8GO) representing the International Amateur Radio Union. The headquarters was based in Hartford, Conn., USA and the letter was posted from Neuilly sur Seine, Paris, dated January 19th 1926. He asks if Marcuse is able to visit

him in Paris in order to discuss matters concerning the
International Amateur Radio Union. Marcuse was Vice-President
of the IARU:

'Could it be possible that you came here when Z4AA* will be
here? It would be very fine, I think if you managed to be here in
Paris at that moment as we could then, discuss different things
about the IARU as we are all 3 members of the E.C. and that as
the Constitution says, we make a majority and we might adopt and
discuss lots of things, of the IARU, as I think that you find, just as
me, that the IARU might do more things than it does till now.
How, OM?
Also, he mentioned that he had been ill and that his father had
tetanus ('He is recovering now, but so slowly (!!!!) and we have all
of us, had a terrible time in nursing him.').
* Frank D. Bell Z4AA Palmerston South, N.Z.

59. Letter from J. H. Leslie, RMC, Camberley, dated 31st January 1926
thanking Marcuse for his card and 'the schedule you arranged with
Saigon'. He says that he worked HBK and X2BG ('Urdaband,
north of Calcutta'). He states that he was dissatisfied with his
Harley receiver 'although I scrapped a straight set for it', giving
adjustment problems as the main reason.

60. Letter from C. D. Roberts, Sydney, Australia dated 26th December
1925 but received on 3rd February 1926. He stated that he had
heard Marcuse 'about 45 metres' and this was the first British
amateur he had heard. He mentions that he had heard:

· 'Over 100 USA stations, 2 from Canada, 1 Argentina, as well as
stations in the Philippines, Samoa, Guam Island, Java, Hawaii. I
have heard KDKA on 63 metres.'
He goes on to say that he had heard 20 American stations in 80
minutes.

61. Second page of (60)

62. Letter from Hamilton, Bermuda from Eva Tucker (Mrs Grosvenor Tucker, Real Estate) dated 27th February 1926, received 15th March 1926. She said that she heard Marcuse on her 2-tube set Radiola III, with ear phones. Also, she heard 'BER' announce that he would endeavour to relay 2LO London:

"I then heard a voice announce from the Savoy Hotel orchestra and then the dance music burst in, I heard it quite clearly at intervals but the local ships in our dockyard had a great deal to say which rather ruined an otherwise good reception... then came over the ocean the wonderful notes of "Big Ben" striking the midnight hour – you are doing a great work as also is our friend "Ber" Mr Hosington..."

63. Four-page letter from a shortwave listener, J. H. Harris, Enfield, Sydney, dated 19th January 1926. This gives a reception report of several transmissions that Marcuse made to the Philippine Islands and Australia, along with the transmission times. He adds: 'Might say your morse is the real thing – you are strongest of G's and always R4 to R6 easily readable'.

64. – 66. Second, third and fourth pages of 63.

67. Letter from C.J. Rockail, Amman, 'TransJordania', dated 16th April 1926 thanking Marcuse for a contact. He says that: 'I've left 6XK and have set up on my very own... I myself have been engaged on search for Spaniards on a Wireless Aeroplane, out searching practically all day and only too glad to turn in on arrival back to aerodrome and out again in the morning at dawn'. At the end of the letter he mentions that 'search for the Spaniards still unsuccessful, am beginning to lose hope for them'.

68. Second page of (67)

69. Letter from J.F. Hall, Cairo, Egypt, dated 13th May 1926. He apologises for the fact that RAF personnel were:

'Forbidden to communicate with stations other than Royal Air Force'. Of course this does not apply to experimental work done outside the R.A.F. in my own time and with my own gear so look out for me with a new call sign and new gear within the next few weeks. Treat this letter as confidential OM, won't you?'

He has included a small sketch of his transmitter circuit at the bottom of the second page.

70. Letter from C.J. Rockail, Amman, Transjordan, dated 17th May 1926. He mentions that the Spanish flyers were on their way home to Spain 'They were in a terrible condition as I think I told you...' Generally a very friendly, chatty letter concerning making contact, his time in the east and his radio work for the RAF.

71. Second page of (70).

72. Letter from Kenneth Ray, Johannesburg, S.A. dated 30th June 1926 in which he says he heard 2NM on 13-06-26 on the 40m-waveband and requests confirmation.

73. Letter from W.G.H. Hiles, H.M. W/T Station, Stonecutters Island, c/o H.M.S. Tamar, Hong Kong, dated 12th July 1926 in which he confirms where he experiences perfect communications and then says that he cannot get his rectified AC supply properly filtered. He includes a circuit used by HMS Ambrose that received 2NM's signals from Singapore as well as Marcuse's re-broadcasts of 2LO. He complains about the 'awful cost of components and the fact that I haven't much spare cash for buying them'. He says he would get on better in the winter 'when it isn't so blinking hot as it is now – the sea itself is generally at a temperature of 85 degrees F.'

74. – 76. Second, third and fourth pages of (73)

77. Letter from 'Brenda', Waihemo, New Zealand dated 9th August 1926 in which she writes a very long narrative receiving certain amateur stations but not hearing 2NM. The stations 2SZ, 2OD, 2LZ and 4AM are all mentioned.

78. Second page of (77).

79. Letter from Barbara Dunn, Steventon, Berks., dated 31st August 1926 in which she thanks Marcuse for his help to get her a transmitting licence. She says that she had returned the form to a Mr Mager but that:

'He is quite mistaken saying I go partridge shooting. I've never shot one in my life! Rabbits, jays, pigeons, stoats, rats and poaching cats are my mark – in fact sort of unofficial gamekeeper!' She continues to write a very interesting letter and adds that she had enclosed the form and a postal order for 15/-. She continues: 'I'm sure I can't be "OM" any longer' and she goes on to say that 'YL' sounds better than "OG" and ends the letter 'Barbara Dunn (OM) Old Maid!'

80. – 81. Second and third pages of (79)

82. Letter (9 pages) from R.H.E. Earle, Singapore, dated 2nd October 1926. He gives a detailed account of the weather conditions but mentions that owing to the 7-hour time difference he hears few British amateurs except from October to March. The 33m-band being good from about 1800 GMT. He states New Zealand and Australian amateurs are heard from about 1100GMT and gives details of the reception of amateurs in many other countries. He had contacted Australia using 25W input and was heard in England with this power level. During February the short-wave licence was withdrawn. Contact with 8QQ, Z2AC, OA3E, F8JN, F8TUV and GFUP (who was on HMS Durban, homeward bound) had been made and he had worked stations in all five continents in 5☐ hours. He had applied for membership of the T&R Section of the RSGB and asks Marcuse for support to enter the IARU. He was already a member of the ARRL.

83. – 90. Eight other pages from R.H.E. Earle.

91. Letter from 2MM, Twyford, Winchester dated 30th October 1926. He asks Marcuse to help him renew his T/A permit with a special

request that it is made for 47.5 and 23.7 metres. He asks after 'Mrs 2NM and Miss 2NM'.

92. Second page of (91).

93. Letter from 'Brenda', Waihemo, New Zealand dated 22nd November 1926 in which she thanks Marcuse for sending her a valve and explained several other problems she had with her equipment.

94. Second page of (93).

95. Letter (five pages) from T. H. Harris, Sydney, Australia dated 1st November 1926. He gives details about Marcuse's and European signal strengths at different times, including CW to A4AN and phone, adding that this was as clear as KDKA. He makes some suggestions about the timing of Marcuse's concert programmes. He sends four photographs of his equipment and requests that Marcuse sends some of his station. He claims to have heard over 200 European amateurs since 1st August 1925.

96. – 99. Four other pages of (95).

100. This is a three-page reception report from T. H. Harris (Australia) that is likely to have been included with letter (95) showing dates, times and detailed observations for amateurs heard or contacted from 8th March 1926 up to and including 27th June 1926. The list includes the callsigns of numerous amateur stations as well as details of Marcuse's concert broadcasts.

101. Second page of (100).

102. Third page of (100).

103. Letter from C. R. Tonting, Bristol, dated 6th December 1926 who mentioned contacts he had made in the Antipodes with A5HG and Z3AR.

104. Letter from Ralph E. Howard, Atlanta, Georgia date missing due to rip on corner of page. Asking if Marcuse rebroadcasted programmes from 2LO.

105. Second page of (104)

o~o

1927 (1 to 122)

1. Letter from W.G.H. Hiles, H.M. W/T Station, Stonecutters Island, c/o H.M.S. Tamar, Hong Kong, dated 18th March 1927 thanking Marcuse for sending him a receiver. He comments on the political situation:

    'Matters at Shanghai are quite quiet and we have enough troops there now to protect ourselves, but all business is coming to a standstill, and all firms, big and small, are hard hit. I am afraid things will never be the same again out here, and it will be years before China evolves a stable government.'

    He mentions that Marcuse used to call his transmitter 'Claude' and that he would be making up a rival called 'Felix' which he would use first for testing out the best circuit and would then run simultaneously with Claude!

2. Letter from E. Hangstarr C3KA, St Catherine's, Ontario, Canada dated 30th April 1927 in which he suggests that Marcuse visits Niagara Falls and the new Welland Ship Canal. He offers to act as Marcuse's guide and to take him to see the local amateur stations. The letter is headed: 'Niagara District Radio Association' with the Board of Directors from 1922 and 1923 listed each side.

3. Second page of (3)

4. Page inserted by Museum to indicate letters for '1924 in other file'.

5. Letter from C. D. Roberts, Sydney, Australia dated 28th August 1927 but received on 4th October 1927. He gives a full reception report based on 2NM's signals received on 28th August at

0620GMT but said that his frequency was in the middle of the Australian and New Zealand band so there was heavy interference. Also, 4AA was transmitting on the same frequency and s FU9 'had his 500 note so broadly tuned that he too was an especial nuisance'. He stated that both speech and music were very clear: '... the former better than PCJJ. He suggests that Marcuse transmits on a lower frequency, 'at least 31 metres or, preferably, below 30m'. He mentions that 2NM was the first English station he heard, on Boxing Day 1925 and on 10th December 1926, 2NM was the first English phone station he had heard. 'Now, 2NM is to be the first English broadcasting station received by me. Congrats OM. I sincerely hope that Australia will soon be able to send her programmes all over the world via the short waves. Station 3AR, a Victorian broadcaster, intends to start shortly but only 250 watts will be used'. Roberts includes A.R.R.L. at the end of his letter indicating membership of the organisation.

6. Second page of (6)

7. Third page of (6)

8. Letter from C. H. Vernon Albany, Western Australia dated 30th August 1927 but received on 4th October 1927. He is responding to Marcuse's request for reports on his transmission of 28th August 1927. He had heard instrumental, vocal and orchestral signals and wished Marcuse every success with his intended Empire Broadcasting. He commented that Marcuse's signal 'was equal to the American 2XAD on 20.02 metres and practically the same as regards 2XAF on 32.77 metres, but your modulation seemed superior to either'. He suggests suitable times for broadcasting to Australia. He ends by saying that 'if you ever get time a little card with 'G2NM thereon will be treasured by me'.

9. Second page of (9)

10. Third page of (9)

11. Letter from W. A. Bousfield, Tasmania dated 4th September 1927 but received on 17th October 1927. He congratulates Marcuse for his enterprise and continues, 'Although we British out here do not like to criticise the policy of the BBC at home, I think that even if only to maintain British prestige, a short-wave broadcaster should be established some time ago.' He mentions the broadcasters that he could receive already: PCJJ Lundhoren, Holland; WGY, 2XAF, 2XAG Schenectady, KDKA, Pittsburgh, and says: 'it can be safely said that your transmission compares very favourably with their commercial broadcasters. Why not rebroadcast 2LO & 5XX as PCJJ did some time ago?'

12. Detailed signal report from Bousfield (12) for Marcuse's transmission on Sept 4th 1927. This includes a full report including interference, signal strength, aerial and receiver used.

13. Letter from Conrad Bischoff, Sidney, Australia dated 4th September 1927 that includes a nine-page detailed reception report. He says that the radio he used, 'was 3 valve low loss constructed by my son Conrad age 16. He concludes: 'you will no doubt agree that the reception is a triumph of your broadcasting we wish you every success in the future'.

14. – 23. The reception report is very detailed and would have provided Marcuse with a clear idea about how his signals were getting out. The last page of reception report repeats the exact words he had heard: 'Empire Broadcasting Station on a wavelength of 32.5 metres. Hello everybody. Hello British Empire 2NM here. Hello 2FC Sydney, Australia. This is 2NM calling.

24. Letter from R. W. Browne, Ebute-Metta, Nigeria dated 5th Sept 1927 confirming reception of a transmission on 1st September using a two-valve 'Radiano' designed by Percy W. Harris with a 'short indoor aerial'. He confirms he can receive W.G.Y., D.D.K.A. Holland. Browne gives his title as the Assistant Works Manager of the Nigerian Railways.

25. Letter from R. G. Ellis, Buenos Aires, dated 6th September 1927 confirming reception of Marcuse's experimental broadcasts on 32.5 metres but added that the transmission suffered very badly from rapid fading. He records items heard: 'This is 2NM Experimental Empire Broadcasting Station, Caterham Surrey, England, British 2NM calling on 32.5 metres' and adds that several remarks were addressed to 2MT in Sidney, Australia. The concluding remark was: 'this station will now be closing down until 7.30 tomorrow morning B.S.T.' and stated that he used a two-valve receiver with an 'L' aerial situated about 15 miles south of Buenos Aires.

26. Letter from F. G. Cornish, Secondi, Gold Coast Colony dated 9th September 1927. He writes a very helpful letter and states that 2NM's signal is not quite strong enough for him to hold it and follow it for any length of time. He concludes: 'I am sure we shall be very grateful to you if you can send us out the latest news from home if it is only once a week (say of a Saturday evening) what a treat it would be.

27. Letter from W. H. Rushohm, Christmas Island, Indian Ocean, via Singapore dated 11th September 1927, received on 17th October. He says he is one of two amateur listeners on the Island and asks if Marcuse would give him the times and wave lengths of his transmissions. He had read in the Singapore papers that Marcuse had been given permission from the Post Master General to transmit two hours per day for three days. He goes on to explain which other radio signals he can receive and concludes by saying: 'I can only address this letter to you by the call sign of your station and should it arrive safely, as I trust it will, I should be pleased to have a reply...'.

28. Second page of (27).

29. Letter from C. H. Vernon, Albany, West Australia dated 12th September 1927. This letter gives a reception report for the morning of 12th September and includes the content of the transmissions, ie, Instrumental record, Song (lady), an overture played by His Majesty's Coldstream Guards, record No 11335. He

mentions that 'dotted line where words were missed owing to not being able to write down quick enough'.

30. Letter from Lloyd Dumas on headed paper from the Australian Newspapers Cable Service, London, E.C.4. He extends a most grateful message of thanks to Marcuse for attempting the first genuine effort to broadcast a concert from England to Australia'. The attempt ended in failure, but he asked Marcuse to: 'please convey to Mrs Marcuse my regret that her self-sacrifice in the cause of science should have been so ill rewarded at the psychological moment'.

31. Letter from H. Grobbelaar, Hopefield, South Africa dated 12th September 1927, received 4th October 1927 in which he confirms having received Marcuse's telephony on 11th September 1927 at 80pm local time using a two-valve short wave receiver; 'signal strength was rather on the faint side...'

32. Front of an envelope addressed to Grobbelaar.

33. Letter from 'Norm Turnbull, Narrogin, West Australia dated 12th September 1927 in which he congratulates Marcuse for his 'wonderful pioneering achievement' having heard the last part of a transmission. He used a Schnell-Reinartz receiver with: 'one audio, plain Ormond condensers with 15-1 ratio Vernier dials. Hand capacity awful. Aerial system 50 feet long and 8 feet high. He suggests that if he used a better receiver, the signals would 'come in here about R7 – 10. Although he mentions sending a map with the places marked where Marcuse's signals had been heard, the map was not present in the file. The letter paper is headed: 'Postmaster General's Dept'.

34. Front of stamped card sent by Turnbull from Australia to G2NM.

35. Reverse of card sent by Turnbull giving reception report including: 'QRB 9000 miles'; the card requests a QSL reply.

36. A very long 3-page letter from A. R. McLean, Pointe-a-Pierre, Trinidad, British West Indies, dated 13th September 1927 in which he confirms having received 'signal 2NM ' and goes on to say 'Your signals were received exceptionally clear and strong on the phones'. He says that he and seven members of the community 'lost many hours of sleep' waiting for what had been advertised in the local press as the 'first British Empire full programme' to be broadcast on 11th September 1927. Unfortunately, the signal was not heard but he had heard '2XAF (WGY's programme) on 32,77 metres at full loudspeaker strength. He complained about being 'unable to use transformers out here, having burnt out seven. I have tried both English and American makes, but they all go after a few weeks use'. He adds that there was no broadcast station in his part of the world, the nearest being in Caracas, Venezuela (AYRE), about 3200 miles away. He continues by explaining the difficulties in receiving radio signals. He asks Marcuse to explain the principle of the 'Truphonic amplifier'. It is likely that the pencil cross against this question was made by Marcuse with a view to answer it.

37. Page 2 of (36)

38. Page 3 of (36)

39. Copy of letter of complaint to the BBC from Sydney W. S. Strong (OZ2AG), Gisborne, New Zealand dated 14th September 1927. The letter includes an article that appeared in a New Zealand newspaper titled 'Publicity Stunt', by Telegraph. – Press Association, London 9th September 1927. The letter condemns the BBC's official announcement as being deplorable (& childlike) and goes on to explain the value of amateur experimentation.

40. The New Zealand newspaper clipping outlines the BBC's official announcement:

"...deplores the present unfortunate exploitation as a publicity stunt, giving a wholly artificial importance to the admittedly unsatisfactory and irregular direct reception available merely to a limited number of experimenters".

It would appear that the BBC objected to amateur experimentation unless full coverage of a transmission to a target area was possible. The popular feeling of people around the world was in complete opposite to the BBC's view if the content of the numerous letters is considered.

41. Second page of (39). The letter states that 'the due and just acknowledgement of credit to the pioneer work of we amateurs throughout the world' is conspicuous by its absence'.

42. Third page of (39). This concludes by offering the BBC advice by telling the Corporation that it should be offering 2NM support rather than negative criticism.

43. Letter from G. H. J. Horan, headed: Observatoire de Ksara, Said-Nail, par Beyrouth, Grand Liban. The letter is from The Lebanon, dated 17th September 1927 and is labelled under the address: 'Call-sign AR OCOBK'. He begins: 'This time good news and I offer you my heartfelt congratulations on your Imperial Experimental Broadcasting'. It continues with detailed reception reports based on transmission over several days. It confirms reception of piano music and an announcement '3LO, Melbourne Calling' followed by a musical programme that was too weak to be enjoyed. He concludes by saying that he would very much like to make radio contact with 2NM using morse code.

44. Reverse of page (43)

45. Second Page of (43)

46. Third page of (43)

47. Letter from Henry Gibson, Lancaster dated 18th September 1927. This letter gives details of programmes received along with a reception report. ie, Sonata for piano and violin, 'Hello Ceylon. Hello Mr Jolly of Ceylon, I hope you are receiving this all right? Hello everybody. B2NM calling on 32.5m. Hello 6AC, you are being received O.K. cornet solo OK. Reduce your wavelength and

put-up power. Will co-operate in Let with you. British Experimental Broadcasting Station 2NM calling'. Then follows another detailed log of what was heard.

48. Second page of (47).

49. Letter from Henry Gibson, Lancaster dated 25th September 1927. He thanks Marcuse for his letter of 21st September and includes a reception report of 2NM's transmissions conducted on 25th September. The transmission included a piece by the Grenadier Guard's band titled 'The Rose'. Following this, another piece, a song by Leighton & Johnson, a medley (a Columbia Record). He reports Marcuse's greetings messages to Mr Jolly of Ceylon thanking him for his cable, a Mr Hurry of Bombay thanking him for his cable and to let him know the transmission times. During the broadcast, Gibson reports hearing Marcuse's comment: 'That was a motor cycle going past'. Also, there is a greeting to Mr Brown of Nigerian Railways saying 'we are very glad to hear you are receiving us well on a 2-valve set'.

50. Second page of (49)

51. ******* Second side of Page 2 missing *******

52. Letter from C. M. Barnitt, Cheltenham, Victoria, Australia dated 19th September 1927 and received on 24th October. He confirms reception of broadcasts made on 18th September and gives a detailed log and reports on the signals. His receiver was a '3 coil detector + 1 Audio', and his aerial was 20ft high and 35ft long.

53. Second page of (52).

54. Letter from G. B. Jolliffe, Radio 7VX, Govinna, Ceylon dated 19th September 1927 explaining the difficulties he had receiving a broadcast, including what he thought was a generator hum.

55. Second page of (54).

56. Letter from Phil Burbridge, OA3 PB, Victoria Australia dated 23rd September 1927, received on 31st October, confirming reception of a broadcast on 22nd September with a signal report. The broadcast included: 'a vocal item on a Columbia record at 4.50 by Harold Williams'. The aerial used was 10ft of copper tube, 30ft high into a 2-valve Schnell receiver.

57. Letter from W. J. Fleet, Geelong Victoria, Australia dated 25th September 1927 and received on 31st October giving a brief reception report; he was using a Schnell receiver and a 40ft aerial.

58. Second page of (57)

59. Letter from A. Tostevin, Mt Lawley, West Australia dated 26th September 1927. He writes to confirm reception of three broadcasts, 'one on your test night, the second was on your opening night and again this morning which was the best of all'. He goes on to say that: 'one of the items played on the 11/9/27 was so perfect that I thought it was Mr Coxon 6AG, who is living near my place, and he plays the same piece on his gramophone when he is broadcasting; that was the Triumphal March'. He writes that he heard a church bell striking and then the church service thus: '1st Choir singing, Hymn 627, Anthem – The Lord is my Shepherd, Prayer (I never missed one word), Hymn 641, Scripture lesson from St Luke. The sermon was from St Luke's Gospel 10th Chapter, the preacher said the 7th verse and then corrected himself and said the 10th verse, The sermon finished 3.10am Perth Time. The Choir chanting and 2NM closing down at 3.35AM Perth Time'.

60. Second page of (59).

61. Letter, (Sender Unknown), undated but received on 27th September 1927 containing a reception report. He complains of fading: 'I made it out to be about 2 seconds in every 10'. He commented: 'My word when, that motor cycle passed your premises it made some difference' [see (49)] and continued: 'The first record I heard when I got you was No 9221, then there was

Layton & Johnstone, * Columbia No. 9219'. The service from London came over: 'wonderful especially it being a relay. I think you were a little too near the mike at times or was it over modulation'.

62. Second page of (61)

63. Letter from Mervyn H. Fletcher, Victoria, Australia, dated 27th September 1927 received on 3rd November 1927 containing a reception report for 25th & 27th September. He reports: 'Reception on both days was at fair strength on a three-valve throttle controlled short wave receiver. The valves are dull-emitters and average 2 years old so the sum total about equals two decent ones'. He continues by giving a fairly detailed account of the programme and the general level of reception heard.

64. Inside pages of (63).

65. Letter from Trevor George Orr, Pietermaritzburg, Natal, South Africa, dated 27th September 1927. In a fairly long, rambling letter he states the parts of the broadcast that he could make out although it would appear that the signal was sporadic and suffered from a lot of fading.

66. Second page of (65)

67. Third page of (65)

68. Letter from C. R. Slingsby, Mowbray, South Africa, dated 28th September 1927. He asks if Marcuse received his cable and he includes a detailed log of 2NM's broadcasts for 25th September and asks Marcuse for a copy of his transmission times. The log includes the time Big Ben and the Sunday Service were broadcast.

69. Second page of (68).

70. Third page of (68)

71. Letter from A. W. Haworth, Tenerife, dated 30th September 1927 thanking Marcuse for his letters of 8th and 25th and for information about station 2FB. He said that 2NM came through with 'tremendous volume, almost as loud as 2XAF but that for some reason the distortion was most terrible and it was only at times that I could understand that was being said'. He continues with a comment about distortion on Marcuse's signal and then mentions the 'Dempsey-Tunney Fight'. He had taken notes as the fight progressed and was able to give these to a local newspaper. He wished Marcuse 'every success in this venture, and trust that it will make the BBC "rig-up" a really tip top short-wave station for the Empire. He suggests that Marcuse should start a subscription amongst British residents towards a station for the Empire and goes on to say: 'It seems to me that the BBC are dead against this business and it is a thing I cannot understand in view of the fact that everybody is clamouring for news and music from England. The main bone of contention the people had against the BBC was that it had perfected broadcasting in England and it seemed that it wanted to keep what they considered a high standard overseas without realising that: 'when one is away from the Old Country, one is not so particular, and that one has to put up with many things, and that one more or less is nothing very much'. He concluded by saying that he had re-wired his favourite set with extremely heavy wire, 'about 5/6 mm gauge' and that the broadcasts were not distorted. 'I heard every word spoken by Mr Tom Spencer to Mr George Spencer, and if the latter gentlemen's reception was anything like as good as mine, he must have received the message very clearly indeed.

72. - 74. Second, third and fourth pages of (71)

75. Letter from the Bombay Presidency Radio Club, Bombay, dated 2nd October 1927, received 24th October. This is signed by H. B. Atkins saying he had passed on a message to W.R. Ballantyne. (After this name, it gives 'or Valantine' in parenthesis.) He thanks Marcuse for all his work and congratulates him 'on the result of the first effort of short-wave broadcasting from G.B.

76. Another letter from H. B. Atkins confirming reception of a message: 'your son Percy sends you greetings'.

77. Letter from J. G. Brooker, Luticorin, South India dated 4th October 1927, headed: 'c/o Ralli Bros'. He thanks Marcuse for replying on 8th September, to his request asking for a circuit. He says that since using it, he had picked up 2NM several times although the speech could not be made out. He said he received Sydney, Perth, Melbourne quite clearly, PCJJ and several amateurs on telephony, morse from all over the world. He goes on to express his gratitude for Marcuse's efforts.

78. Second page of (77).

79. Letter from E. H. Pereira, Georgetown, British Guiana, dated 8th October 1927 confirming reception of 2NM on 32.9 metres. He suggests that 30 metres would be a more appropriate due to the strength of W.G.Y. that transmitted 60Kw. He sends his best wishes for making Empire Broadcasting possible and concludes: 'You are certainly warming up THEIR cold feet'.

80. Letter from K. N. Rastomjee, Poona, India, dated 10th October 1927. This is a copy of a letter asking for confirmation that a broadcast that included a song (Grieg's "Solveig's Song") was actually from 2NM.

81. Letter from Joseph F. James to W. R. Valentine of Cawnpore, dated 10th October 1927 asking for verification that a message had been sent by 2NM to his (Valentine's) son.

82. Letter from J. C. Standen, Travancore, South India, dated 10th October 1927, received 31st October. He confirmed that he had received a Broadcast on 9th October (9.30 and 11.45pm both at Indian standard time and that both signals had suffered from fading to various degrees. He congratulates Marcuse for relaying 'Langenberg' and asked if he could persuade 'the-powers-that-be' if they could relay (at least) Big Ben 'if we cannot have one of their programmes per week'. He concluded by saying that although he

could get GMT from Marcuse's pips, 'it is not Big Ben and that is what most of us want to hear. It brings us nearer Home'.

83. Letter from Robert Halle, Colombo, Ceylon, dated 12th October 1927, received 31st October confirming reception of a Broadcast on Sunday 9th October. He was using a 'Bowyer-Howe, 3 valve receiver' that had 'excellent results from Holland, PCJJ. He states that 'the BBC will, before long, start a short-wave station as this would be a great boon to exiles like myself. I would mention before closing that we had full loud speaker reception of the bantam-eight fight transmitted by Daventry and relayed by PCJJ and it was great to listen in to a London crowd.

84. Letter from the Bombay Presidency Radio Club, signed Sd/-, Hon. Secretary, dated 12th October 1927. This is a copy of a letter sent to Messrs. Jost's Engineering Co., Ltd., in Bombay thanking them for sending him notice of 2NM's transmissions 'for the Sunday list'. He gives a reception report that is very mixed and mentions: 'Fading was very bad, in addition, reception at the club, was marred by interruption from electric fans working in the building'.

85. Letter from E. J. C. Herring, general manager & secretary of Jost's Engineering Co. Ltd., Bombay, dated 14th November 1927. He confirms and gives the contents of an exchange of cables with 2NM. He mentions attaching a newspaper cutting from the 'Times of India' (Scrapbook page 75). He discusses 2NM's tests and concludes 'It is most remarkable, because you are using 1200 watts against the BBC, 25 Kw. You are to be congratulated' but adds, that the Chief Engineer of the Indian Broadcasting Company suggests that what he had really picked up was a harmonic of the local station.

86. Second page of (85).

87. Front of Post card from Hans Flittner, Budapest, Hungary dated October 16th 1927 stating reception in the evening was far better than in the earlier hours.

88. Reverse of Post Card from (87) in which he confirms reception and gives a brief report on readability and atmospheric conditions.

89. Letter from William F. Fell, Phoenixville, Pa., USA, dated 19th October 1927, received on 31st October. He confirms reception of 2NM on 32.75 metres and asks for confirmation of wavelength and power.

90. Letter from Clarence Horton, Pernambuca, Brazil, dated 21st October 1927 confirming reception of 2NM, commenting: 'I found the modulation excellent'. He asks if Marcuse could 'influence the BBC to give us a short-wave Empire station'. He adds that he can receive: Schenectady & Gettysburg programmes; 'I have heard the sporadic efforts of Ottawa (Canadian Marconi, Drummondville, Quebec)'.

91. Second page of (90).

92. Letter from J. W. Fraser, East Finchley, London, dated 21st October 1927. He reported that the 'Evening News' had stated 2NM had not been heard nearer than 200 miles from Caterham, but he had heard 2NM on 32.5 metres, calling 'Hello Canada, Hello USA followed by gramophone music. He mentioned that fading was bad but quality of speech and music very excellent.

93. Letter from R. W. Browne, Ebute-Metta, Nigeria, dated 26th thanking Marcuse for his letter of 29th September. He stated that: 'the dry season will be with us in a week or two after which reception will improve'. He adds that he hoped the BBC would soon appreciate Marcuse's efforts and realise the value of short-wave'.

94. Second page of (93)

95. Letter from R. N. Shaw, New South Wales, Australia, dated 31st October 1927; the letterhead is: 'THE COUNCIL OF THE SHIRE OF HASTINGS'. He gives a reception report (28 metres) and mentions he heard 2FC, Sydney. He requests a card and confirmation that Marcuse had rebroadcast the Australian

programme. He concludes: 'Your name has been quite famous in Australia during recent months'.

96. Letter from A. W. Haworth, Tenerife, dated 1st November 1927. This confirms reception of one of 2NM's early morning broadcasts and it comments: 'Reception was the best I have ever heard of your station being both strong and clear. Some fading was present at times but speech etc was always audible, you made me feel very much that I wished I was in good old England – giving you description of the sunrise and the birds in the garden'.

97. Second page of (96).

98. Letter from H. Russell Crane, Sydney, Australia, dated 3rd November 1927 addressed to Marcuse's 'Mincing Lane' business address. He says that his reception of 2NM's re-broadcast of 2FC's Australian programme on 30th October was: 'so poor that I was not going to write to you, but apparently reports from others are going to be scanty, so I send you my notes for what they are worth'. He explains that he has problems with his receiver due to a broken connection in the grid coil but gives an account of what he heard from 5.14 – 5.40am (Sydney time).

99. Second page of (98).

100. Letter from A. W. Haworth, British Consulate, Tenerife, dated 7th November 1927 thanking Marcuse for his letter of 14th October. He responds to a question concerning a British short-wave transmitter that had started transmitting on 24 metres 'a few days ago' by saying he would send him a duplicate report of the original sent to the station itself. He went on to say that 2NM's signal was 'jammed by a code station and a very powerful one at that'. He concludes by asking: 'have you ever experienced the matter remarked on in the enclosed report and marked *? It would be interesting to know. It does not often happen but is sort of impressive, as it gives on the idea of absolute 'infinity feeling'. You might let me know'.

101. Letter from W. C. Begley, Catford, London, dated 14th November 1927 in which he congratulates Marcuse for his broadcasts and requests transmission times for the Australian broadcasts.

102. Second page of (101).

103. Letter from G. W. B*****, Maylands, West Australia, dated 14th November 1927 confirming reception of a transmission: 'Speech was clear but very quiet and only a word here and there could be got at 20 past 12 our time & soprano solo, then a Tenor solo, or it might have been a duet as I thought I heard a ladies voice as well, but morse was bad at the time...'.

104. Reverse of (103).

105. Letter from J. G. Brooker, c/o Ralli Bros., Corripore, dated 16th November 1927 saying that he had excellent reception of 2NM's Armistice Relay while in Tuticorin, South India. He concluded by saying that he did not even receive a carrier wave from the BBC.

106. Letter from Sydney Chambers, Perth, West Australia, dated 19th November 1927. He confirmed having received the 'Armistice Community Singing' that included: 'Keep the Home Fires Burning', 'John Browns Knapsack', 'It's a Long Way to Tipperary', 'Auld Langsyne', also prayers followed by hymns, including 'Lead Kindly Light, 'Abide With Me' and the Prince's Speech, ending with 'God Save the King'. The transmission had been received on the 33-metre band'.

107. Letter from Robert Fittall/Tittal, Kenya Colony, Nairobi, dated 21st November 1927. He reports using a Reinartz circuit and states the music was rather faint but the speech was clear. He continues, 'as 3LO was rather better I did not persist with your wave but think you would like to know that you were heard here'.

108. Letter from Leslie Ford Smith, E.T.C. Staff Mess, Ascension Island, 3rd December 1927. This confirmed he had heard 2NM's transmission although it was not very strong & suffered very badly

from severe fading. He had hoped to 'give you a more useful report – however as the mail leaves tomorrow and there is not another for a month, I thought I would drop you a line now'. His receiver was similar to the 'Empire short-wave set described in the Wireless World for June 29th last'. He mentioned that 'whilst in Port Sudan during 1925 & 1926 I constructed the short wave set described by you in P.W. and got very satisfactory reception from KDKA on 62 metres'.

109. Second page of (108).

110. Third page of (108).

111. Letter from G. H. Jolliffe (7VX, 32.5 metres, Ceylon), Frocester, Govinna, Ceylon, dated 12th December 1927. He congratulates Marcuse for his short-wave transmission on Armistice night as reported in 'Wireless World' on 23rd November having listened to it all. He asks about meeting Marcuse during his home leave starting in June 1928.

112. Second page of (111).

113. Letter from Conrad Bischoff, Crow's Nest, Sidney, Australia dated 15th December 1927 in which he enclosed a log of 2NM's transmissions and acknowledges receipt of Marcuse's QSL card.

114. Letter from Michael G. Eber, Singapore, S.S., dated 21st December 1927. He confirms reception of the Armistice broadcast on 33 metres using a two-valve Reinhartz receiver. He expresses that: 'I can hardly mention the disappointment arising out of the failure of the BBC to, at the last moment, cancel their proposal to broadcast this programme'. He confirms that all the amateurs here were on the 24-metre band that night searching and for 5SW's carrier but that he found 2NM's transmission a little higher: 'I must say that your transmission was superb considering the immense distance and the 1 Kw power used'. He continues by giving a log of what he had heard from 3.20am and gives a very detailed signal

report and requests 2NM's transmission times. He gives a list of stations he had heard:

PCLL on 17.5 metres, a Dutch Laboratory based at The Hague.
PCJJ on 30.2 metres, Eindhoven, Holland.
PKI   on 17.5 metres, Radio Service Bandoeng D.E.J.
(?)   on 35 metres, Radio Sourabaya, Java, D.E.J.
2FC   on 28.5 metres, Sydney, N.S.W., Australia.
6AG   on 30 metres, Perth, West Australia.
2ME   on 30 metres, Australia
2AK   on 38 metres, New Zealand.
2SA   on 42 metres, Australia.
6XP   on 46 metres, Japan.

He adds that he had not heard 5SW but hoped to pick her up 'sometime this week as it has been officially announced that they will be on the air 'till the end of February 1928'. He ends by confirming that had included some newspaper cuttings with his letter.

115. - 117. Second, third and fourth pages of (114).

118. Letter from Sergeant G. Baker (?), Punjab, India, dated 27th December 1927 in which he thanks Marcuse for a letter of 5th December (received on 25th December). This is a personal letter in which he mentions his receiver, the fact that he had just started learning morse and if Marcuse could send him two condensers suitable for his short-wave set because they were the only ones he was able to obtain: 'besides having to wait a deuce of a time for anything it is nearly always inferior'.

119. Second page of (118)

120. Third page of (118)

121. Letter from A. W. Haworth, Tenerife, dated 21st December 1927. The letter consists of a very detailed, typed reception report of several stations heard from December 10th through to December 20th 1927. The stations include 2XAF, 2NM, 3LO, K.D.K.A.,

E.D.K.A., 5SW, and requests answers to queries contained in the report.

122. Second page of the report (121).

o~o

1928 (1 to 154)

1. Marcuse Letters 1928 Title Page 1 – 86 (MD28 1 – 86)

2. Letter from Thomas Cooper dated Jan 1st 1928, Lighthouse Randon Head, Trinity Bay, Newfoundland (50 miles NW of St Johns). The letter acknowledges receipt of Marcuse's (speech) signal and music using a receiver with three UV199 valves and a battery power of 22.5v.

3. Second page of (2)

4. Envelope addressed to Mr G. D. Rudram, 79 The Boulevard, Worthing, West Sussex. Dated 24th July 1987.
   (Incorrectly filed in the 1928 letters folder.)

5. Letter from Marcuse to Frank Brittain, Barnet, Herts. The letter appears to respond to a complaint about Marcuse's station interfering with 3LO "… My wave cannot move on account of the crystal, and 3LO being an 'A' Station, they can afford to have as many crystals ground as they like….. I do not think the fault is mine as I am using the same crystal, the same drive and the same aerial; therefore my station is tied down to 32.5 Metres…."

6. Second Page of (5)

7. Letter from James H. Cole, Survey of Egypt, Giza (Mudiriya), Egypt dated 23rd January 1928. The letter confirms reception of Marcuse's 'Gramophone records' on 32 metres. Cole's receiver is given as O-V-3, the first two L.F. being resistance coupled using poor valves, Phillips B2, 2v. Signal strength reported as R8-R9,

'slight fading but never below R7'. Cole mentions that his receiver was made up of old spare parts 'from the junk box'. He ends, 'my wife and I thank you for a very enjoyable evening'.

8. Second page of (7).

9. Letter from P. Pah, Radio Section, Post Office No 1., Bankok, Siam, dated 23rd January 1928. The letter confirms Marcuse's signals were received at R3 level on 22nd January. He requests an appointment for testing: "Our AEA Wavelength 37 metres, 300 watts, AED 36 metres, 150 watts and AEP 37 metres 150 watts are at your service".

10. Letter from (signature not readable) addresses: The Athénée Palace Hotel, Bucharest, dated January 24th 1928. The letter advises Marcuse not to earth any part of any circuit on the valve side of the filament chokes, or he would short them out. He continues: "The city is damned awful and dirty – in more ways than one…. I heard today that we are on the edge of a local revolution, anything will add a zest to life!".

11. Second page of (10)

12. Letter from Joseph Adams, Wittet Road, Ballard Estate, Bombay, PO Box 371, dated 30th January 1928. A reception report is included that confirms Marcuse's speech and music broadcast. He comments: "I got my short-wave set going only three days back; I never heard anything like it on the Broadcast Band. Empire Broadcasting must go on". The letter is headed: 'Indian States & Eastern Agency Ltd. Pioneers of Wireless in India'.

13. Letter from the General Manager & Secretary of Jost's Engineering Co. Ltd., Hararwala Building, Wittet Road, Ballard Estate, Bombay, dated 7th October 1927. Jost's Engineering represented several very large firms in India (ie, Standard Telephone & Cables, Edison Storage Battery Co.). The letter included cuttings from The Times of India Oct 6th and 7th 1927 and promised further reception reports.

14. Letter from J. C. Standen, Kottayam, Travancore, S. India, dated 30th January 1928 confirming reception of Marcuse's broadcast on 32.5 metres. Standen comments: "...I received you at wonderful strength ... strength R7... your modulation could be considered almost perfect". It also comments that 3LO 'was always in the background ... I am of the opinion that 3LO Melbourne is off its wavelength, or else it is your station, which I doubt, in view of the position of the dial for 2XAF on 32.77 metres".

15. Letter from A. C. de Oliveira, The Rio de Janeiro Flour Mills & Granaries Ltd., PO Box 486, Rio de Janeiro, Brazil. dated 30th January 1928. It was sent to 'Engineer in Charge of G2NB, Caterham, Surrey, c/o The British Broadcasting Co.' The letter confirms reception of Marcuse's signals on 23 metres "extraordinary clearness and strength". The receiver was a "Reinartz type with a "Metro-Vick S. P. – 18 Red Spot" for detector followed by two Philips "dry battery amplifying valves". "For aerial I use 4 yards of flexible wire fixed up anywhere in the room".

16. Second page of (15).

17. Letter from C. R. Slingsby, 'Scriven', Thelma Road, Claremont, South Africa, dated 2nd February 1928. A detailed report is attached giving exact times and readability strengths of Marcuse's broadcasts during six days in January 1928 complete with detailed comments of what was heard and weather conditions.

18. Reception report attached to (17).

19. Letter from C. S. Taylor, in Stewiacke, Nova Scotia, Canada dated March 4th 1928. It is addressed to Marcuse at: Radio Station 'G2NB', Caterham and confirms reception of a broadcast on 32.5 metres.

20. Letter from A. R. McLean, Pointe a Pierre, Trinidad, British West Indies dated March 5th 1928. It confirms reception of a transmission made at 7.50pm on 22nd February 1928. "Your

transmission was received by me on the evening of the 22nd ult., with exceptional strength and clarity and with practically no fading".

21. Letter from W. R. Rowsell, c/o Salvage Factory, Delta Barrage, Egypt, dated March 26th 1928. The letter is addressed to: The Editor, Popular Wireless, The Fleetway House, London EC4. He requests the Editor to inform Marcuse that he had heard some of his music broadcasts on 25th March. He confirmed that he had heard: 5SW, PCJJ, KDKA, WGY and many other amateurs including GBS. He continues by comparing the various signal strengths of these stations.

22. Second Page of (21).

23. Letter from Henry Cousin, Cherapia St., Alexandria, Egypt, dated 8th march 1928. The letter confirms reception of Marcuse's transmission at 12.30am on 8th March. He reports using a 'Bourne', home-made receiver 'followed by an L.F. amplification stage'.

24. Letter from unknown person due to just page 1 of the letter being present. It is from: Pilot Station, Harrington, Manning River, New South Wales, Australia and is dated March 10th 1928. He confirms having received Marcuse's transmission that included a variety of music on March 9th between 10 and 12pm on or around 25 metres.

25. Letter from A. E. Hewitt, Heavy Repair Shop (M.T.) Class 11., Peshawar, India, dated 12th March 1928. The letter includes a reception report taken 1915hrs GMT on 12th March and recorded as R7. The report includes details of the various musical items transmitted (HMV record P3247. He reports hearing Marcuse calling a Mr Drudge-Coates of Rawalpindi, thanking him for a message received through 6MU. He states that he used a '0 – V – 1' receiver.

26. Letter from (J?) G. Brooker, 10 Cossipore, Calcutta, India, dated 12th March 1928 in which he confirms reception of a Marcuse

broadcast conducted on March 11th with a signal strength 'almost equal to P.C.J.J.'.

27. Second page of (26).

28. Letter from B. R. Beveridge, from 2, Drummond Road, Allahabad, India, dated 12th March 1928. He confirms reception of Marcuse's transmission made on 11th February as being 'particularly good'.

29. Letter from Captain Quarter Master Sergeant A. Patterson at 2nd Royal Warwickshire Regiment, Bombay, India on 14th March 1928. This is a request for Marcuse to confirm if he was broadcasting on the night of 11th March, 'I heard an organ and some words as follows: 'I am going over to 2LO, afterwards I heard Church bells quite plainly'. He continues: "you can imagine what pleasure it gave me to hear Church bells from Blighty".

30. Second page of (29).

31. Letter from Jos Rawlings, Holmes Lodge, Customs Street, Gisborne, New Zealand dated 14th March 1928. The letter confirms reception of Marcuse's broadcast on 32.5 metres, made on 12th March from 5.45 – 6.30am N.Z. Standard time that included the William Tell overture. The signal strength is given R3 – R4.

32. Letter from Allan Parcell, Waikiwi, Invercargill, New Zealand dated 15th March 1928 to confirm reception of Marcuse's broadcasts on March 5th, 6.50 – 7.20am, New York time and again on 11th & 12th March, all on 32.5 metres.

33. Letter from John T. C. Vigurs, at Piraeus, Greece on 17th March 1928, but signed 24th March. The letter is addressed: S.S. Maid of Syra, c/o Byron S.S. Co. Ltd., P.L.A. Building, Seething Lane, London E.C. At Matsuma Bay, East Coast of Naxos Island, Grecian Archipelago. The letter confirms reception of Marcuse's relay of a broadcast from Daventry on March 17th between 1045 –

2400 hrs G.M.T. He ends: "2XAF and PCJJ were also well received at above place".

34. Letter from A. Tostevin, 46 Railway Terrace, Mt Lawley, Western Australia on 19th March 1928. He confirms reception of a singing and orchestral concert from G2NM on 32 metres, 2am Perth time. Also heard was: 3LO (Melbourne). He used a three-valve receiver '… only put together temporarily, no soldering done on it'.

35. Second page of (34)

36. Letter from A. P. Talbot, Box 368, Porto Rico Railway Light & Power Co., San Juan, Porto Rico on March 21st 1928. In what is a very appreciative letter, it demonstrates just how much a broadcast offering a basic level of entertainment was needed. "To an Englishman and living so far from home it sounds good to hear old 'Big Ben' again." The letter comments about where the broadcast originated: "I believe you said it was from the Ambassador's Club, not quite sure of this however as it faded a little at that point…". It also mentions: "…. If you expect to continue on a more or less regular schedule of broadcasting. There are a great number of listeners on short waves down here who are picking you up and we want to know if we can count on you as a regular station". There are copious 'shorthand notes', presumably either written by or dictated by Marcuse at the bottom right-hand corner of the last page of this letter.

37. Second page of (36)

38. Letter from R. G. Collingwood, Maison Abound, Avenue Rameses, Heliopolis, Egypt, dated 22nd March 1928. This confirms the strong signal that 2NM was transmitting: 'The reception was better than anything received from nearest official stations, Naples, Constantinople etc, and again on Sunday 18th particularly the bells of St Martins which filled the house!".

39. Letter from John Borthistle, Effernogue, Ferns, Co. Wexford, Ireland dated 26th March 1928. The listener was using a Popular

Wireless magazine two-valve receiver called the 'Sydney Two'. Clearly Marcuse's signal was strong: ".... I unexpectedly came on your transmission which was the most powerful I ever heard here". The transmission was timed at 6.45pm.

40. Second page of (39).

41. Second letter from Henry Cousin (see 23), Alexandria, Egypt, dated 27th March 1928. In this letter to Marcuse (in 1928) he asks for advice. He discusses dismantling his 'Bourne' short-wave receiver due to the length of time it takes him to tune into stations, and replacing it with either a 'Schnell' or a 'Reinartz' receiver.

42. Letter from Herbert Knirbl (??), dated 27th March 1928 in GERMAN.

43. Second page of (42) in GERMAN.

44. Letter from unknown person in Ambala, India. Part of the top section is missing but the word 'Hospital' appears in print at the top. The letter thanks Marcuse for getting him some condensers but goes on to say that the parcel was held up pending an application for an import licence for electronic goods.

45. Second page of (44).

46. Another letter (see 17) from C. R. Slingsby, 'Scriven', Thelma Road, Claremont, South Africa, dated 30th March 1928. The letter contains another very detailed signal report as in the first letter. He complains that 'some commercial Morse station is blotting out your signals, and imagine it is an Italian station'. He also mentions a French station on 31 metres: 'The volume of his speech beats even 2XAF!'. A blank section of the lower left-hand corner is partly filled with shorthand notes.

47. Detailed signal report from (46) on March 4th, 10th & 18th giving times, signal strength, weather conditions, remarks and Barometric readings.

48. Letter from Henri R. Griner, 121 Harrison Avenue, Baldwin, L.I., N.Y., dated March 31st 1928. The letter confirms reception of dance music from the Savoy orchestra in the Savoy Hotel, London that had been already broadcast by 2LO. Marcuse's broadcast was recorded as, 32.5 metres. The listener gave details of his receiver: "I am using a two-tube shortwave receiver employing two Cunningham tubes, type CX301-A, manufactured S.W. coils, plug-in style, seven plate variable condenser, controlled regeneration with a fixed tickler coil. The receiving aerial is given as an outdoor (90 ft) and an indoor (25ft).

49. Second page of (48).

50. Letter from William C. Savage, Shoeburyness, Essex, dated March 31st 1928. This is a reception report for a broadcast made by Marcuse on 18th March from 1900hrs on 32.5 metres. "Reception on daylight on O-V-1 is at splendid LS strength…". The listener provides a list of the music heard and mentions "… that records played were kindly loaned by the Columbia Gramophone Company for broadcasting that they were 12", Blue label".

51. Second page of (50).

52. Letter from C. Taylor, B.R.S. 149, Berkshire, dated 1st April 1928 reporting on a broadcast transmission on April 1st at 1915 hrs GMT, signal strength R8 using an O–V–1 receiver (A vacuum tube regeneration circuit). He thanks Marcuse for his short-wave articles in Practical Wireless magazine appearing in 1925.

53. Letter from C. S. Potts, London, E11, dated 1st April 1928. A listener using a 3 valve Reinartz with a homemade coil and R.F. choke. He confirms reception of Marcuse's broadcasts on 1st April, timed 1815 – 1945 hrs; "the strength was too loud to be comfortable. I was particularly anxious to see if the coil would really cover the short-wave band between 20 & 60 metres". (Marcuse had announced that his power was 1KW.) The listener continues: "I was glad to hear that you were being received so well in Vienna & Egypt".

54. Second page of (53).

55. Letter from Alfred France, 33 Church Street, Rotherham, dated 1st April 1928. He confirms reception of Marcuse's broadcasts on 1st April timed 1830 – 1955 hrs; "I picked you up 6.30 and have never had better reception, the power was enormous and the modulation perfect". He continues with a description of the programme received and explains how grateful he is for the broadcasts.: "I hope you won't think me a nuisance, but I could not help writing to thank you for such a lovely evening. I have really enjoyed 'listening in' for once".

56. Letter from David Richardson, Edinburgh, Scotland, dated 1st April 1928. He confirms reception of Marcuse's broadcast on 1st April on 32.5 metres from 1911 – 2000 hrs. He lists the programmes heard on his three-valve receiver.

57. Letter from M. W. H. de Gorter, a Dutch receiving station (I.A.R.U., en-R005, N.V.I.R.), Essenburgstraat 120b, Rotterdam, Holland. He confirms reception of Marcuse's April 1st transmission on 32.5 metres at 1910 hrs. GMT. De Gorter was the editor for the short-wave part of the Dutch Wireless paper 'Radio Wereld'. He asks for particulars and photos for publication in Radio Wereld. Short-hand notes in the bottom left-hand corner.

58. Letter from P. L. Helhêne, Villa Cecilia, Avenue Des Sources, S'Maurice, Nice, dated 2nd April 1928. The listener is a member of the Radio Club de la Côte d'Azur and confirms reception of Marcuse's broadcasts on 25th March and 1st April. He continues: "Big Ben which I had not heard at 2000 for months came through quite clearly". The listener used a Schnell receiver with an L.F. amplifier.

59. Second page of (58).

60. Letter from Gst. J. Horan, Observatoire de Ksara, Saïd-Naïl, par Beyrouth, Grand Liban. (Beirut, Lebanon), dated 2nd April 1928, (AR. OCOBK). The letter is a 'catch-up' letter to Marcuse after they had not been in correspondence for a long time. The author

asks four questions to which outline answers have been 'penned – in', presumably by Marcuse.

(i) What Power are you using (input to plates) and approximate aerial energy?
Answer: 1200 watts and 900 watts

(ii) What make of pick up are you using for the gramophone transmissions?
Answer: Bessiswis ? & Igranic ? (Norman Field ~ re: pick-up arms)

(iii) What make of micro for ordinary transmission?
Answer: Reiss & Amplion

(iv) About what % of modulation are you using?
Answer: 60%.

He goes on to comment: "You are still 'facile princeps' as far as modulation goes.

61. Page 2 of (60). The writer goes into great detail about a superheterodyne receiver he was constructing with three IF stages. The IF transformers used formers that he made from hard wood, boiled in oil, to expel all moisture as he had no ebonite available. Length: 45mm, diameter: 40mm.

62. Page 3 of (60). Reception reports for 1st April 1928 at 1800 hrs GMT: "very poor results with 0-V-0 (receiver) and headphone"; "very poor with 0-V-2 + L.S."; "Excellent L.S. strength at times with the Super-het, still in unfinished condition". He continues: "my transmitter is silent for a good while now – I have just got the 2nd valve from Phillips – and hope soon to be on the air again".

63. Page 4 of (60). Reception reports taken on Sunday 18th December 1927 at 1600 – 1830 hrs GMT. Another taken on 22nd December at 2000 – 2010 hrs GMT. Another taken on 25th December at 1600 – 2100 hrs GMT. Another taken on 1st January 1928 at 1600 hrs GMT.

64. Page 5 of (60). Reception reports taken on Sunday 8th January 1928 at 1600 – 1840 hrs GMT. Another taken on Sunday 22nd January

1928 at 1600 - 1830 hrs GMT. Another taken on Sunday 29th January 1928 at 1600 – 1950 hrs GMT. Another taken on Sunday 5th February 1928 at 1600 – 1825 hrs GMT, continued on page 6. All the reports are very detailed.

65. Page 6 of (60). Reception reports taken on Sunday 12th January 1928 at 1600 – 1900 hrs GMT. Another taken on Sunday 19th February 1928 although 2NM was not heard ("3LL on the contrary came through very well. Heard Frank Webster singing and greeting his 2LO friends, he says that it is a bit early in the morning for singing", continued on page 7.

66. Page 7 of (60). Reception reports taken on 26th February, 4th March and 25th March.

67. Letter dated 3rd April 1928 from K. Stewart, Rossal Oban, Scotland confirming reception of Marcuse's broadcast of 1st April 1928. Confirmed he had heard 3LM on 18th March 1928 'splendid on speaker'.

68. Letter dated 4th April 1928 from F. P. Crowther, Caldecot Cottage, Caldy, Cheshire, B.R.S. 99, enclosing a reception report for 1st April, using an '0-V-2 Circuit 1 BIS'. The times were 1800 – 2000 hrs G.M.T. Very detailed report with remarks.

69. Second page of (68).

70. Letter dated 8th April 1928 from Charles W. Slatham, 37 Castle Road, St Albans, Herts., confirming reception of a broadcast made on 8th April with no detail.

71. Letter from George A. Clark, 4a Bedford Street, Watford, Herts., dated 9th April 1928 confirming reception of a 32.5 metre broadcast on 8th April. The broadcast included gramophone records by The Columbia Gramophone Company, a religious service and 'Bells and organ recital' from 2LO. The receiver used was a 'Sydney SW Two'. Readability given as R7&8.

72. Letter from Ian More, 48 Hackthorn Road, Cashmere Hills, Christchurch, New Zealand, dated 9th April 1928. This is a report for 2NM's broadcast on 8th April confirming reception of organ music, chanting of Psalms, prayers, a soprano solo, sermon and a hymn from 0540 – 0715. In addition he comments: "the Hallelujah Chorus came in very plainly". The receiver is described as being: "a 2-valve homemade receiver using (Detector) & one stage Audio. The aerial 80 ft long, 35ft high".

73. Letter from H. C. Woodcock, 13 William Morris Close, Forest Road, Walthamstow, E17, dated 9th April 1928. This is a reception report taken 8th April on 32.4 metres and reports hearing 'Hungarian Rhapsody No 1 in F'. The listener mentions he used a O-V-1 receiver, 'a most primitive affair' and congratulates Marcuse 'on your wonderful achievement'.

74. Second page of (73).

75. Letter from Clarence E. Roach, Windsor, Nova Scotia, Canada, dated 10th April 1928 and addressed to 'G2NB'. The listener reports that he heard 2NM on 8th April: 'on about thirty-three metres on my three-tube shortwave radio which I constructed myself'. He mentions hearing a church service 'from some Cathedral… it ended in –ham'. A note is pencilled in at the bottom 'Birmingham'.

76. Circuit pencil sketch of a tuned circuit.

77. Letter from Harry F. Hoerner, 309 N. Pulaski Street, Baltimore, MD., USA, dated 11th April 1928 (7pm). The letter confirms hearing a dance programme on 32.5 metres, concluding with an announcement to a party in San Juan, Porto Rico, thanking them for their reception report; he ends with: "The rain is coming down fast and temperature is 44 above".

78. Letter from Rafael Carmoega, Arquitecto, Carrion's Court, Santurce, Porto Rico, dated 12th April 1928. The listener reports

hearing 2NM's 11th April Broadcast, calling Porto Rico and he writes: "you had been heard very well".

79. Letter from Frank N. Bridge, 12, Warren Avenue North, Fleetwood, Lancs., dated 15th April 1928. He provides a reception report for 2NM's 15th April, 32.5 metre broadcast and mentions that: "I suppose the Beirut music was a compliment to the Rev Horan of Beirut, Syria. He would be delighted." The receiver used is described as a home-made, 2 valve set using Mullard valves and no chokes with an indoor aerial about 15ft long, 9ft high and a 5ft earth wire to a tap".

80. Second page of (79).

81. Letter from C. A. Tucker, Ranelagh, Sunny Bank Road, Griffithstown, Nr. Newport, Monmouth, dated 15th April 1928. The letter gives a reception report of 2NM's 14th April broadcast that included a piano solo, the 'Volga Boatman by the Don Cossack Choir and 'Ride of the Valkeries' (Wagner). He had failed to hear 3LO on 32 metres.

82. Second page of (81).

83. Letter from F. Huyser, Amsterdam (O) Guerickestr. 76, dated April 16th 1928 in which he gives a reception report saying: ".... to send you a report of your station that I heard yesterday evening with a strength equal to our local station Hilversum". This is followed by a detailed report of 2NM's broadcast from 1815 to 1930 hrs GMT on 15th April.

84. Letter from J. Hubert, Aussig, C.S.R. Kottage 140, Tschechoslowakei, Wohlgeb, dated 16th April. The report given was based on 2NM's broadcast on 15th April. The letter is typed in German.

85. Letter from T. H. Wait, Denver House, Croesyceiliog, Newport, dated 17th April 1928 reporting on 2NM's broadcast of 15th April using a 1 valve Reinartz reaction receiver.

86. Letter from Theo Dunwody, Villa Florida, les Coteaux de St. Cloud, Nr. Paris, dated 17th April 1928, confirming reception of 2NM's broadcast on 15th April. He used a 1 valve receiver with a French double grid valve with an antenna at 30ft and an H.T. of 15 volts.

87. Letter from L. H. Pruce, c/o Khanaqin Oil Co. Ltd., Naft Khana, Khanaqin, Iraq, dated 17th April 1928. He confirms reception of 2NM's broadcast at 1915 hrs (to 2015 hrs) GMT on 15th April (incorrectly written as 15th March). He used a 2-valve 'Bower-Lowe' short-wave receiver. He wrote: "… Apart from an annoying quick fade at intervals the reception was excellent, speech being beautifully clear and distinct".

88. Letter from James Russell, Burn Cottage, Longcroft, By Bonnybridge, Stirlingshire, Scotland dated 18th April 1928 who confirms reception of 2NM's 32.5 metre broadcast of 15th April and asks for the times and days of transmission.

89. Letter from Alfred France, 33, Church Street, Rotherham, dated 18th April 1928. He confirms reception of 2NM's relay of 5GB's Service. He confirms having heard Marcuse's message to the Rev Horan, Beirut, Syria. He mentions that 2NM's signal "… could not be better than 5XX, 5GB or Sheffield my nearest Station, no fading whatsoever…". He continues: "5SW is a poor affair to me, a perfect wash out, in comparison with your station; PBJJ comes in well, 2XAD very clean but poor strength. 2XAF very good, 3LO very satisfactory at times".

90. Letter from a listener (signature unreadable) in "Rillington" Wellawatte, Columbo, Ceylon, dated 18th April 1928. The listener states that he listens to 2NM's broadcasts every Sunday and that since January 1928, 2NM came in as well as 3LO, Melbourne. He received 5SW "with remarkable clarity and volume". The listener used a 'Radiano', 2 valve receiver built from the June 1927 issue of 'Wireless Constructor' magazine. Copious short-hand notes are written at the bottom of the letter.

91. Letter (6 sides) from George H. Freeman, 27 Spring Bank Road, Chesterfield, Derbyshire, dated 22nd April 1928. The listener includes a report of 2NM's Sunday broadcasts for the month of April starting 1st April and gives details of all the programmes heard along with readability strengths.

92. Second page of (91).

93. Third page of (91).
94. Fourth page of (91).

95. Fifth page of (91).

96. Sixth page of (91).

97. Letter from C. W. Dreyer, 17 Victoria Avenues, Hull, dated 22nd April 1928. He writes that he listens to 'LO Melbourne (3LO) and there is only about ½ a degree difference between 2NM & 3LO that made it very difficult to cut out adjoining stations ie, for the average man in the shack'. The listeners aerial was 143ft long and 65ft high with what he described as an 'efficient earth and most selective American receiver and brings in 2XAD & 2XAF' .

98. Second page of (97).

99. Third page of (97).

100. Letter from John C. Hardy, 66, Cardoness Street, Dumfries, Scotland, dated 22nd April 1928. The listener had built his own two-valve receiver. He explains: 'Previous to tuning in 2NM I had received W.G.Y. but owing to German re-broadcasts, I was decidedly sceptical. I have been lost in morse stations for a week with only occasional traces of speech or music, so you will perhaps realise how glad I was to hear your announcement of your station, wavelength and power'. He confirmed having receiving 2NM's military band records.

101. Second page of (100).

102. Letter from G. W. Duke, 154 Mortimer Road, Kensal Rise, London, NW10, dated 22nd April 1928 confirming reception of 2NM's broadcast of 21st April on 32.5 metres using an 'indoor aerial and the set in the kitchen where all the cooking is done'.

103. Letter from J. Vergouw, Haarlemmerweg 193, Amsterdam, (Telefoon 46517), dated 22nd April 1928. The listener confirms he had heard 2NM's transmissions for a few weeks and says 'they are brilliant'. He stated that the modulation was as good as Daventry.

104. Letter from Thosa Fawcett, Oak Lea, 48 Park Road, Windermere, Westmoreland, dated 23rd April 1928. The listener includes a reception report of 2NM's transmission on 32.5 metres on 22nd April at 1700 hours GMT for which he used a $0 - V - 1$ receiver and an Amplion Cone loudspeaker; the signal strength is given as R8–R9. He mentions that 5SW was a very weak signal both at noon and at night and he sent his regards to G2DX.

105. Second page of (104).

106. Third page of (104).

107. Letter from Thomas G. Sayers, Causeway Cottage, Monkwearmouth, Sunderland, dated 23rd April 1928. He includes a reception report for 22nd April made using a two-valve receiver with a 'swinging coil reaction, on an ordinary two-way coil holder, not loose-coupled'. He used a six-foot wire aerial hung on a picture on his wall. He explained that 'the coils used, consisted of 5 turns of 28 D.C.C. on a 9 slotted former for aerial coil and 10 turns for reaction also 28. D.C.C. on a cardboard former'.

108. Second page of (107)

109. Letter from J. Hart Davis, Nicosia, Cyprus, dated 23rd April 1928 confirming reception of 2NM's broadcast on 22nd April at 8.10pm; the signal strength was given as R2 – R3. He used a 3-valve receiver 'Det. 2.LF'. He stated that he was unable to make his receiver oscillate on the short waves with 3 valves so he used only

the detector valve. He complained that in the summer months, long wave was 'quite impossible owing to the static'.

110. Second page of (108).

111. Letter from Mr J. W. Burnell, dated April 19th 1928, 522 High Street, Thurnbury V17 (Thornbury?), Victoria, Australia. Only one side of this letter is present. The listener mentions that he had listened to 2NM for 6 weeks but includes a reception report for April 28th, 7am to 8.30am Melbourne time with a readability of R9 using a 2-valve receiver.

112. Letter from George E. Morcroft, Jr., 481 Dawson Avenue, Bellevue, Pittsburgh, Pennsylvania, USA., dated 29th April 1928. The letter is headed with the address of the Pittsburgh Fruit Exchange Building of which the listener is Traffic Manager. A reception report is included for 28th April for 2NM's 32.5 metre broadcast at 0655 G.C.T.

113. Letter from S. Hait-Davis, Skouriotissa, Cyprus and is dated 30th April 1928. The letter confirms reception of 2NM's broadcast on 29th April at '8.50pm' (1950 BST). The listener reports hearing a voice say: "… we are going to take you over to 2LO for a bit till 8 o'clock when we shall close down. This is 2NM, Caterham, Surrey." The signal strength was reported at R4 -5 with occasional fading. He continues to say: "This place is so much out of the way that it is wonderful to get communication with the outside world and it gives you a feeling of communication again". The listener gives details of his receiver as a Reinartz 2 valve O-V-1 and states that this was the very first short-wave telephony station that he had identified.

114. Second page of (113)

115. Letter from Fernando Castaño, Ingeniero Industrial, Princesa 54, Madrid, Spain, dated 3rd May 1928. The listener starts his letter with: "My dear old friend Gerald" and congratulates Marcuse following the birth of his daughter 'Peggie': "My kindest regards to

your wife and 'un besito' to 'Peggie'. Is this not the name of the little girl?" he reports having heard 2NM's broadcasts very often and discusses the difference between a moving coil loud speaker and a 'Horne-less Cone Amplion'. He asks Marcuse to send him a moving coil speaker if he considers it to be best.

116. Second page of (115).

117. Letter from Mr N. Dyer, Chermside Road, East Ipswich, Queensland, Australia, dated 6th May 1928. The letter confirms reception of 2NM with very little detail; 'at good head-phone strength using a 3-valve short-wave receiver'.

118. Letter from Albert Wheeler, The Prk, Pinjarra, West Australia, dated 8th May 1928. The letter includes a reception report for 7th May from 0150 – 0300 hrs and adds: 'The clarity of your transmission was all that could be desired, I had one handicap in reception, which was what I call rolling static; it was similar to the distant rolling of the waves on a sea beach". He confirms reception of 5SW – RFM Russia, a USA station or Holland PCJJ or PCLL. He explains an elaborate procedure for his receiver: 'I wound two fresh coils. An 8 turn Grid Coil and an 8 turn Reaction Coil, both being 1.5inches in diameter, but my aerial coil was 3 turns, 3 inches in diameter. The coupling of the aerial coil consists of completely encircling the grid coil (I have found that to be the best so far) while the reaction coil was coupled close to the grid coil. On a certain wave band, morse stations came in so thick, like someone putting them through a hopper, with the above arrangement I find the set more stable, and less capacity effects and it certainly loses no efficiency as against 3-inch coil throughout.'.

119. Second page of (118).

120. Letter from B. Vermehren, Park Street, 12., Berlin-Hermsdorf, Germany, dated 30th May 1928. The listener thanks Marcuse for his letter of May 21st and hopes that he is able to have his licence renewed; 'I know and can imagine what it is like to have to deal with the authorities in question, we have some jolly bureaucratic

folk here too, while some governments as that of the Argentina are doing all they can to further amateur experiments, by permitting the erection and function of amateur station without even charging any permit fees…'. He shared Marcuse's opinion that Argentinians listening on the short waves did not hear 2NM's broadcasts because they did not know the schedule. He explained that he would have 2NM's schedule published in the Radio Club Argentino club paper and in two others, 'Radio Revista' and 'Revista Telegrafica'. He offered to provide Marcuse with a list of all South American amateurs after discovering the Marcuse was beginning work on the 20m band. He provides a reception report for 2NM's broadcasts on 25th May, ascribing them as 'R8 M9'.

121. Second page of (120).

122. Letter from a Dr. Winckler, Berlin-Lichterfelde, Dürerstraße 31, dated 26th May 1928. He writes to tell Marcuse that '2NM seems to me to be the best shortwave broadcast transmitter that exists in Europe …. You are much clearer, louder as the two big stations, 5SW Chelmsford and PCJJ Eindhoven. Once you announced that your power is only 1KW. The two other stations have 15 and 30KW, you know, but you are the best'.

123. Letter from B. Vermehren, Park Street, 12., Berlin-Hermsdorf, Germany, dated 19th May 1928. The listener congratulates Marcuse for his Empire broadcasts and says he hopes Marcuse will be able to renew his licence: 'I understand your audiences are to stop with the last day of May. Is that so, or has your licence to operate the 1KW broadcast station already been prolonged?'. He mentions that only radio clubs and associations could possess and use transmitters. The listener had just returned from Buenos Ayres and said that he had heard over 300 Argentinian and other South American phone stations within six months and that there were more than 1500 Argentinian amateurs transmitting. He had almost finished building a transmitter in Argentina using 180 volts H.F. and two UX201 valves.

124. Second page of (123).

125. Letter from W. A. Bousfield, York Street, Bellerive, Tasmania, dated 19th May 1928 in which he says he encloses a page from Amalgamated Wireless's handbook from 1928. [AWA was Amalgamated Wireless Australia, an early radio station based in Sydney. In the early days, stations picked their own call signs, all Sydney stations began with a '2' followed by two letters. Then there was a reshuffle ie, the reshuffle re-allocated the call signs. 2FC was started by the catholic church, but the ABC finished up with it, 2FC and 2KY are still going in Sydney. 2FC & 2SM were two of the original stations.] The listener disputes the claim in the handbook that 2ME was the first 'Empire Broadcast Programme', because he had heard 2NM on phone and had an entry in his log book on September 5th 1927 to prove it. He asks Marcuse for the exact date that he started because he was sure that he had heard him before this date. He continues: 'A.W.A. made a great fuss about the feat of transmitting from Tilbury Dock, London on the S.S. Jervis Bay to Sydney when the amateurs had been in regular communication with ¼ the power and I think it is about time they were taken down a peg.'

126. Second page of (125).

127. Letter from S. Beckwith, Walmer Downs, Balranald, N.S.W., Australia, dated 21st May 1928 confirming reception of 2NM's Sunday morning transmission from 1600 hrs to 1700 hrs, N.S.W. time, on 20th May. He added that was hoping to add a stage of R.F. amplification using a screen grid valve to his set.

128. Second page of (127).

129. Letter from L. N. Miller, Canterbury Road, Ringwood, Melbourne, Victoria, Australia, dated 21st May 1928. The listener confirms reception from 4.25am to 5am on Monday 21st May at R2 to R4. He used a 'Schnell' receiver with a detector and two audio stages.

130. Letter from Gerald Morrice, Murranumbla, Dalgety, Via Cooma, N.S.W., Australia, dated 22nd May 1928 with a reception report of 2NM's transmission on 20th May on 32.5 metres from 4.15pm

Sydney time. He complained of interference from a morse station in Hawaii but confirmed reception at R5 from a three-valve receiver. He states: 'I live 40 miles from the nearest railway and six miles from the nearest town and neighbour, in other words I live in the good old bush.' He had heard 5SW rebroadcasting 2LO.

131. Second page of (130).

132. Third page of (130).

133. Letter from J. A. Pierson, 66 Hoon Hay Road, Spreydon, Christchurch, New Zealand, dated 22nd May 1928. The listener confirms reception of 2NM's transmission ('O Solo Mio') on Sunday 20th May 1928 at 5.45pm, R3 strength using a three-valve receiver. He reported that he could receive PCJJ and 2XAF.

134. Letter from R. T. Stanton, 9 Forbes Street, Sydenham, Christchurch, New Zealand, dated, 27th May 1928 that includes a reception report for 2NM's 32.5 metre transmission on 27th May. From 5.30 to 6.20pm. the listener used a 3 valve, home-made receiver with one detector and two transformer coupled audio stages. He states that the signal strength was R7, reducing to R2-R3 at close. This was the listener's 50th telephony station that he had heard. He writes that 5SW (BBC station) at Chelmsford came through every morning at good strength and PCJJ (Holland) on Wednesday and Friday mornings. He comments on other stations heard on his loudspeaker: 'RFM Eastern Siberia, 2XAF, 2XAD New York, ANE Jeura, JHBB Japan, 3LO, 2FC Australia, KDKA Pittsburgh, 6AG Perth, Western Australia are about the best of the distant stations heard here, not forgetting of course your own station 2NM'. He had heard several amateurs in Australia and New Zealand.

135. Second page of (134).

136. Third page of (134).

137. Letter from C. Zinnecker, Hampton Street, Bridgetown, West Australia, dated 28th May 1928. The listener confirms reception of

2NM's 32 metre broadcast on 19th May from 6.35pm to 7.45pm, West Australia time. He gives incomplete details of other stations heard and asks for a programme of 2NM's broadcasts.

138. Second page of (137).

139. Letter from A. Tostevin, 46 Railway Terrace, Mount Lawley, Western Australia, dated 3rd June 1928. The listener thanks Marcuse for sending him a 'Leydon Condenser' and mentions how pleased he was with the results. [Note: A Leyden jar, or Leiden jar, is a device that "stores" static electricity between two electrodes on the inside and outside of a glass jar.] he continues: 'I had been using a .00035 for tuning the grid, but I find the .0005 gets down to 20 metres quite easily and I have no trouble getting 5S.W. with it'. He reported that he had heard 3LO, Melbourne on 371 metres and would hear 6WF on 1280 metres that evening. He explains the coils used for his aerial circuit in detail.

140. Second page of (139).

141. Another letter (see 17 & 46) from C. R. Slingsby, 'Scriven', Thelma Road, Claremont, South Africa, dated 6th June 1928 in which he thanks Marcuse for his letter of 17th April and to who he sends another reception report. The listener mentions in a hint that 2NM would be closing down ('… which I suppose will be the last until you start up again) but says he would listen out on 23 metres as well. He mentions that the morse interference affected reception of 2NM: '… but for the morse interference, your signals on the 13th were the best I've ever heard for some time'. The listener lists other stations heard: 5SW, 2XAF, 2XAD, KDKA, 2XE and Radio LL (Paris) and Copenhagen.

142. Second page of (141).

143. Reception report from (141) taken over four days with a significant amount of detail, including: Date, Time, Barometric Reading, Signal Strength Carrier & Signals), Weather and remarks.

144. Letter from W. Diefenbach, Aurach, Kempten, Bavaria Germany (in German), dated 18th June 1928. He sends two reception reports and thanks Marcuse for his stable signal and for the clear natural playing of the performance. He asks for a QSL card.

145. Second page of (144) also in German. This is the first reception report for 17th June, 0700 – 0753 hrs, and includes a detailed report giving the times, details of what he heard and the strength of the signal. Both the carrier and modulation were reported as being excellent.

146. Third page of (144) also in German. This is the second reception report for 17th June 1900 – 2000 hrs with a similarly detailed reception report as the previous one.

147. Letter from F. G. Weber, Goethe Str 1, Sommerda, Erfurt, Germany, dated 20th June 1928 in German. The listener reports that the signal was received in spite of fading but it was not a good short-wave signal in Germany. He had to tune around to pick out 2NM's signal.

148. Letter from A. Tostevin, a post office worker living at 46 Railway terrace, Mt Lawley, Western Australia, dated 24th June 1928 containing a reception report taken on 17th June. He reported that he had heard 3ME and then 2NM at R6 – R7 and comments on the music played: 'these three pieces (from you) were the last played and were quite as good as if they were coming from 3LO Melbourne 1400 miles from here, instead of the other end of the earth'. He describes his receiver as: 'an all wave Reinhartz using plug-in coils for the higher wavelengths and the Cyldon .0005 condenser (that you gave me) for the grid tuning with the plain 4" Dial (no Vernier) and a .00035 condenser for Reaction'. He asks Marcuse for the name of the components and their values along with the circuit of a short-wave set he had read about by the Short-Wave Communication Development Company of Wickford.

149. Newspaper Clipping attached to (148). This clipping addresses a question from a listener asking about the addresses of 2NM & 5SW and which mornings that 5SW transmits.

150. Second page of (148).

151. Third page of (148).

152. Letter from Thomas H. Mottram, 27 Crawford Road, Maylands, Western Australia, dated 1st July 1928. The listener states that he was receiving 2NM's Thursday and Saturday transmissions from 6am to 7am Australia time. He explains that voices and music are heard well but some names cannot be heard.

153. Letter from C. R. Slingsby of Scriven (see 17, 46 & 141), Thelma Road, Claremont, South Africa, dated 13th July 1928. He writes that he was surprised to hear Marcuse had so much to do with a Nairobi radio station as he had spent 'seven years in Kenya during the war'. He says that he had not heard the 22-metre broadcast from 2NM on Sunday afternoons but that he had heard PCJJ from 8pm onwards. 2XAF running 100KW was 'erratic' and suffered from fade out on the 30-metre band for the past three years at about the same date. Neither 2XAD nor 3LO were heard. He continues: '5SW is most peculiar, some nights from 8 to 9, reception is good, fading out at about 9.30pm, on other evenings signals are good from 10 to 11 after which they fade out completely'. He states that 2XE was the best of the Americans, beating KDFKA (German station). Slingsby states that he was, "contributing half a column of radio notes weekly for the Argus now, so if you want anything published, be sure and send it along."

154. Second page of [153].

o~o

1930 (1 to 25)

1. Title Cover page: "Marcuse letters 1930 1-18".

2. Letter from J. Mahoney, Royal Army Medical Corps from the British Military Hospital, near Calcutta, India, dated 29th May 1930. The letter includes a reception report taken at "3 to 4am when you were calling Sydney and Sussex". He reported that "he could hear every word distinctly" and that Marcuse's signal was the only English transmission he could receive whilst in India, "5SW is a dead loss as far as we are concerned."

3. Letter from J. W. Brauner, a member of the International Short-Wave Club. The letter is addressed, 17 Spring St., Williamsville, New York, USA and is dated August 3rd 1930. He reports G2NM's transmission on 20.9 metres from 1.46 to 2.05 EST and confirms that the carrier was very steady with little fading. He thanks Marcuse for his "splendid work in short-wave radio" of which he had read about in 'Radio News and other publications'.

4. Letter from Jaap de Heer, UO1JH, from Grinnzinger, Vienna, Austria, dated 23rd November 1930 confirming reception of Marcuse's transmission dated 16th November at 23.30hrs. The letter is headed notepaper for the 'Austrian Brass-Pounders club'. He congratulates Marcuse "not only for your excellent modulation but also for your excellent German! Only few English people speak that difficult language in a way that you can also understand what they want to say." He invites Marcuse to visit him after noting that Marcuse had visited Innsbruck in 1929.

5. Letter from J B Sessions, a member of the International Short Wave Club, from Bristol, Connecticut, USA, dated July 28th 1930. He confirms reception of Marcuse's broadcast on 27th July, 1.20 – 1.40 EST on 21 metres and had heard piano music playing very faintly.

6. Another letter from J B Sessions saying that his letter of July 28th had been returned but he was sending it again with this new letter. He confirms reception of Marcuse's broadcast on August 17th 1.06 – 2.11pm EST. Marcuse's shorthand notes are added to the bottom of the letter. (J B Sessions is printed at the top of the letterhead as President of 'The Sessions Foundry Co.')

7. Letter, unsigned but likely to be from Arthur J. Green (See letter 10). It is dated March 16th 1930 and is typed onto stationery from the International Short-Wave Club (ISWC) which had its headquarters in: Klondyke, Ohio, USA. He responds to a request from Marcuse for his letter to be included in the ISWC magazine. Green emphasises the difficulty of hearing European stations, "… reception of European Stations has been almost unknown for some time." He had heard a Siberian station RA97.

8. Letter from Ralph G. Van Name from 168 Prospect Street, New Haven, Connecticut, USA, dated April 8th 1930. He sends a reception report of Marcuse's broadcasts of March 24th & April 6th although complained of only having heard just a few parts. He was really responding to a request in the March 10th 1930 bulletin of the International Shortwave Club asking for reception reports. He complained of the signal fading but added that he had heard stations in Java and Australia

9. Second page of (8).

10. Letter from Arthur J. Green dated 5th May 1930 written on International Short Wave Club headed paper with home address (Klondyke, Ohio, USA) missing. He thanks Marcuse for sending details about when he would be on the air and that this had been printed "… in the May issue". He writes about, "… some fellows confusing G2GN on the Olympic and also on about 21 metres". He notes that Marcuse would be "… on the new power" on the 18th.

11. Letter from Stephen Sluka from 20 Spring Street, Trenton, New Jersey, USA, dated July 10th 1930. The letter includes details of what he had heard of Marcuse's broadcast of June 20th although very little of the signal appears to have got through to his location.

12. Second page of (11).

13. Letter from C. Runeckles (sp?), SU8RS addressed No. 1 Coy. Egypt Signals, Polygon, Cairo and dated 18th August 1930. He writes to thank Marcuse for his card, for the "very good news it brought and for "all the interesting QSO's we have had." It

appears that Runeckles had been awarded the R.O.T.A.B. Cup and in his letter he expresses great surprise at this achievement, "By the wildest stretch of my imagination I cannot put my radio efforts in the same street as those of the O.M.s that have been awarded the cup in other years." The rest of the letter is devoted to responding to Marcuse's request to 'arrange a sked'.

14. Second page of (13).

15. Third page of (13).

16. Letter from Arthur J. Green, dated September 8th 1930, written on International Short Wave Club member's notepaper and addressed: Klondyke, Ohio, USA. The letter includes a reception report for Marcuse's broadcast dated the same as the letter. He comments; "The reception was not wonderful by any means, but better than I have heard from G5SW the past few evenings." Interestingly he states that the I.S.W.C. "...is going to organise an International Association of Short Wave Broadcast stations soon".

17. Letter from Raymond Yard, dated September 28th 1930 and addressed: 1319 Bradford Avenue, New York, NY., USA (Bronx). He thanks Marcuse for sending a QSL card and sends a reception report for Marcuse's broadcast dated the same as the letter. He states that he had heard a lady announce G2NM, at "-Sonning-on-Thames" at 12.50hrs and that the signal was a good R8 but only modulating 60-70% carrier. As a stamp collector, he asks Marcuse to send him any postage stamps "you have laying around foreign or USA."

18. Second page of (17).

19. Letter from A. R. Timothy (headed notepaper indicated he was a photographer). It is dated September 28th 1930 and addressed, 180 Wellington Street, Kingston, Ontario, Canada. He confirms receiving Marcuse's broadcast and asks if he could recommend an English radio magazine dealing with short waves. His receiver was a "Silver Marshall 735 ac receiver."

20. Letter from J. W. Brauner, dated September 29th 1930 and addressed 17 E. Spring St., Williamsville, N.Y. He confirms reception of Marcuse's 21 metre broadcast on September 28th, "… I picked up the signal and heard what appeared to be sacred or concert music played by an orchestra, this continued until 1.45 when the announcer spoke with a rather high-pitched voice…". His receiver was a battery operated, 'Pilot Super-Wasp' and he confirmed that Marcuse's broadcast, "between 1.30 and 1.40 the signal was quite strong and at times was perfectly readable, tone quality was very good, being much better than that usually noted when musical programs from your country are being sent over by way of the Transatlantic phones, your modulation too was very good."

21. Letter from David W. Jefferies, W8BEN dated September 29th 1930 addressed, Canaseraga, N.Y. USA. The letter confirms successful reception of Marcuse's test transmission conducted on September 28th, on 20.95 metres, using a 3-valve receiver, consisting of one untuned RF stage with a screen grid 222 valve, 201a detector and a one stage transformer couple amplifier with a 201a valve. He used a two-stage valve driven audio amplifier. This is a very detailed letter that includes all kinds of signal information that would have been useful to Marcuse.

22. Second page of (21).

23. Letter from Arthur J. Green, dated October 19th 1930 once again written on International Short Wave Club member's notepaper and addressed: Klondyke, Ohio, USA. This is a reception report coupled with a note of thanks for all Marcuse was doing to publicise the I.S.W.C. Reception was confirmed of Marcuse's broadcast on 20.95 metres and he mentions that American stations, "… are on your wave at times and mess up your program terribly, but still you cannot go lower or you will bump right into GBW on 20.7 metres…". He concludes by thanking Marcuse "… the club is with you 100% and we wish you all the success in the world. Your past work, carried on under adverse conditions, proves that you

should have the backing of every radio club or organisation in the world".

24. Letter from George E. Moorcroft Jnr., dated November 22nd and addressed, 481 Dawson Avenue, Bellevue, Pittsburgh, Pennsylvania, USA. He thanks Marcuse for replying to his reception report and requests scheduled communication with two other American amateurs (W9DEF & W8CF) on the same Sundays that Marcuse broadcasts.

25. Letter from Arthur W Lunn, dated November 22nd and addressed, 32 Sagamore Road, Maplewood, New Jersey, USA. He includes a reception report and comments, "G2NM is surrounded with code stations, I am sorry to report". He confirms reception of the September 28th broadcast, "... you had a lady announce, who frequently said, 'This is G2NM testing'. Your station was very good that day".

o~o

1931 (1 to 60)

1. Title Cover page: "Marcuse letters 1931, 1-34".

2. Letter from J. S. Riddile, dated February 8th 1931 and addressed 3431 Redpath Street, Montreal, Quebec, Canada. The letter confirms reception of Marcuse's transmission on 20.95 metres at 1955 hours GMT, Sunday February 8th. He writes, "I heard your signals quite strongly all the time, fading being only slightly evident". He used a 'Pilot Super-Wasp' receiver and a 'light-socket aerial' but stated that he hoped to construct a good antenna in the near future.

3. Second page of (2).

4. Letter from E.D. Thomas, dated February 8th 1931 and addressed 133 West Poptor Street (*likely to be West Poplar Street*), Mount Airy, North Carolina, USA. He writes to confirm reception of Marcuse's

February 8th transmission at 2pm EST, "… modulation very good, there was little fading and no code interference". The listener used a four valve receiver, one stage RF, a regenerative detector and two transformer coupled audio stages".

5. Circuit diagram drawn by E.D. Thomas (4), showing his receiver.

6. Letter from H. Collins dated, February 8th 1931 and addressed, Counties Electrical Construction Co., Horsham, Pennsylvania, USA, (H. Collins, Mgr.). He confirms reception and a report of Marcuse's broadcast of Sunday February 8th at 2.30 EST 'on about 20 metres' although mentions, "We received much interference from code messages from WMC otherwise your music came through 100%". There is evidence here that the Lady who was announcing during this broadcast (stated female in many other listener's letters) was called Emma. Collins asks about an aerial design that Marcuse had mentioned in an earlier broadcast and mentions that he tuned into G2NM every Sunday 1.30-3.00 EST. His receiver was a 'Pilot Super Wasp' with an additional audio stage to #106 RCA dynamic speakers.

7. Second page of (6)

8. Letter from Lewis R. Greenman, dated February 8th 1931 and addressed 397 Liberty Street, Conneaut, Ohio, USA confirming reception of Marcuse's February 8th broadcast on 20.9 metres at 2.30pm EST. Once again the listener complains of interference from morse code operators and confirms that a lady announcer took part in the broadcast.

9. Letter from Joseph B. Sessions, dated February 9th 1931 at 2.30pm EST. The address was given as Bristol, Connecticut, USA and the letter acknowledged reception of Marcuse's broadcast of February 8th although he mentions that "…. Your signals are quite weak and faded badly".

10. Letter from Paul Harrison (?), dated February 26th 1931 and addressed 7020- Place, Glendale, Long Island, New York, USA. The letter confirms reception of Marcuse's broadcasts conducted

on Monday February 23rd from 3.30 to 4.30 EST. He identifies a discussion about the value of old coins and Treasures. The frequency (announced) was 25.53 metres, reception strong but fading.

11. Letter from Nick Gang, dated March 1st 1931 and addressed 2136, 42nd Street, Astoria, Long Island New York, USA. The letter confirms reception of Marcuse's broadcast of concert music on March 1st at 1.35pm EST on 20.97 metres. He reports that, "… the signals were very weak and fading a lot … you were also bothered a lot by Code signals almost on top of your station and sometimes they drowned you out … a little below your station was a transatlantic phone … a little bit above you I heard some amateurs calling each other here in the States". The listener was using a 5 valve receiver which he built himself, "and wound my own coils".

12. Second page of (11).

13. Letter from Lyndsay Wolfe, dated March 1st 1931 addressed, Clermont, Florida, USA, confirming reception of Marcuse's broadcast from 1930 to 2000 GMT on March 1st, at Readability 4. His receiver was "… a three-circuit regenerative detector with two stages of audio amplification". Penned in at the bottom are notes, quite likely written by Marcuse: Photos, 1KW, no.95 1830-2000.

14. Letter from William H. Leeds, dated March 2nd 1931 and addressed, 21-38 42nd Street, Long Island, New York, USA., in which he confirms reception of Marcuse's March 1st broadcast on 20.95 metres. The letter is fairly long-winded but includes sufficient detail to provide confirmation of reception. He states that he is using an 'electric set' and adds that the signal was spoiled by morse code signals "pounding away a mile a minute".

15. Second page of (14).

16. A brief letter from L. Heading, an Englishman but living in New York, dated March 3rd 1931 and addressed 495 Wolf's Lane,

Pelham Manor, New York, USA. He confirms having heard Marcuse's March 1st broadcast from 2.30 – 2.45pm EST.

17. Letter from William H. Leeds, dated Sunday March 8th 1931 and addressed as in (14) above. This letter contains a similar reception report to the previous one but he states that Marcuse's signal was stronger than the previous week but "blanketed with code making speech or music almost very intelligible". He gives details of his receiver, "… regenerative screen grid detector two tuned screen grid RF's with a power amplifier, two resistance coupled audios and two 45's in push pull using 300 volts. The RF circuit is on the style of the Pilot Super Wasp AC".

18. Second page of (17).

19. Letter from John Ginocchio, dated Sunday March 8th 1931 and addressed 543 Post Area, Lyndhurst, New Jersey, USA. This contained a reception report of Marcuse's March 8th broadcast which was received on a home made two-valve receiver very clearly but subject to the interference from morse code operators reported in other letters. He reports being in the middle of a very heavy rain and hail storm.

20. Second page of (19).

21. Letter from Garry Hooker, dated Sunday March 8th 1931 and addressed P.O. Box 244, Camden, New York, USA in which he confirms reception of Marcuse's broadcast on March 8th from 2.00 - 2.20pm EST on 20.95 metres. No detail concerning the quality of the signal was given.

22. Second page of (21).

23. Letter from Lloyd J. Bonham, dated February 8th 1931 and addressed Upper 33 Scarboro Beach Blvd., Toronto, Ontario, Canada. He writes, "After two months of patient waiting I've been rewarded and have heard G2NM, … I have a five tube, battery operated SW receiver employing one stage of RF amplification and

a regenerative detector both using screen grid tubes. This is followed by a two stage AF amplifier the output being push-pull. My aerial is 45 feet of No. 22 copper wire in the form of a loop around the plate rail of a small room". He writes that Marcuse's broadcast came through with remarkable clarity, modulation excellent and that the carrier was held until 3.02pm (EST). He heard G5SW, "practically five days a week from 7.30 8.30 am". He ends, "I shall certainly listen for you again- providing the da-dit-da boys aren't too active". He goes on to say that "… almost continuous interference which comes in here like the proverbial ton of bricks".

24. Second page of (23).

25. Letter from George F. Brooks, 9408, 78th Street, Ozone Park, New York, USA dated March 8th 1931. Once again complaining about the interference but he was able to hear parts of Marcuse's 2.30 EST, March 8th broadcast using a "… S.W. superheterodyne, (1st RF, Det; Osc; 3 screen-grid I.F.; linear 2nd Det; 1st AF res/tance; and D.P. 2nd AF.). He reports that he was unable to identify any of the actual items but there were several Organ Selections and violin solos.

26. Letter from D.B. L. Hinds dated March 9th 1931 and addressed 85 St Andrew's Place, Yonkers, New York, USA confirmation reception of Marcuse's broadcast on Sunday March 8th at 1.52pm, on 20.95 metres until 3.00pm EST. He states "I was hampered throughout with a very persistent code station (could not tell who), who would just not keep quiet at all during the broadcast and who annoyed me very much".

27. Letter from G. A. Jones, dated March 8th 1931 and addressed 85-44, 152nd Street, Jamaica, New York, USA in which he confirms reception of Marcuse's March 8th broadcast from 2.30 – 3.10 EST. His receiver was a three valve set, one detector and two audio stages and mentioned hearing "LSX in the Argentine on 28.98 metres as his best catch".

28. Letter from Fremain Charles Hait, dated March 8th 1931, addressed 241 Shinnan Street, Albany, New York, USA confirming reception of Marcuse's March 8th broadcast at 2.45pm EST. He describes the signal as coming through clearly except for periodic fading and being "… cut up by CW".

29. Second page of (8).

30. Letter from Adolph Puttrich dated March 8th 1931, addressed 3024 N. Bailey Street, Philadelphia, USA confirming reception of Marcuse's broadcast on March 8th between 3.05 and 3.15pm EST; coming in at R9 to R10. He mentions "…. A barrage of code stations operating on and around your frequency of 14.340 Kc" (!). The listener's receiver was a six valve set: one stage inductive reactance coupled RF using a screen grid valve, a screen grid detector followed by three stages of audio. The first stage transformer coupled using a screen grid valve. The last stage was push-pull using the same valve as the resistance stage, resulting in: "This outfit is very stable and has been giving good results for quite some time".

31. Second page of (30).

32. Third page of (30).

33. Letter from Herbert Taylor, dated March 8th, 1931 addressed Box 4, Lawrenceville, Virginia, USA confirming reception of Marcuse's broadcast of March 8th from 2.00 – 3.10pm EST on 20.95 metres using a five-valve receiver.

34. Letter from Robert H. Haas dated Sunday March 9th 1931 addressed 311 Fourth Avenue, Pittsburgh, Pennsylvania confirming Marcuse's broadcast of March 8th, 1.45 – 3.05pm EST, on 20.95 metres. The report correctly identifies the programme details. The listener states, "… you were interfered with from time to time by amateur stations in the twenty-metre band, and the worst offenders seemed to be several English stations which

heterodyned you at times rather badly". He confirms that the signal quality was very good.

35. Second page of (34).

36. Letter from A. J. Wright 2nd, dated March 9th 1931 and addressed, 34 Ardmore Place, Buffalo, New York, USA confirming reception of Marcuse's broadcast of Sunday March 8th at 2.28pm EST.

37. Letter from Gilbert L. Peters JR, dated March 8th 1931 addressed, 3067 Decatur Avenue, New York City, USA confirming reception of Marcuse's March 8th broadcast between 1.30 and 3.10pm EST. He gives a very detailed account of the actual musical pieces heard from Bizet, Brahms and mentions, "Reception was attained during a rainstorm, which had been raging since last night".

38. Letter from Jos. P. Walsh dated March 9th 1931 and addressed, 4503 N. 17th Street, Philadelphia, Pennsylvania, USA. The listener provides a reception report for Marcuse's March 8th broadcast from 9.33 – 9.54am EST, the 3rd of Marcuse's tests and from 1.57 – 3.13pm EST, in fact the 4th of Marcuse's tests. The listener further breaks down the broadcast into a detailed account showing a blow by blow account of the times and programme content.

39. Second page of (38).
40. Letter from Charles Edwin Wilson, dated March 9th 1931, addressed Hillsdale Box 302, Bergon County, New Jersey, USA. The listener is 15 years old and writes a very long letter confirming reception of Marcuse's broadcast of March 8th from 2.00 – 3.00pm EST. His receiver was a 'Super Wasp' using, "a 224 RF, 227 regenerative detector, a 227 resistance and a 227 audio". He mentions that he had received over 250 commercial stations and that although he was not yet an amateur, he had a transmitter, know morse code pretty well and hoped to get his licence soon. His report of Marcuse's signal would have been very useful as he provided a lot of detail.

41. Second page of (40).

42. Letter from W. Ray Milliron, dated March 9th 1931 and addressed, 250 S. Jefferson Street, Kittanning, Pennsylvania, USA. This confirms reception of Marcuse's March 8th broadcast using very similar comments as other letters have for this date.

43. Letter from Fred Lawrence, dated March 9th 1931 and addressed, 483 Fargo Avenue, Buffalo, New York, USA. The listener is a Yorkshire man living in the USA and he confirms reception of Marcuse's broadcast of March 8th on 20.95 metres at 3pm EST using a, "Silver Marshall 4 valve screen grid set". He mentions that, "G5SW and 12RO Rome, Italy all coming in fine".

44. Second page of (43).

45. Letter from John P. Martin, dated March 10th 1931 and addressed 117 Main Street, Elmira, New Jersey, USA. He confirms reception of Marcuse's March 8th broadcast at 1.45pm EST and requests a QSL card. The letter head is titled with the Elmira Arms Company logo.

46. Letter from Harry W. Phair, dated March 10th 1931 and addressed 364 Page Avenue, Lyndhurst, New Jersey, USA. He confirms reception of Marcuse's March 8th broadcast from 2.45 – 3.15pm EST and states that the signal came in clear.

47. Second page of (45).

48. Letter from Robert L. Stuart, dated March 10th 1931 and addressed, Law Offices, Commonwealth Building, Allentown, Pennsylvania, USA confirming reception of Marcuse's March 8th broadcast, 7pm GMT. In his letter the reader says that The International Short Wave Bulletin (March 1931) states that Marcuse operates the **"world's most famous amateur station"** and ends by saying that "I heartily agree with the bulletin's comment".

49. Letter from W. J. Matthews, M.I.Mech.E., dated March 16th 1931 and addressed, Waterport, Gibraltar. He confirms reception of Marcuse's March 15th broadcast from 7.00 – 7.30pm and says that

he heard nearly all the announcements and records on his uncalibrated shortwave receiver. He mentions that "Ultra S.W. Radio" is the only good reception we get here" and that "America swamps the ether every night and often jams G5SW.

50. Letter from Lewis R. Greenman dated March 16th 1931 and addressed as in letter (8). He reports on Marcuse's 'Test Program' of March 16th and monitored it until 5pm EST. He states that, "… before you began broadcasting, your signal strength was so strong I thought it was the powerful 'GBW' at Rugby on 20.7".

51. Second page of (50) in which the listener reports that the March 8th broadcast was 'very fine' but the March 15th broadcast was poor.

52. Letter from Bernard Dunne dated March 22nd 1931 and addressed, 704 Washington Street, Olean, New York, USA. The listener thanks Marcuse for his card and admits to making a mistake on his previous report, saying that he copied "… the report of 7ANT in Great Falls, Montana. Your report is as follows, QSA 4 R7 about 2.00pm EST".

53. Second page of (52).

54. Letter from Harold J. Christmas dated March 22nd 1931 and addressed, 3425 Princeton Avenue, Mayfair, Philadelphia, USA confirming reception of Marcuse's March 22nd broadcast from 3.12 - 2.45pm EST. The listener complains of interference, "… from code stations and electrical appliances in our neighbourhood, not to mention almost a continuous stream of motor cars down the street and setting up a steady rattle of static from their magnetos, that it is no pleasure to listen in during the daytime or early evening".

55. Second page of (54).

56. Letter from H. F. Weber, dated March 22nd 1931 and addressed, 159 Roup Avenue, Pittsburgh, Pennsylvania, USA. The listener confirms reception of Marcuse's March 22nd broadcast at 2.00pm EST. Apart from fading, he was able to identify the broadcast.

57. Letter from Hiram Shafer, dated march 22nd 1931 and addressed, Wilpen, Westmoreland County, Pennsylvania, USA. The listener confirms reception of Marcuse's march 22nd broadcast from 2.50 – 3.11pm EST on 20.95 metres. He used a National AC operated short-wave 5 receiver and from the tone of his letter was a very enthusiastic listener.

58. Second page of (57).

59. Letter from James H Webb, dated March 23rd 1931 and addressed, 22 Elsie Street, Springfield, Massachusetts, USA confirming reception of Marcuse's March 8th 20.95 metre broadcast providing a clear listing of the programme contents from 2.10 – 2.55pm EST.

60. Letter from Harry Benn dated Sunday March 29th 1931 and addressed, 5295 Spencer Street, Vancouver, British Columbia, Canada. The listener writes a fairly long letter detailing reception from 10.55am Pacific Standard Time and he includes hearing Big Ben strike at midnight over short-wave station G5SW. He states that he wrote to G5SW and I3RO, Rome describing the different types of interference they had been subjected to by "USA Morse stations" and says "… they have no code of ethics, international agreements are disregarded for convenience of any aircraft that wishes to wander around off its frequency, and I might say here that when I look at my chart of the S.W. Stations of the World, there are very few of the frequency channels that are not subjected to the whim or will of American dominance".

He continues, "… Your own programme of this date was ruined by amateurs on their allotted frequency of 14.300K.C. wandering on to your own of 14.340K.C. Then again W.N.C. of Deal, New Jersey. 14.480 K.C. came in with Transatlantic telephone completely blanketing you".

The listener describes himself: "I am a burnt-out ex-war veteran, and radio is my hobby". He closes by saying, "… with every good wish that you may continue to give people the same thrill that it gives me to hear you".

He used a seven-valve superheterodyne receiver with a dynamic loud speaker.

o~o

1935 Onwards (1 to 8)

1. Headed folder containing letters, etc for 1935, 1938 & 1953.

2. Letter from Les M. Mellase, Wanganui, NZ, dated May 1938 (day missing) (See letter 45 in 1923-1926 letters). He states that he is enclosing newspaper clippings and has appended a form on the back (3).

3. A form attached to reverse of (2) providing a "Report on Reception of Signals" from Les M. Mellase whose address is given as: P.O. Box 178, Wanganui, NZ dated 14th September 1925. The report lists a total of 9 dates, some with more than one entry and shows the date, time and details Marcuse's communications heard in that year.

4. Letter from Flight Lieutenant (unreadable) dated 23rd February 1935 and addressed, Headquarters, Royal Air Force, Far east, Singapore. He gives his callsign as, VS8AJ. The amateur was Chief Signals officer of the R.A.F. Far East and he writes that he logged Marcuse working a VK station at approximately 1915hrs GMT on 17th February. He continues, "Mr Hall is my Signals Warrant Officer who conducted early experiments from Mosul, Iraq in 1925". He ends with an offer to make a schedule by calling G2NM every Sunday at 1900hrs GMT.

5. Reverse of (4) showing the sketch of part of a circuit.

6. Letter from Austin Forsyth OBE, G6FO, dated 30th December 1953 and addressed, Old Mill House, Maids Moreton, Buckingham, in which he says he enclosed a copy of the editorial for the January edition of Short Wave Magazine. He sent advance copies of the editorial to Douglas Ritchie (BBC Publicity) and to Sir Noel (Ashbridge), Chief Engineer of the BBC, asking for a

208

statement for publication in the February Edition. He also sent a copy to the editor of the Daily telegraph suggesting he may like to print the substance of the editorial as a letter to the Editor.

He said he was considering writing to the Lord Lieutenant of Sussex, drawing his attention to the fact that Marcuse had no public recognition of his pioneering work in radio and would propose that Marcuse's name should be put forward for the next Honours List, adding that he would not do it until he had heard that Marcuse had no objection.

7.   Second page of (6).

8.   This entry is a proof version of the Editorial for the January edition of Short Wave Magazine signed by Austin Forsyth OBE, G6FO, in which he highlights the regrettable omission by Sir Noel Ashbridge during a talk entitled 'Service on Short Waves', by failing to make any mention about the pioneering work done by Marcuse on short waves before the BBC.

The talk was in commemoration of the 21st anniversary of the BBC Overseas Service. The talk was billed in the Radio Times as being for, among others, "fans and hams".

He says, "it is much more regrettable that he failed, by so much as a single phrase, to give any credit at all where the record proves it to be abundantly due".

o~o

Recollections, some undated (1 to 112)

1.   Folder containing the letters and documents titled 'Marcuse Letters ND'.

2.   Cartoon on an ARRL letterhead showing "F. H. Schnell of the QST Champion Cricket team" bowling towards a hot dog stand.

3.   Letter from John E. Lingo addressed, 225 Walnut Street, Audubon, New Jersey, USA. The letter confirms reception of Marcuse's 2.35pm EST broadcast on 21 metres when he was living at Sonning-on-Thames and is dated February 8th. The letter mentions a female voice and mentions CW interference. This is likely to be 1931 as the contents are consistent with other letters of this year.

4.   Letter from H. J. Smith, undated and addressed Oak Wood, Church Road, Flixton, Nr. Manchester. He thanks Marcuse for agreeing to send an updated circuit for short-wave and discusses practicalities of speaker design. He confirms reception of Marcuse's music broadcast, "the clarity then was the best I have ever heard from any station". He continues, "it makes one think there is no limit to Wireless and that our great BBC has a long way to go. The great 5GB, at first it came in fairly good here, but whatever they have shifted the studio or what, but it now comes in rotten and I can get 2LO good on my Everyman 3". There is a chap I get on about 380 when the BBC closes down, I get from Liverpool calls himself '6 Something Bootle' and suspect he is an army officer, I can hear him talking and coughing and he nearly always starts off with Colonel Bogie. The French are doing a lot on SW and the row some of them make and jabbering is awful".

5.   Second page of (4).

6.   Third page of (4).

7.   Fourth page of (4).

8.   Letter from R. G. Bain, undated and addressed, Eldenside Cottage, Peterculter, Aberdeen, Scotland and dated, March, the day and year missing. He confirms reception of Marcuse's 6.00 – 8.00pm broadcast using a two-valve short-wave receiver. This letter is very rambling but contains some interesting little gems concerning others the listener knows.

9.   Second page of (8).

10. Letter from S. J. Wollard, undated, addressed, 249 Victo***, East B****, Victo(*ria*), *Australia,* (unreadable as corner of letter missing but contents reveal country: "… we have been receiving the short-wave of 3LC Melbourne in the land of Sunshine very well…"). The listener provided a reception report for Marcuse's 4.30pm (Sunday – Australia time) broadcast, with R5-6 using a three-valve receiver. He reports intelligibility 95%.

11. Letter from (unreadable) dated 25th October and addressed, c/o Taranaki Oil Fields Ltd., New Plymouth, New Zealand. Judging by the informality of the letter, this is obviously a friend of Marcuse. He is conducting geological tests in a remote area, "I'm about 50 miles from anywhere in general and right in the mountains doing more geological survey work…". He mentions another amateur, 4AG, who he says is "up to his eyes in (work)…".

12. Letter from Leonard Holdrup, dated Sunday 18th August and addressed, H.M.S. Volunteer, C/O G.P.O., London. The listener describes himself as a Leading Telegraphist and he states, "… position of receiver at time of reception was at Argostolion (Kefalonia, Greece)…". It is likely he is referring to the position of the tuning dial on his receiver. He sends a reception report for Marcuse's broadcast around 1845hrs GMT on 20.95 metres.

13. Letter from L. Ford Smith, dated circa 28th February and addressed, E.T.C. Staff Mess, Ascension Island, per SS Guildford Castle. He thanks Marcuse for his letter of 20th December listing transmission times. He says that he is unable to pick up the Sunday daylight broadcasts (0600 – 0800 & 1600 – 1700) nor the Sunday evening broadcasts (1800 – 2000), but he "… gets 3LO by accident… ". He could receive the transmissions on Wednesday and Friday (2300 – 0100) but "… hardly say they come in sufficiently well to be a pleasure to listen to…", "… but compared with the power used by 5SW I am surprised that we get anything at all". He goes on to say that as he lived in a bungalow with a corrugated iron roof, he had difficulties putting up a suitable aerial by including a counterpoise.

14. – 17. 2nd, 3rd, 4th & 5th pages of (13).

18. Letter from R. Smith, undated and addressed 85 Dawson Street, Brunswick N10, Victoria, Australia. The letter confirms reception of Marcuse's Sunday 27th May broadcast at 4.15pm (Melbourne time). The listener reports using a 3 valve, Schnell receiver "of my own make".

19. Letter from Don C. Wallace, NU6AM (ex-9ZT) a member of the A.R.R.L., OWLS Committee, on official A.R.R.L. headed paper, undated and addressed "Office 109 West Third Street., Long Beach, California". The letter appoints G2NM 'Official Wave Length Station (OWLS) #45-C'. This was given to amateurs who were within 2% accuracy on their frequencies but "among ourselves require an accuracy of 1% or better". The other requirement was that amateurs should end every other transmission with the wavelength they were using "… Example NU6AM 39K".

20. Letter from J. P. O'Neill, dated February 8th 1926 and addressed, 216 E. Evergreen Avenue, Chestnut Hill, Philadelphia, Pennsylvania, USA. It includes confirmation of reception on Thursday February 4th at 6.30pm EST., Friday 5th at 5.30pm EST on the 45-metre band. He stated that the signals came in best "during the half hour at which day was changing into night". The listener mentioned that he was learning morse code and was able to copy 10 words per minute and that he had only had a short-wave set for five days and this had been the first foreign broadcast he had ever heard.

21. Second page of (20).

22. Letter from Andrew Peterson, undated and addressed, 71 Lexington Avenue, W. Somerville, Massachusetts, USA in which he confirmed that he had enjoyed hearing Marcuse's transmission during two consecutive Sundays on the 20-metre band. The first had been a talk about Lincoln the second about Washington.

23. Second page of (22).

24. Letter from * Urquhart, undated and addressed Hawkestone Street, Cottesloe, Western Australia. The listener gives a reception report for January 25th at 2.30am (Western Australia time) although he says it was a weak signal "… that is weak compared with the din kicked up by 3BD & Co". He states he had heard, 3Bm, 2GQ, 3OT, 5BG & 3BD. His receiver is described as, "detector & 1 low with usual haywire tuner". He complains that every night he can hear the "6's, 5's & 9's in the USA", but no Englishmen. He continues to say that there had been an item in the local press on January 24th, "saying that Mr Partridge & Mr Marcuse of England were successful in receiving Mosul and Melbourne during an eclipse of the sun, that being the first time Australian stations had been heard in England prior to 7 o'clock". He asks, "who Mosul actually is as I have a lot of strange calls I can't identify". He had heard A3BQ on phone working G2OD.

25. – 28. Second, third, fourth & fifth pages of (24).

29. Letter from Charles J. Holton, 19 Glen Street, Milson's Point, Sidney, N.S.W., Australia, undated but confirming reception of Marcuse's transmission on 19th January 1925 at 5.16am Sydney time. He states, "I only identified you from your final OK given to A3BQ, your signals were received here at strength R4. He reports having a 40-foot indoor aerial, 6 feet high and used "The set is a standard 3 coil (American circuit) using plug in coils, all coils are homemade. Detector and 1 or 2 stage amplifier using Radiotron UV201A valves throughout". He continues, "I have logged 30 Yanks since 29-12-24 on the short waves". He had an experimental receiving License only: No. 2203.

30. Second page of (29).

31. Letter from Pierre Louis, F8BF, in French, in which he includes a circuit diagram of the final stage of his transmitter. Amateur stations 8BE, F8AB and 8CT are mentioned.

32. Second page of (31).

33. Letter from R. H. Marchant, dated Monday April 9th and addressed 10, Park Street, Dawlish, South Devon. He confirms having heard Marcuse's transmissions on April 8th and on Sunday April 1st using a receiver he made himself; a four-valve set using "a set of dynamic short-wave coils to receive short waves". He comments "the strength and purity of your transmission is great here". He mentions hearing 3LO and 2FB.

34. Second page of (33).

35. Two letters sharing the same stationery on 'Holland-America Line' headed paper containing reception reports that included the date, September 1st (year missing). The first letter is from A. R. Moss, on Steamship R.M.S. Moerdijk (on its way from London via the Panama Canal to San Francisco and Vancouver) and addressed, 3rd Officer, C/S Sherry Holmes, St Thomas Virgin Islands, West Indies, USA. The listener confirms reception of one of Marcuse's Empire broadcasts when he was a passenger on board this ship and that the captain had tuned in Marcuse's broadcast using a three valve Schnell receiver. He reports the concert broadcast was "... received very loud and clear with remarkable absence of atmospherics" from 10.30pm to 11.30pm BST, which was 6.36 – 7.36 at ship owing to westerly longitude. The ship was Latitude 33 – 27 degrees N. and Longitude 43 – 40 degrees W. (2333 miles from Caterham). He reported hearing an American station from Schenectady, 2XAF who was also broadcasting (Jazz) music on 33.77 metres. The second listener, writing in the same letter, signed himself as 'L Rijnink', Master SS Moerdijk, Rotterdam, Holland.

36. Second page of (35).

37. Letter from Leonard Dasler (D?), dated November 11th 1924 and addressed, Ruddington, Near Nottingham. This is a friendly letter from someone who was obviously well known to Marcuse. In his letter he says that he was dismantling his gear to make a clear start on 90 to 100 metres. He had worked 8WV on 90 metres.

38. Second page of (37).

39. Letter from George H. Atkins, dated Sunday May 6th and addressed 2 Alexandra Place, Combe Down, W. Bath. The listener writes a congratulatory letter to Marcuse for his Empire transmissions on 32 metres, "in particular this evening up to 8 o'clock BST". He was using an experimental three valve set, "1 – V – 1 … with extremely high quality of modulation".

40. Second page of (39).

41. Letter from a boy who attended Bromsgrove School, Kenneth Dunsford, dated May 3rd and addressed 88 High Street, Reigate, Surrey. The listener explained that he was at home in Reigate and as he often cycled to Caterham, would Marcuse allow him and a friend to visit and see Marcuse's equipment. He mentioned that he had often sent reports to Marcuse.

42. Verso of (41) showing Marcuse's shorthand notes written in corner.

43. Letter from K. L. Radburn, G2ABA, dated "on the 15th of this month" and addressed Maison De Ville, Loudon Avenue, Radford, Coventry. The listener reports hearing Marcuse on the 64-66 metre band at R7-8 and comments on the band conditions.

44. Letter from E. A. Jackson, dated March 5th and addressed, 51 Prospect Road, Prospect, Adelaide, Australia. In this very brief letter the listener requests a "DX card" and reports hearing G2NM "at fair phone … received about 30 metres". No time, date or signal report is given.

45. Letter from Chas. H. Mills, dated 15th April and addressed 8 Cumberland Road, Oxford. He writes that he was listening to 3LO, Melbourne when he stumbled across G2NM and commented, "… yours was the best I have ever heard". He gives a programme report: A woman singing, Entry of the Guards followed by a call to Rev Moran, Syria, thanking him for his report; finally, concluding with two organ solos and the chimes of Big

Ben. He mentioned that he could not understand why he couldn't "… hear 5SW with as much volume as yours is a short wavelength (32.5m) as well as 5SW".

46. Second page of (45).

47. Fragment of a letter just containing a few words.

48. Letter from Henry Gibson, page four only of a general discussion about radio. In his discussion about a receiver, "… the set is Det. & 2LF using 4.6.9 coils, Schnell Reaction", Gibson writes that he had built and sold dozens of sets. He was working on a set that he intended to send out to Nyassa Land in October and that he was calibrating it to G2NM's station so that the owner could pick him up.

49. Two letter fragments. The first is from the station (D-7EC) of an unnamed amateur in Denmark, dated July 7th and addressed Charlottenlund, Denmark. The amateur thanks Marcuse for a test and QSO the previous Sunday and comments, "Your signals were sure f. b. although stronger at 1800 than at 1200 GMT. Your signals were very steady and the strength at 1200 was about R6 and at 1800 GMT about R8, your phone was very good when I first got you tuned in, the tuning for telephony is very critical but the quality was excellent".

The second fragment is from Neill, Belfast who comments on G2NM's speech quality, "… at 2pm your speech was nearly perfect – very loud indeed – every word followed easily except for some fading and modulation good. He ends by saying he had heard 2KF on phone at 2.20pm.

50. A long, six page letter from 'H.J.S.', a short-wave enthusiast, it is undated but addressed, Oak Wood, Church Road, Flixton, Manchester. He reports hearing, "KDKA (62.02), 2XAD (22.02), WLW (32), 2XAF (32.77), and PCJJ Eindhoven (30) one or two German French also at good strength". He continues, "Let me say that if the BBC shuts you off at any time it would be a rotten piece of work, after in my opinion your showing them the way and if

that were to come about, a petition signed by Amateurs too numerous to mention both here and abroad(?) would make them reconsider. I heard every word of the Lindberg speech & presentation medal in N.Y. being relayed by KDKA of Pittsburgh & got a letter from their station master corroborating my letter statements complimenting me". He discusses aspects of his receiver, speakers, gives a report of the contents of Marcuse's broadcast and asks Marcuse for a circuit diagram and other advice.

51. – 55. 2nd, 3rd, 4th & 5th pages of (50).

56. Letter from H. W. Steele; a date of Nov 27th has been written in and circled at the top. The address is given as Lumut Rubber Estates Limited, Sungei Wangi Estate, Sitiaiwau, Federated Malay States. The listener confirms reception of a broadcast dated 11th November 1927 at 3.00 – 5.00am Malayan time. The letter provides an interesting insight into propagation conditions in Malaya as well as the type of broadcast that Marcuse was transmitting (Armistice Concert, Speech by H.R.H. The Prince of Wales). He says, "As one, who if not actually in the real wilds, is somewhat cut off, I really am extraordinarily grateful to you".

57. Second page of (56).

58. Letter from E. G. Yeardley, dated (at top in different hand, April 3rd). The address is The Limes, Humberstone Road, Humberstone, Nr Grimsby. The listener had picked up Marcuse's Australia broadcast and commented that he was astounded at the power both in "volume and clearness. It is almost equal to 5XX".

59. Second page of (58).

60. Folder entitled, 'Recollections of 2NM'.

61. Letter addressed to Mr Ham (Ron Ham), dated 6th July 1984, from J. H. King. In the letter he states that "Gerald Marcuse was of Austrian ancestry; his commercial interests were mainly concerned with importing wheat to Europe and the UK. He was in very

comfortable 'upper' middle class". He continues, "In his many visits to 2NM, my father never met Mr Marcuse. In fact, it became apparent to my father that 2NM's enthusiastic dedication to his pastime was already a big barrier between husband & wife. I believe this situation ended in some form of domestic tragedy in the late 1920's – possibly divorce – I am not certain. Another point, did you know that Gerald Marcuse was forced to wear a brown wig?".

62. Second page of (61).

63. Another letter from J. H. King, dated 6th July 1984 and addressed, 1 Meadow Close, Marlow, Buckinghamshire, SL7 1QJ. The letter was sent to Ron A. Ham, Faraday, Grayfriars, Storrington, Sussex and offers further information about Marcuse that he calls, "youthful recollections of him".

He says, "In those days about 1921-23, wireless was passing through a period comparable to that which satellite T.V. is passing through today. Enthusiasts had to build their own receiving apparatus by D.I.Y. by purchasing basic items at rare suppliers who were few and far between". When King was a schoolboy, he passed the Marcuse's house on his way to Caterham school and remembers an elaborate aerial extending the length of the house high above the tennis court. The antenna reminded him "of a typical man-of-war aerial with its rings supporting six or eight strands of wire".

He first came across Gerald Marcuse when he was with his father, at a time when the Marconi company had arranged a 'sales promotion' that was a demonstration of the new, novelty 'wireless'. Part of the demonstration included a one-off broadcast by 2LO, the future British Broadcasting Company not yet formed. The demonstration was held, late evening, in the Territorial Army drill hall in Caterham Valley.

The public were invited, free, to hear a live broadcast of the opera 'La Bohème, starring Dame Nellie Melba (La Bohème, the opera in four acts, composed by Giacomo Puccini). The audience was at full capacity and at the end a voluntary 'silver collection' was made in support of the local cottage hospital on a table near the door. On the table was receiving apparatus, components, home-built crystal sets and commercial literature.

King says, "while examining this table's contents, my father became engaged in conversation with a total stranger. So contact was made with 2NM". He continues, "a week or so later my father was invited and accepted 2NM's invitation to visit him in late evening – 9pm onwards in his 'den' at the top of his house surrounded by all his gear". From that point onwards his father visited Marcuse many times in the late evenings for the next 2-3 years.

Marcuse encouraged his father to build a crystal set with a carborundum (silicon carbide) crystal and King remembers sliding the contact on a metal bar above a coil with headphones on, moving the Cat's Whisker over the surface of the crystal to find a sensitive spot, "Woe to the person whose vibration in the room jerked the cat's whisker".

King describes their aerial "by now we had our long wire supported by a 25-foot pole, half way down our garden". He says that the only telephonic/speech and music stations which could be received "on the long wave were: Eiffel Tower, Paris; also Hilversum Holland and "Morlala Sroeder".
King remembered the Marconi Company experimental transmission every Tuesday evening at 7pm from Writtle near Chelmsford, especially the "clear precise articulation of Captain P.P. Echersley: Hello, Hello Hello, this is 5IT, 5IT, Wrrrrittle, Wr…….r, the testing station". He said that Captain Echersley became the Chief Engineer of the British Broadcasting Company, later to become the British Broadcasting Corporation.

Marcuse continued to help and encourage King's father from building a one valve receiver to a five valve set, all from discrete components.

King remembers that every morning Marcuse used to exercise his spaniel dog across Queen's Park, Caterham. King and his school friend met him there at 8.30am and raised their caps with a 'Good Morning Sir"; Marcuse replied, "Good Morning boys". Every weekday, Marcuse took the 9.16 to London Bridge.

King ends by saying that he was sorry the recollections did not contribute to the technology, but he was not technically minded.

64. – 68. Second, third, fourth, fifth and sixth pages of (63).

69. Folder for Mrs Marcuse's correspondence.

70. Letter from Mrs (Irene) Marwood dated 9th February 1973 and addressed, Tidewaters, Windmill Field, Old Bosham, Chichester, PO18 8LH. The letter is to a Mr W. K. E. Geddes, Assistant Keeper Radio Collection, The Science Museum, South Kensington, London, S.W.7. In her letter she offers to lend material for a forthcoming exhibition at the Science Museum which she had been able to locate.

The materials included, letters from the GPO authorising transmission to Australia under certain conditions, the photograph of the Australian artists who took part in the first concert transmitted to Australia, photographs of Gerry with some of his early equipment, a log book with programmes of concerts and other material.

71. Letter from A. A. Moss, Keeper, British Museum, Dept. of Natural History dated 19th April 1972 to Mrs Marwood at Tidewaters, Bosham. In his letter, he says that the Science Museum might be interested in her material and confirms the contact as a Mr W. K. E. Geddes, the address is included on a business card attached to the letter. He suggests that Mrs Marwood writes to Mr Geddes saying what action she would like him to take and to include a brief description of the material.

72. Letter to Mr Geddes as (70), same addresses and dated August 9th 1972 from Mrs Marwood who thanks Mr Geddes for his phone call. Mrs Marwood points out that she had "a trunk full of documents relating to her late husband Gerald G2NM, comprising four volumes of QSL cards from 1930, early wireless magazines, letters, photographs of dinners of the Radio Society, including such famous radio personalities as Sir Oliver Lodge, Capt. Eckersley, Admiral Somerville, Sir John Reith, etc., her own volume of press cuttings".

Also, she pointed out that much of this material records early achievements in radio communications, such as first contacts by short-wave radio with countries such as New Zealand, Australia, America and the radio contact with the Hamilton Rice Expedition up the Amazon in 1925.

Mrs Marwood says that he was welcome to visit and view the material but she was unwilling to part with it just yet as she would want some of the documents deposited "in a safe place where they can be referred to and consulted in the future".

73. Letter dated 13th October 1972, to Mrs Marwood from Keith Geddes at the Science Museum thanking her for her kindness and hospitality shown to himself and Geoff Voller for the day they spent at Tidewaters. He asked what had become of the numerous papers not now in her possession that included official correspondence with the GPO, the BBC and other members of the RSGB as well as his log books and circuit diagrams of his equipment.

He continues by asking questions: 1) had Gerald conducted much of his correspondence from his business 2) had Gerald disposed of any material during his lifetime and 3) could she give any clue as to occasions since his death when substantial correspondence could have been removed without her being aware of it and had John Clarricoats had borrowed much when compiling his book.

Pencilled in the margin of this letter, are three notes, 1) Yes, destroyed 2) No 3) Clarricoats. Geddes states that he hoped to be in a position to seek to borrow most of the papers for a short period to select suitable items for an exhibition, "making use of showcases already available in the room that houses our own radio station, GB2SM.

74. Letter to Mr Geddes as (70), same addresses and dated October 26th 1972 from Mrs Marwood who stated that she was awaiting a reply from Mr Newnham about the points he raised. She said that Gerald's business address was blitzed during the war and everything was destroyed, including possibly, some of the early correspondence.

She mentions that there were two moves, one from Caterham to Sonning and another from Sonning to Bosham during which papers which at that time may not have been considered important, could have been thrown away. She confirms that as far as she knew, Gerald did not dispose of any papers during his lifetime.

Mrs Marwood continues by stating, "…when John Clarricoats was preparing his book he took all the papers away for inspection. I am sure that the correspondence you refer to with the GPO and the Australian photograph were included in this parcel. Indeed, the fact that they appear in the book (Photo opposite p.116, letter p.131, is a proof of this. I did not examine the parcel in detail when it was returned to me but when I unpacked it, prior to the recent visit of the local Radio Society, I discovered the letters and the photograph were missing. I wonder whether these items were retained by John for some reason and on his death, perhaps, they found their way into the archives of the RSGB. It is on this point that I have written to Mr Newnham (as Radio Society Historian) asking him to make a search for them, and I await his reply. When I hear from him I will certainly let you know". She ends by saying that she would be happy for the Science Museum to borrow the papers for inspection and to lend such items as thought suitable for display.

75. A newsletter from the Hastings & District Amateur Radio Club dated December 1961.

76. Verso of (75). An article is included under the title 'Bit of History' saying, "Painters and decorators invaded offices where Bill G3MQT does daily stint. Turning out cupboard, colleague found old record cards, handed over to Bill as they contain information of Tx licences. Made interesting reading as following notes show:-

(i) Issued to S. H. Freeman of Otford, Kent on 27.5.1913, experimental licence call sign FXK, to use up to 50W on wavelength 200 metres. Renewed on 6.1.1920, the licence endorsed 'No valves – receiving only'. Later endorsement says 'Valves authorised 30.6.1920'. Source of power shown as 100V accumulators and station allowed to work 'Sterry, Riverhead' and 'Lucas Malling'.

(ii) Issued to V. R. Mills of Hastings on 7.12.1921, a permit to operate a 4-valve receiver. On 23.1.1923 licence issued for experimental Tx station, call sign 5QM. This allowed 2W spark, 10W valve. Source of power shown as 'Spark'. On 10.10.26 authorised until 15.4.27 to make experimental trans-oceanic transmissions with 1KW power on wavelengths 23, 44 to 46, and 90 to 200 metres. See notes in (5) & (9) below – there might be some tie-up! Vic still holds call-sign G5QM.

(iii) Issued to R. M. Sutherland on 29.9.1924, experimental licence call sign 2AYN. This later changed to one we knew so well, G5RO. Authorised: 10W (later 100W), aerial 100-ft, wavelengths 42.83 to 41.12, and 21.43 to 20.83 metres.

(iv) For three weeks commencing 10.2.1926, temporary commercial experimental licence for 100W on fixed wavelength of 90 metres, to Messrs, Autoveyors Ltd., Westminster SW.1, for 'Fixed Station at Chiddingstone, Edenbridge, Kent, on motor van XP.4255'. No call sign was allocated to this station!

(v) In May 1929, Marconi Wireless Telegraph Co., Marconi House London, granted licence for experimental transmissions, call sign G2FT, frequency 23077khz (13m) power not to exceed 20KW. Record says 'Site of station near Fairlight, Hastings'.

(vi) Have you sig. gen. in shack? What about licence for it? Few years ago you needed one, for on 3.4.1933 licence issued to radio renovations Ltd., Tunbridge Wells, Kent for 'Local Oscillator for testing Wireless receiving Sets'; Power 1W max. Firm gave up licence on 30.1.1935.

(vii) Experimental licence issued on 19.4.1934 to C. S. Bradley (G5BS) on behalf of Hastings & St. Leonards & District Radio Society, call sign G6HH. Licence later vested in R. M. Sutherland, and was for portable Tx power 10W, battery power supply and wavelengths 173.4 to 151.1, 42.7 to 41.24, and 21.38 to 20.88 metres. This station permitted only to 'Exchange Signals' with G2AX, G2FC, G2MC, G5BS, G5QM, G5UY and G5YA.

(viii) G3OHV take note: Issued to G. J. Parris on behalf of son G. A. Parris, 'South Lodge', Harley Lane, Heathfield on 29.3.1938, licence to transmit, call sign G4GW.

(ix) Perhaps most interesting of all, couple of cards concerning the late Gerald Marcuse G2NM, licenced a 2NM on 19.4.1922. Cards bear much small writing in red ink regarding concessions on 13.10.1926 to make experimental trans-oceanic transmissions with 1KW power on wavelengths 5, 23, 32 to 34, 44 to 46, and 90 to 200 metres. Address was 'Dunedin', Caterham Valley. Also reference to private wire between 'Coombe Dingle' and 'Woodside', Caterham. This connected 'studio' to (unprinted). Intriguing red markings at head of many cards, e.g., 'E. S. Con' and 'HS Con'. If necessary to refer to East Sussex Constabulary and Hastings Constabulary, seem amateurs regarded as potential criminals or other sort of bad hats in those days.

77. Page 3 of (75).

78. Page 4 of (75).

79. Letter from John Clarricoats on 'Radio Amateur Old Timers' Association' headed notepaper, dated July 13th 1968 and addressed, 16 Ashridge Gardens, Palmers Green, London, N13. The letter is addressed to Irene (Marwood) in which he hoped that her wedding was a very happy day and that she and Geoffrey Marwood were settled at Tidewater. The rest of the letter concerned a teak garden seat bench placed outside Bosham Church to commemorate

Marcuse's life. He mentions that it needed cleaning and re-varnishing and that RAOTA would pay for the work.

80. Second page of (79).

81. Letter on the Radio Amateur Old Timers' Association (founded 1959) headed paper from 'May', dated 7th February 1973 and addressed 79 New River Crescent, London, N13 5RQ. In her letter she explains that she went to the RSGB headquarters to help with subscription queries but instead she was asked to identify people on some photographs when she came across some missing papers. Included in these were early photographs and Marcuse's Log Book of Broadcasts. She ends, "When you no longer require the papers and early photographs, I know the RSGB would like to have them in their files".

82. Letter from May to Mrs Marwood on R.A.O.T.A. headed paper addressed as in (81) and dated 5th February 1973. This letter was not posted as dated but sent with the previous letter (81) in which, this is confirmed. In this letter she states that John Clarricoats would not have destroyed the missing correspondence as "everything was filed away when I saw the house before he died". She sent three missing photographs with the letter in (81). She confirms that, "Mrs Clarricoats now lives in a flat at 414 Bowes Road, London, N11". She apologies for the missing papers and adds, "as nearly four years has elapsed since they went to the RSGB anything could have happened there especially with the turnover of staff and general managers they have had in recent years".

83. Second page of (82).

84. Letter from R. F. Stevens (RSGB) dated 24th March 1969 to Mrs Marwood confirming that she would be paid direct for repairs to the bench. He ends by saying that "the passing of John Clarricoats, G6CL, will leave a gap which will be very difficult to fill. Mrs Clarricoats and the RSGB have received messages of condolence from all over the world.

85. Letter from R. F. Stevens, (RSGB), dated 11th December 1972 to Mrs Marwood. He thanks Mrs Marwood for her letter of 4th December and apologies for her not being able to contact Mr Newnham. He states, "a considerable amount of sorting out of the material in Headquarters has been done but as I have not been involved I do not know precisely what has been found". He continues, "I can tell you that Mrs Clarricoats does not have any of her husband's papers, these were either destroyed or removed before she left Ashridge Gardens. I was responsible for the production of (the book) 'World At Their Fingertips', and the photographs were retuned by Garden City press to me after blocks had been made. In turn, the photographs were sent to John Clarricoats. I can appreciate the urgency of your request and I will do all I can to obtain a suitable reaction from Mr. Newnham".

86. Letter from R. F. Stevens, (RSGB), dated 9th July 1969 to Mrs Marwood thanking her for her letter and saying that it had taken a long time to deal with the affairs of the late John Clarricoats. He stated that the RSGB had not yet had time to sort out and classify the books and pictures that had come to the society from Mrs Clarricoats but hoped that this work would be started in the near future.

87. Letter from Mrs Marwood to Mr L. E. Newnham, dated October 16th 1972. In her letter she states that when John Clarricoats was preparing his book, he borrowed the papers and photographs to browse through. She explained that the Chichester & District Amateur Radio Club had a successful field day at 'Tidewaters' on October 8th and for this event she arranged a display of photographs and documents concerning the early days. On unpacking the parcel returned by John Clarricoats, she discovered some of the items were missing, eg, the photograph of the Australian artists who took part in the broadcast to Australia (opposite page 116 of Clarricoats's book), and the correspondence with the GPO regarding available wavelengths, etc (page 131 of the book). She went on to say, "I know these items were in the parcel that I let John have and, indeed, the fact that they appear in the book is proof of this. I am wondering whether John retained them

for some reason and if they found their way, on his death, into the archives of RSGB". She asks Newham to make an urgent search for the documents as the Science Museum wanted them, in particular the GPO correspondence. Also, she asks for Mrs Clarricoats's address so she could write to her and make enquiries about the missing items.

88. Copy of letter, same date and addresses as (87); possibly the copy referred to in (89).

89. Letter from Mrs Marwood to Mr Stevens dated December 4th 1972 in which she encloses the letter (88) and says she had no reply and had heard nothing since writing. Once again she asks for the missing letters to be traced in order for the items to be displayed by the Science Museum celebrating the 60th Anniversary of Amateur Radio.

90. Copy of (89)

91. Letter from Mrs Marwood from May, dated 16th January 1973 asking for the missing papers and stating that she had written to both Newnham and Stevens (at the RSGB) but had heard nothing positive from them. She commented, "I understand Celia (Clarricoats) had left Ashridge Gardens and has probably destroyed a lot of John's papers". Perhaps you will be kind enough to find out if any of them got into RSGB archives".

92. Letter to Mrs Marwood dated May 27th 1961from Norman A. S. Fitch, G3FPK, the Hon. Secretary of the Amateur Radio Mobile Society. The letter is addressed, 79 Murchison Road, Leyton, London, E.10. He states that he enclosed a copy of 'Mobile News' and would send the previous edition if there was a spare copy. He extends his sympathies for Gerry's passing and adds, "…. he was the most popular, respected and well-loved person in amateur radio". He adds, "… after the wonderful tribute paid to Gerry in the May edition of the RSGB Bulletin there is little I can add save to extend to you and David, on behalf of the Committee and

members of the Amateur Radio Mobile Society throughout the world, our deepest sympathies in your great loss".

93. An Obituary note on the back of an Amateur Radio Mobile Society (A.R.M.S.) letter, undated but worded: "It is with deep regret that we learned of the death at his home at Bosham of Gerald Marcuse, G2NM, on April 6th (1961), at the age of 73. As many will recall, Gerry was a founder vice-president of the international Amateur Radio Union in 1925 and later president of the Radio Society of Great Britain in 1929 and 1930. He joined A.R.M.S. in June 1959 and was an active 'mobile' preferring to operate in quiet country lanes, away from the traffic and QRM. Our sincere sympathies are offered to his widow, Irene, and his son, David, in their loss."

94. Letter to Mrs Marwood from A.R.M.S. dated June 25th 1961, signed by the Hon. Secretary, Norman A.S. Fitch. In this letter he confirms that at the AGM, Mrs Marwood was made an Honorary Member of the Society and that she would be receiving the newsletter, 'Mobile News'. He confirms that there was only one other Honorary member, that of a Major Peter Kravchonok, W9CWL who had done much to make the first Barford rally a success.

95. Radio Amateur Old Timers' Association newsletter dated April 1st 1962. It notes that the Association was founded on October 10th 1958 and at the time of this newsletter had 118 members; this issue commemorated the 'Fourth Reunion = April 6th 1962'. It mentions the passing of Marcuse, G2NM and records that Christmas gifts were sent to Irene Marcuse and another widow, also, £13. 2s. 0d. was transferred to the Marcuse Memorial Fund Account at the express wish of the donors. It was also recorded that the surplus of £45 would be used to provide a Gerald Marcuse memorial Prize for the next 20 years. Thanks were recorded for May Gadsden for her secretarial work for the society. The newsletter is signed by John Clarricoats.

96. Second page of the newsletter of (95).

97. Radio Amateur Old Timers' Association statement of Account for the year ending March 31st 1962.

98. A (typed) draft, dated 5th September 1927, of a request to the Postmaster General to agree to a concert being broadcast by G2NM on the 11th or 18th September 1927. The draft includes written amendments and suggests restrictions to the experimental broadcast to comply with Post Office rules at the time; ie, "I undertake that after the 11th or 18th September, unless prior authority is obtained for any specific transmission, no further concerts of the kind will be given from my experimental station, that no artistes will be permitted to broadcast from the station, and that the transmissions will be restricted to experimental matter, readings from books (no item of current news value being included) and gramophone records up to a limit of 50 during the period of the experiments."

99. Letter from John Clarricoats on Radio Amateur Old Timers' Association headed paper dated February 24th 1962 and addressed: 16, Ashridge Gardens, Palmers Green, London, N13. The letter announces that £135 7s 4d had been raised for Gerald Marcuse Memorial Fund to purchase a teak bench to be placed near Bosham Church and a plaque to be fixed to 'Coombe Dingle', Queens Park, Caterham, Surrey; (now, 14 Queens Park Road). The seat and the plaque had been designed by Mr H. A. M. Clark G6OT. The plaque would be unveiled by the Chairman of the Caterham & District Urban District Council (Councillor J.P. Blair, J.P.) at 3pm on Saturday, April 7th 1962. The seat would be handed over at a later date. Any monies left over would be devoted to a Gerald Marcuse memorial Prize Fund (see 95).

100. Letter to Marcuse from A. J. Gill (for the Engineer-in-Chief, Col. T. F. Purvees, M.I.E.E.) dated May 1925 and addressed: Office of the Engineer-in-Chief, General Post office (West), London, E.C.1. The letter informs Marcuse that his signals had been heard by the Japanese Telegraph Authorities, "the hours during which the signals are heard are very limited and are between midnight and morning. The dates and times and wavelengths are not stated". He

asks Marcuse to supply "precise information regarding the wavelength and power normally used during February and March. The information is furnished will be regarded as confidential and used for technical purposes only, while if the limitations of your licence have been exceeded ion the tests steps will be taken if possible to amend the licence to regularise such tests".

101. G2NM's QSL card addressed Tidewaters, Old Bosham.

102. Mrs Marwood's Amateur radio Mobile Society Honorary Member card, dated May 30th 1962.

103. QSL card from G5SN and photo of house (Tidewaters, Old Bosham).

104. Two cards, one from Molly & Myself (Noesman), addressed to Irene thanking her for her card and how pleased they were to hear that she had enjoyed meeting with E19F. It said that now (Irene) had a sister-in-law with a car, she would be visiting the beauty spots of Ireland. The second card from (???) and Fernando EA4CK, dated December 1960, said, "I had some news from Alan that you have been rather ill and I hope and wish that you are already recovered and quite well".

105. Letter to R. Ham dated 15th September 1985 containing a QSL card for the museum archives from Marcuse, G2NM that confirmed a 5metre contact with him (E. A. Perkins – 'Pat' – G3MA) in 1948. The letter is addressed from 40, Carlton Road, Gloucester, GL1 5DY. The QSL card is below and confirms the contact on 26th September 1948 at 1255 BST

106. Front of envelope addressed to Mr E. A. Perkins, 40, Carlton Road, Gloucester (addressee of (105).

107. Letter to Mrs Marwood dated 25th February 1974 and addressed, East Pits, Penselwood, Wincanton, Somerset from Douglas Chisholm, G2CX, formerly RSGB QSL Manager and former member of RSGB Council during G2NM's time. He thanks her for

her greetings and reports that on the 'Old Timers net' on 80
metres, he passed on her message to a number of old friends of
G2NM's. They sent their best wishes back. The names are listed:
Kenneth Alford G2DX, Col. Sir Evan Nepean Bt. G5YN,
Geoffrey Thomas G5YK late Editor of the RSGB Bulletin, G.
Garratt G5CS late curator of the Science Museum, Douglas
Johnson G6DW, Harold Chorley OBE G5YH, Jimmy Matthews
G6LL Assistant Editor of the RSGB Bulletin, S.K Todd G2KV,
Brig. C.R. Templer DSO G3RDX, E.M. Wagner G3BID, and G.F.
Bloomfield G2NR.

108. Second page of (107).

109. Five QSL cards from, GW4FOI, GB2NM, G4AET, EI9F
(Dublin) and G2DX

110. Four QSL cards from, GW4***, G5VS, G3TYD and verso of
Special event station GB2NM (card in 109).

111. Letter to Mrs Marwood from the Secretary of the Chichester &
District Amateur Radio Club, G3TYD dated 11th October 1972.
He thanks her for allowing the club to establish a Memorial station
at 'Tidewaters'. He adds, "The station stirred the memories of
several 'Old Timers' who have been contacted on the sir since, and
who knew Gerald and yourself, and they feel that the Station was
well worthwhile". Signature unreadable.

112. A list of those who donated to the Marcuse Memorial Fund:

V.M. Desmond,	G5VM	D.H. Johnson,	G6DW	C.R. Plant, G5CP
A.C. Edwards,	G6XJ	J.V. Rushton,	G2JZ	E.Y. Nepean, G5YN
J.P. Blair,	GM5FT	E.S. Shackleton,	G6SN	B. Dasvis, G2BZ
F.W. Garnett,	G6XL	S. Rieson,	G6SR	E.M. Corry, G2YL
E.R. Frarey,	G3DMK	L.W. Gardner,	G5HR	J. Paine, G6PR
W.E. Thomson,	G3MQT	C.W. Andrews,	G2TP	A.W. Fawcett, G2HQ
H.C. Page,	G6PA	H. Littley,	G2NV	W.E. Corsham, G2UV
T.A.St.Johnston,	G6UT	H.G. Collin,	G2DQ	A. Douglas Rose, n/a
J.W. Davies,	G6NH	E.S. Cole,	G2EC	R.L. Royle,G2WJ
C.A. Butler,	G2YB	H.H. Lassman,	G2PX	R.W. Bailey, G2QB
F.J.H. Charman,	G6CJ	F.C. Crocker,	G2NN	L.W. Jones, G5JO

A.J. Mathews,	G6QM	A.E. Tillyard,	G2IJ	Southampton, (RSGB Grp)	
A. Desmeules,	VE2AFC	V.H. Hayes,	n/a	G.H. Samways, G6OH	
J. Proctor,	G2AKC	S.A.G. Cook,	G5XB	R.E. Griffin, G5UH	
H.W. Pope,	G3HT	Bristol Group,	n/a	R.L. Varney, G5RV	
J.D. Chisholm,	G2CX	D.N. Corfield,	G5CD	H. Longuehaye, G8KC	
E. Sydenham,	G3LOK	N.H. Munday,	G5MA	G.P. Anderson, G2QY	
J.N. Roe,	G2VV	A.E. Watts,	G6UN	J. Clarricoats, G6CL	
May Gadsden,	n/a	R.L. Smith-Rose,	n/a	R.A. Bartlett, G6RB	
G.C. Price,	GW2OP	N. Carter,	G2NJ	W.J. Thompson, G2MR	
F. Briggs,	G4RD	V.A. Sims,	G5VS	W.G. Sherratt, G5TZ	
H.N. Ryan,	G5BV	G.A. Spencer,	G2KI	H.A.M. Clark, G6OT	
A.O. Milne	n/a				

o~o

Appendix 6. Certificate from Crystal Palace

Marcuse achieved 10 certificates which confirmed the levels he achieved by examination. One certificate is included below to show the format: Dynamo Construction (2nd in order of merit in 1907). The certificates are all very well preserved and are in the possession of the family.

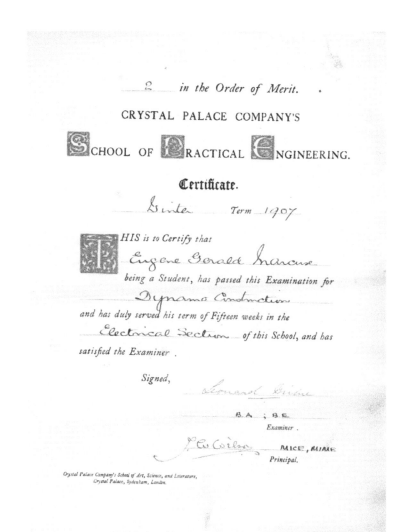

_____ in the Order of Merit. .

CRYSTAL PALACE COMPANY'S

SCHOOL OF PRACTICAL ENGINEERING.

Certificate.

Winter   _Term_ _1907_

HIS is to Certify that

Eugene Gerald Marcuse

being a Student, has passed this Examination for

Dynamo Construction

and has duly served his term of Fifteen weeks in the

Electrical Section _of this School, and has_

satisfied the Examiner .

Signed,

Leonard Gwise

B.A. ; B.E.

Examiner .

MICE , AIAIE

Principal.

Crystal Palace Company's School of Art, Science, and Literature,
Crystal Palace, Sydenham, London.

o~o

Appendix 7. Marcuse's Scrapbook

The scrapbook is stored at the Amberley Museum, West Sussex but this is the first time that its contents have been made readily available in text and electronic form in the public domain. This analysis can serve as a basis for further research into the little-known beginnings of amateur radio and the incredible obstacles that had to be overcome with

233

equipment that was very limited and primitive by modern day standards.

Amateurs faced the legal problems of obtaining licences to transmit, although these were always granted on the basis of it being a 'licence to experiment'.

The British Post Office was the organisation responsible for issuing amateur licences in the early days and the application procedure was not made very easy. In the 1920's many radio amateurs knew much more about the technical complexities than the officials in the Post Office who were controlling them.

It was in this climate that Marcuse was granted a licence to 'carry out test broadcasts' and thus become the first person to transmit music and entertainment to the British Empire.

Gerald Marcuse's scrapbook contains over 100 documents, letters, photographs, certificates and newspaper cuttings. It was one of Marcuse's most prized possessions and it catalogued his achievements through his life. Marcuse was unable to complete it but after his death, his wife Irene took up the task and she organised and dated most of the material.

At least one item is missing, eg, a photograph was borrowed from page 90 on 12th October 1987 for an article in Practical Wireless magazine but it was not returned to the scrapbook, a note has been inserted in its place.

<u>Page</u>   **<u>Contents (1 to 139)</u>**

1   Marcuse's house at Little Coombe, Coombe Dingle, Bristol,
     G2NM's Transmitter circuit diagram, 1920.

2   Radio shack and QSL contact card from 9HP, Louisville,
     Kentucky, USA.

3   G2NM's Radio shack and power supply at Coombe Dingle, Caterham, Surrey, 1925

4   Letter to a Bristol newspaper in 1921 describing the R36 Airship that passed over the city. Marcuse's name appears at the bottom of the letter as well as stating his membership of the 'Bristol & District Wireless Society'.

5   Telegram from a friend, Paddy Doughty from Wellington, New Zealand on Aug 25th 1922. Also, 'delighted with message many happy returns (for the) twentieth'.

6   Four newspaper clippings:

(i)   The merits of Marcuse using the 32 or 33 metre band to re-broadcast the London Armistice day celebrations against the British Broadcasting Company's use of the 24 metre band.

(ii) The Argus, Melbourne dated August 10th 1922 headlined 'BBC bans an Empire Relay' in which Marcuse complains of the 'Dog in the Manger' attitude of the BBC.

(iii) The Cape Argus, Cape Town South Africa dated Aug 29th 1922 complaining about a regular Empire Broadcast being held up by the BBC.

(iv) 'A Step to Empire Broadcasting', congratulating Marcuse for his pioneering work and pointing out the 'official reluctance' to proceed with Empire Broadcasting.

7   Letter to Marcuse from Jack Ludlow at Oundle School dated 14th Dec 1923 in which he informs of a transmission of Bach's Mass as sung by the Boys of the school. Below the letter are four newspaper clippings:

(i)   A report that Marcuse's tests had been heard by the Canadian steamer 'Arctic' when that ship was 'far to the north of the Arctic Circle.

(ii)　A clipping stating that Marcuse's re-broadcast of '2LO, London' was clearly heard in Halifax.

(iii)　Another similar to (ii).

(iv)　Another similar to (i) but with more detail.

8　Table of Trans-Atlantic Test transmissions allocated to G2NM from Dec 22nd 1923 to Jan 10th 1924 giving code words, dates and transmission times.

9　Three clippings from newspapers dated 1924:

(i)　A report from an Australian newspaper confirming radio communication between G2NM and the American fleet that was sailing towards Australia, 67 miles from Sydney.

(ii)　A report from the Daily Express dated May 1st confirming that Marcuse had sailed on board the Canadian pacific liner 'Melita' for a two-month tour of American amateur transmitting stations. Marcuse is quoted as saying: "I have reached places as far distant as Los Gatos, California and Port Arthur, Texas". He goes on to say: "There are not more than a dozen of us in Britain who are sufficiently enthusiastic to carry on these tests night after night, between one o'clock and seven o'clock in the morning, but we are the real pioneers in two-way communication...".

(iii)　An unknown clipping titled: 'Just Voices – Til Now'. It describes a meeting of 200 short-wave experts in London that including the well-known woman radio amateur, Nell Corry (G2YL) who was the first Britain to talk to Australia on 10 metres.

10　A clipping from The Evening News dated May 13th 1924 and a Telegram dated May 16th 1924. The clipping reports on Marcuse's arrival in Halifax from Montreal and his proposed tour of Canadian amateur transmitting stations. It lists the call signs of ten ARRL members in Halifax and Dartmouth who he would visit. The Telegram is really a plea for Marcuse to visit Chicago: "...your trip not a success unless you come to Chicago...". The name of W E Schweitzer is at the bottom.

11 A note from the RSGB dated March 19th 1924, signed by Philip R Coursey confirming reception of Marcuse's transatlantic tests heard in the United States (1ANA, 1BCF) and Canada (1AF) from December 28th 1923 to January 6th 1924.

12 Five clippings dating from July 26th to Dec 23rd 1924:

(i) A clipping from Melbourne confirming that Marcuse was overheard calling a Sydney amateur and later that music and speech were heard clearly.

(ii) An article in the Daily Mail from their Ottawa correspondent titled 'Arctic Wireless' mentions the officers on the steamer 'Arctic' listened to the Wills-Firpo-fight (*Sept 11th 1924)* and that G2NM was the most distant message received.

(iii) An unknown clipping titled: 'In Touch with New Zealand' and dated October 21st 1924 confirming communication between G2NM and New Zealand amateur 4AG using a wavelength of 'approximately 96 metres'.

(iv) An unknown clipping that congratulates G2NM on his pioneering feats in radio.

(v) A clipping from the Daily Mail dated December 23rd 1924 reporting that the Postmaster-General had refused to permit a chess game being played across the Atlantic between Oxford (England) and Haverford (USA) Universities on the grounds that "a chess match could not be regarded as a bona-fide experiment in wireless telegraphy".

13 Two Telegrams both congratulatory:

(i)   The first dated October 20th 1924: 'Heartiest congratulations overheard whole business here please listen tonight at eleven if possible = Frankie'

(ii)   The second dated October 21st 1924: 'Hearty congratulations on two-way working & with 4-way New Zealand NOW for telephony Mortley Sprague'

14   Two photographs dated April 1924 taken from a page in Experimental Wireless showing a dinner reception held for attendees at a meeting resulting in the formation of the International Amateur Radio Association. Marcuse is seated fifth from the left in the upper photograph. A short poem is attached to the bottom of the page:

> A Wise old owl lived in an oak
> The more he saw the less he spoke
> The less he spoke the more he heard
> "Hams" should imitate that old bird

15   Telegram of unknown origin, dated December 5th 1924, confirming excellent signals, it is signed 'Benzie'. The telegram in very poor condition with quite a lot missing; this is the first example from the Eastern Telegraph Company. It includes the time the telegraph is originally sent using a coding system with circular lettering that follows a clock face in which each letter represents the time. The inner circle indicates P.M., the outer circle A.M. ie, LF represents 11.30am.

16   Two clippings and a cartoon image:

(i)   An article from the Christian Science Monitor, Boston, Mass., USA dated January 8th 1925 and is titled: 'Amateur sends Music across the Atlantic'. It reports on Marcuse's 45m band concerts broadcast from the Savoy Hotel, London to amateurs in Canada and the USA.

(ii) An article from the Evening Standard dated January 19th 1925 and reports on Marcuse being the first person to communicate between Britain and South America. In fact he spoke to someone called McCaleb who was the radio operator with the Rice Expedition camped at Boa Visto de Rio Branco in Brazil.

(iii) The cartoon is taken from an American amateur's QSL card: '4BQ The Uncured Georgia Ham'.

17 Three clippings all dated January 20th-26th 1925:

(i) A Daily Express article dated January 20th 1925, '...Caterham to the Wilds of Brazil' is a report on the Rice Expedition.

(ii) A similar report by The Times dated January 26th 1925.

(iii) A report from the Evening Standard dated January 20th 1925 in which Marcuse discusses the merits of using short over long waves for worldwide transmission.

18 Two clippings and a message:

(i) The Daily Express article dated January 21st 1925 that is a discussion about the use of short-wave lengths titled 'The Wonder Wave'.

(ii) An article dated February 7th 1925 that comments on Marcuse's radio contact with the Rice Expedition.

(iii) A congratulatory message dated January 28th 1925 to Marcuse for being the first person 'to Link up a New Continent with Europe'.

19 A letter titled 'Hamilton Rice via 2NM and W.J.S. stating: "Delighted (to) receive today by courtesy Mr Marcuse first message ever transmitted by radio to this Society from expedition in field..." The letter is terminated: 'HINKS Geographical' and dated February 8th 1925.

20 Three clippings:

(i)   Titled 'Wireless to Brazil', dated February 8th 1925 that comments on Marcuse transmitting a reply from the Royal Geographical Society to the Hamilton Rice explorers in the Amazon.

(ii) A clipping from the Baltimore News, dated February 9th 1925, with the title 'Radio Reaches Scientists on Amazon'. This comments on the request by the expedition radio operator that Marcuse should inform the RGS that the expedition had reached the junction of the Rivers Urari and Uricatara on January 19th. (The Rice expedition had left New York on March 29th 1924).

(iii) An article from The Times dated February 7th 1925 commenting that Marcuse had first contacted the expedition on January 19th. The article continues with some details about the status of the expedition.

21   A telegram of unknown origin sent by 'Benzie' at 2.05 pm on February 4th 1925 commenting on Marcuse's signal: 'Heard you 'exceptionally' strong thirtieth cannot listen first two Wednesday'.

22   A letter from Arthur Hinks of the Royal Geographical Society, dated 6th February 1925, in which he requests that Marcuse should transmit a hand written message to Dr. Hamilton Rice. He says: "We very greatly appreciate your skilled and friendly assistance in this matter".

23   A letter from John Swanson, sent February 21st, received May 1st 1925. Swanson was the U.S. Supervisor of radio at the Customs House, New York, NY. He explains his function in respect of the expedition and gives much detail in a three-page account in which he congratulates Marcuse for his radio link with the expedition. This is a very important letter of great historical significance.

24   A programme leaflet for the Annual Radio Banquet of the Massachusetts Institute of Technology Radio Society and the Commonwealth Radio Association dated May 17th 1924. On the front a message in pen is inscribed: 'Old thing: This is where you should have been on May 17th. The other old thing.' The address

at the bottom is given as Walker Memorial Hall, Cambridge. Inside the leaflet Marcuse's name is given and listed as 'British 2NM'. Under the leaflet is a clipping with a photograph and a brief comment titled: Amateur's Wireless Feat: Contact with Amazon Explorer.

25   Two clippings:

(i)   A Morning Post article dated May 7th 1925 that is titled '2000 miles up the Amazon'. It reports on the position of the expedition, the radio equipment and the Swanson letter sent to Marcuse.

(ii)   A Daily Telegraph article dated February 7th 1925 reporting on Marcuse's contact with the expedition and the Swanson letter.

26   A letter from Arthur Hinks, Secretary of the RGS dated May 8th 1925. He mentions "I do not quite understand how it is that we have not heard more from the expedition" and goes on to say that he hoped to meet Marcuse to discuss questions that Marcuse had raised with him about equipment; "At the moment my interests are in waves of 19,000 metres instead of 20 for time signals".

27   A clipping from a Spanish newspaper (in Spanish). A hand-written note under the clipping states: 'ABC – The most important newspaper in Spain' and is dated May 14th 1925.

28   Three clippings:

(i)   A long article from the Ceylon Observer, Colombo, Ceylon dated May 30th 1925. It comments on Marcuse's communication and includes most of the information contained in the Swanson letter.

(ii)   A short article taken from the Christian Science Monitor, Boston, Mass., USA dated May 19th 1925 announcing the first International Amateur Radio Congress with 'enthusiasts from all over the world'. It concludes that 'Gerald Marcuse, of England, was elected as vice-president'.

(iii) A clipping titled 'Word from the Jungles' comments on Marcuse's contact with the Rice expedition.

29 A long-typed article titled 'Amateur Wireless Telephony. Long Distance Communication on Short Wave' dated 22nd July 1925. It ends 'With the compliments of Marconi's Wireless Telegraph Co., Ltd., Marconi House, Strand, London, W.C.2. The article looks as if it has been written for the radio press. It remarks that 'A remarkable wireless exploit has been achieved by Mr Gerald Marcuse, ... using very short waves, has affected communication by telephony with the U.S.A. "SEATTLE", when she was 400 miles from Sydney, new South Wales.' It confirms the type of valves used and gives more technical information.

30 Four Clippings:

(i) An article from the Denver Colorado Rocky Mountain News, dated July 22nd 1925, titled: 'The Achievements of Two Brothers'. It gives a brief account of Marcuse's achievement and expands on his brother Walter's exploits concluding with a curious observation that the Masikora who were paid silver or gold for their labours in the production of the Madagascar butter bean had nothing to spend their earnings on other than red wine from Greek traders. 'Those who do not patronize the wine-seller generally give their silver to their wives to be melted down and made into bangles, or if they accept gold, the coins are woven with pearls into their wives' hair and never parted with again. It is amazing what an amount of English golden coinage is thus locked up upon the skulls of fair Malagasca (sic) subsequently to be buried with them'.

(ii) An article from the New York Herald Tribune, dated July 22nd 1925 commenting that Marcuse's contact with the Seattle established a record for telephony on short-wave lengths at 8000 miles from England.

(iii) An article from the New York Times dated August 24th 1925 reporting that Marcuse had sent a concert program 14000 (sic) miles from Caterham to the warship Seattle in Wellington harbour.

(iv) An article, most likely from the Westminster Gazette, commenting on Marcuse's contact with the Seattle '... he and Schnell exchanged communications in the telegraph code for two hours on Monday. The signals were so strong on Tuesday that Marcuse suggested that telephone be tried. He says this was done and he and Schnell talked for twenty minutes.'

31   A page from Popular Wireless & Wireless Review, dated August 15th 1925, page 1025 and a very small, unidentified clipping. The page is, in effect, advertising Marconi & Osram valves but it confirms the contact between Marcuse and the Seattle (400 miles out of Sydney) and gives the distance as nearly 12000 miles from England.

32   Three clippings and a Telegram:

(i) Clipping from the Wanganui Chronicle, New Zealand dated 11th August 1925 reporting on the advantages of short-wave lengths, Marcuse's Seattle contact and some technical details on receivers and aerials.

(ii) Clipping from the Wanganui Herald dated 31st August 1925 that mentions Marcuse's disappointment with the 'unreadiness of Australian and New Zealand amateurs to undertake two-way telephony'.

(iii) A Telegram originating in Buenos Aires, dated 20th August 1925, that congratulates Marcuse for his telephony signal: 'your phone heard four GMT fine reception congrats on achievement try work my wave 40 MA8 Radio Revesta'.

33   Two enclosures:

(i)   A letter from the Agent General for Tasmania dated 14th October 1925, at Australia House, London in which he thanks Marcuse for a message from the Director of Education in Tasmania and asks Marcuse to send back a message. This could be the first instance of a radio amateur handling diplomatic messages.

(ii) A certificate of membership for The Wireless Society of London dated October 1923 giving Marcuse's membership number as 696 signed by the Treasurer L. F. Fogarty and the Hon Secretary, L. McMichael.

34   A poster and a clipping.

(i)   The poster advertises The 3rd Great "P.W." Wireless meeting (Organised by Popular Wireless) at 7.30 p.m. on October 23rd 1925 at Central Hall, Westminster. A programme of speakers is listed with 'Introductory Remarks by the Chairman. Mr Gerald Marcuse'. The speakers listed were: Hon. J. M. Kenworthy, Chairman of the Radio Association; Captain P.P. Eckersley, Chief Engineer of the BBC; Viscount Wolmer, Assistant Postmaster-General; Sir Oliver Lodge, Scientific Advisor to Popular Wireless, Major R. Philips, I.O.M.; and Senatore Marconi. The Managing Director of the BBC, Mr J. C. W. Reith was presenting prizes for a "Radio Sounds" competition.

(ii) The clipping is another account of the Seattle contact but with more technical detail.

35   Two clippings and two telegrams

(i)   Clipping from the Vancouver Daily Province, dated December 7th 1925 that reported an English play was broadcast by 2LO based on two acts of a play presented at the Savoy Theatre to two Halifax Radio amateurs.

(ii) Clipping from 'The Herald' dated August 28th 1925 titled 'The Wireless Champions", referring to Surrey, as having lost the cricket championship; 'through the efforts of Mr Gerald Marcuse entertaining an American warship lying in new Zealand waters with songs by Caruso, violin selections by Heifetz, jazz music by Jack Hylton's orchestra and the 'Savoy Orpheans' and other gramophone records, 'at wireless she will take some beating'. (The Savoy Orpheans was a British dance band of the 1920s. They were resident at the Savoy Hotel, London, between 1923 and 1927. Debroy Somers, an ex-army bandmaster, formed the band in 1923.) The reader, in a letter to the editor, mentions that the 30th birthday of the invention of 'wireless', was going to be celebrated at the Royal Albert Hall in the middle of September. The reader was a Frederick Wenman of Chapel Lane, Smallfields in Surrey.

(iii)   The first telegram dated November 22nd or 29th 1925, is a congratulatory message to Marcuse for his 'telephony piano very clear when working Sunday morning congratulations – Benzie'. There appears to be an error in the coding for the time sent as the two letter used appear in both inner and outer circles.

(iv)   The second telegram is dated 14th December 1925 from Cpl Alway in Ismailia, a city in north east Egypt on the west bank of the Suez Canal. The message gives a brief signal report to Marcuse: 'Relay and speech very good Sunday please acknowledge Tuesday Cpl Alway'.

36   Four clippings, three of unknown origin.

(i)   The first clipping, dated December 21st, from the Christian Science Monitor is a very detailed article by Marcuse in which he gives an account of using short waves for long distance communication. The article is titled 'Short Waves Discussed by G. W. Marcuse' and is prefaced with comment, '...Mr Marcuse is regarded as the most successful British amateur in long-distance radio work with short waves...' Marcuse discusses the merits etc, of using different wavelengths at different times of the day and night. Remarkably, after contact with the American Commander on board the Seattle, he says that "...he would not believe that these signals emanated from a British amateur, and, do what I may, I could not convince him of the fact". The Commander of the Seattle suspected that he was a victim of an elaborate hoax by some New Zealand amateur "pulling his leg". However, at some stage during the communications, Marcuse was visited by a 'representative of an enterprising American newspaper service, who also seemed to have some doubt that this was possible. He sent four lengthy questions to the Commander of the Seattle and every question was replied to without any repetition and, at last, our friend the Commander was satisfied that his (sic) was an amateur from England speaking by wireless telephony.' Marcuse goes on to say that he mentioned the incident because he felt sure that this was the first-time wireless telephony had ever been used from England to a vessel sailing within Australian waters. Marcuse goes on to discuss (without using the term) the 'skip distance' of short-wave signals and the phenomena of signals bouncing off the 'ceiling or the Heaviside Layer' (ionosphere). He discusses French engineers, belonging to the radio corps, attempting transmission on short waves in 1918 believing that the signals would not be audible to the Germans but would be audible in Palestine and Egypt.

(ii)   An undated clipping from an Australian newspaper that reports on the first broadcast to the Empire from Australia by station 2FC. It mentions '... short addresses were given by many prominent people, including the Prime Minister of the Commonwealth and the Premier and Governor of New South Wales and a message to Mr. Marcuse acknowledging good receipt of his Empire broadcast concert'.

(iii) This clipping responds to Marcuse's comment about amateurs in Australia and New Zealand being unprepared to experiment in short-wave telephony. It remarks that Marcuse 'is apparently a wealthy man with a considerable amount of time to spare, but unfortunately very few New Zealand amateurs were in that delightful position'. It goes on to comment on the very stringent Government regulations and the high price of equipment.

(iv)   This undated clipping of unknown origin is most likely written by Marcuse and states that he was unable to give details of his transmitting equipment as it '... is of my own construction and contains certain details which I am not anxious to publish'. However, he did give details of his superheterodyne receiver.

37   Four clippings, two of unknown origin.

(i)   A clipping from an unknown source and undated. Title: 'Radio Romance', this reports on a New Zealander on honeymoon in England (Mr F. D. Bell of Otago, New Zealand). He uses Marcuse's station in Caterham to communicate with his father and sister 12,000 miles away in New Zealand using morse code.

(ii)   This clipping is in German and is dated January 16th 1926. It is from 'Neue Freie Presse', a Viennese paper that was printed until 1938.

(iii) A clipping from the New York Herald Tribune that is dated January 10th 1926. It reports on Marcuse's 'meritorious performance on radiophone'. At this time Marcuse was secretary of the RSGB and was using the 45-metre band to broadcast from the Savoy hotel. The clipping goes on to say that Marcuse's broadcasts were being received in Halifax, Nova Scotia on January 9th (1926) by a number of stations including Joseph J. Fassett of Dartmouth, N.S., 'C1AR'.

(iv)   This clipping is dated '1926', most likely originating from an English newspaper is titled 'Talking to the Old Folks Back Home'. It reports on Mr F. Bell (nephew of Sir Francis Bell, the New Zealand statesman) and is similar to (i).

38   Three clippings.

(i)   The first is an article written by Marcuse for the Christian Science monitor dated March 20th 1926 and titled 'Short Waves Continue to get Distance'. In this he discusses the advantages and problems with wavelengths below 50 metres when transmitting to America, India and Canada.

(ii)   A clipping on unknown origin and date written by Marcuse in which he gives a pre-amble on the progress and development of radio. Also, he discusses the advantages of resistance-coupled amplifiers and the availability of rectifier valves removing the need for dry batteries.

(iii) A clipping from The Evening Star in New Zealand dated June 7th 1926. It is titled 'Chatting with Surrey – Lengthy Morse Communication – Waihemo Station Claims Record'. It mentions a Miss Bell with 150W input power on 33.5 metres to communicate in Morse code with her brother for two hours from Waihemo, New Zealand.

39 Three clippings.

(i) The first is an article written by Marcuse for the Christian Science Monitor dated January 25th 1927. He reports on his short-wave broadcasts to Australia & New Zealand from Caterham via the post office telephone trunk line system, gives more technical details about the amplification of the signal and discusses the possibility of Empire Broadcasting.

(ii) The second clipping is from The Courier (Queensland, Brisbane) and is dated July 7th 1927 and is titled 'From London – Nightly Short-Wave Talk'. It reports that Marcuse had completed plans to give a nightly talk at 3am and 4am Australian time. It raises the question about how the BBC's plans had progressed.

(iii) The third clipping is taken from the Cape Argus, Cape Town, South Africa and is dated July 30th 1927. Under the title 'Short Waves from England' it mentions that Marcuse had been given permission to conduct experimental re-broadcasts of the BBC programmes on short waves and that these would start on or about August 15th using the 23-metre and 33-metre bands.

40 Six short clippings each of which relates to Empire Broadcasting.

(i) The first is from the Adelaide Register, South Australia and is dated July 9th 1927. The content is similar to Page 39(ii) but states the wavelength would be the 34-metre band.

(ii) The second clipping is from the Ceylon Observer, Colombo, Ceylon and is dated July 10th 1927. The content is similar to (i) but it states the wavelength used would be of 23-33 metres.

(iii) The third clipping is from the Cape Times, Cape Town and is dated July 26th 1927. The content is similar to (i) but mentions that G2NM's transmitter was recently re-built and had a new power supply system installed using Marconi rectifying and transmitting valves. It states the experimental transmission might begin on August 15th 1927.

(iv) The fourth clipping is from 'The Age', Melbourne and is dated July 9th 1927 and it is titled 'Empire Broadcasting – English Amateur's Plan'. The article explains that Marcuse planned to give a nightly broadcast for Empire listeners on the 34-metre band from 3 – 4am Australia time. It discusses the BBC transmission plans.

(v) This clipping is from the 'Farmer & Settler', in Sydney and is dated July 22nd 1927. It discusses the possibility of the BBC 'planning for transmission specially to Australia' and explains that British, Dutch, German and French stations have been re-broadcast from Sydney.

(vi) This is taken from 'The Sun', Melbourne and is dated July 30th 1927. It mentions the Dutch station PCJJ and the American stations WGY and KDKA and reports about the BBC: 'at last a move has been made to install a British short-wave broadcasting station' but 'As Mr Marcuse has already transmitted speech to Australia, the BBC's effort may take second place'.

41 This page contains seven clippings.

(i) The first is taken from The Times of India, Bombay and is dated August 1st 1927. Titled 'England Calling', it explains a little about 2NM's tests from Caterham to India and the Dominions on '23 and 33 metres'. It mentions that these would commence 'on or after August 15th'.

(ii)   The second clipping is taken from the Natal Advertiser, Durban, South Africa and is dated August 4th 1927. It is titled 'Broadcasting for the Empire – Outcry Against Delay – Successful Tests at Eindhoven'. It mentions that the Dutch station at Eindhoven had conducted tests on shortwave that could be heard 'in all regions of the Empire' and complains about the delay in giving South Africa a similar station for the benefit of the British Empire. It goes on to report that 'Mr Gerald Marcuse begins broadcasting on August 14 from his Caterham station a series of programmes for the benefit of Dominion listeners-in'.

(iii) A curious article from the Adelaide register, dated August 12th 1927 appears in two parts. The first is titled 'Wireless Pioneer' and quotes Marcuse deploring the 'present-day lack of enthusiasm in serious wireless experiments'. The second is titled 'Can it be Done?' and states 'Mr Marcuse told me that he had a letter from India in which the writer claims that he has perfected a means of broadcasting smells! Would Mr Marcuse find money to exploit this discovery?' It continues by saying that the writer had asked Marcuse to send over a few valves 'to assist the experiments, as times are hard and valves none too easy to come by'. In return the writer offered to transmit by wireless a few choice Indian scents and aromas! The ultimate begging letter!

(iv)   The fourth clipping is titled 'Empire Broadcasting – Amateur's Six Months' Test.' It is dated (London) August 10th (1927) and gives details of the licence that the Post office issued to Marcuse so he could provide Empire Broadcasting. It quotes the Morning Post stating "Meantime, the British Broadcasting Corporation is maintaining a dog-in-the-manger attitude, by not rendering itself open to criticism by not showing more active interest in the scheme".

(v)   The fifth clipping from the Cape Argus, Cape Town, South Africa is dated August 4th 1927 and is titled 'Listening-In to Britain – Empire Broadcasting Service Needed'. The article is very similar to (ii) but mentions the reasons for delaying the 'Imperial Conference resolutions' for an Empire Broadcasting service; these are given as 'distortion and fading'.

(vi)   This very small clipping from the 'West Australian', in Perth, dated August 4th 1927 is titled 'Wireless Concerts'. It states that Marcuse would begin his Empire Broadcasting on August 14th but he was waiting for 'departmental sanction and the hours proposed' before broadcasting on the 34-metre band. The 3-4am times are confirmed.

(vii) The seventh clipping is from The Argus, Melbourne dated August 4th 1927 and is titled 'English Programme'. The article is very similar to the others on this page.

42   This page contains four clippings, two from the same newspaper printed on the same day.

(i)   The first, titled 'Empire Broadcasting – Most Baffling Problem' is from the 'West Australian', Perth and is dated August 5th 1927. The article quotes extensively from a BBC statement in which the Corporation declares its commitment to the broadcasts but states that relaying programmes on short waves 'would arouse a temporary interest, but would inevitably be followed by keen disappointment and disillusionment'. It goes on to say that the problem 'is one of reception rather than transmission' and that 'The eventual service, if it is to reach the majority, will have to be re-broadcast through the existing Dominion stations'. The article comments about the importance of the transmitter output power being similar to the Dutch station P.C.J.J. for a reliable signal to be received.

(ii)   This article is from 'The Friend', Bloemontein (Bloemfontein), South Africa, is dated August 5th 1927 and is titled 'Empire Broadcasting – Criticism of Delay in Establishing a Service'. The content is much the same as the others with no new points raised.

(iii) & (iv) Both these two articles from The Courier, Brisbane, Queensland and are dated August 3rd or 5th 1927. The content is much the same as the others printed near this date, both refer to the official BBC statement and to Marcuse's Empire tests.

43   Four short clippings

(i)   The first is from the Natal Advertiser, Durban, South Africa dated August 9th 1927 and is titled 'A Mystery Studio – Broadcasting to the Empire – London Man's Enterprise – Plenty of Offers of Help'. The article develops the theme of the Empire Broadcasts and goes on to mention that as Marcuse's offer to relay BBC broadcasts was rejected, he was setting up his own studio, '…the whereabouts of the studio is at present a closely guarded secret. A first-class orchestra has offered its services and offers of gratuitous performances by dance bands and artists in all parts of the country are said to be pouring in'.

(ii) The second clipping is from the New York Herald, Paris dated August 9th 1927 and is (again) titled 'Empire Broadcasting'. It raises the subject of international copyright and states that Marcuse 'has already received warnings and he is more concerned with this difficulty than any other'.

(iii) The third clipping is taken from The Star, Johannesburg, dated August 9th 1927 and is titled 'Broadcasting to Dominions – Plans of Amateur – A mystery Studio in London'. The content is very similar to (i).

(iv) The fourth clipping is taken from the Cape Argus, Cape Town, South Africa, is dated August 9th 1927 and is titled 'Broadcasting to the Dominions – A London Amateur's Plans'. This is almost the same as (i) and (iii).

44   This page contains two articles.

(i)   The first is from the Cape Times, Cape Town, South Africa, dated August 9th 1927 and is titled 'Dominion Broadcasting: First Experiments. – How Listeners Can Assist'. This is a very long article; it announces Marcuse's intention to re-broadcast BBC transmissions from August 14th 1927 following the grant of a special licence that allowed him to use '1kw of power'. Marcuse would be transmitting on 33 metres two or three times each week from 1700 to 1900 hours GMT. The article mentions that the Umlazi Radio Society had written to the BBC enquiring about when Dominion broadcasting would commence. Mr J. W. Reith's (the Director General) reply is printed in full. The article asks South African short-wave listeners to keep reception reports of the broadcasts.

(ii) The second article is a clipping from the Adelaide Register, dated August 10th 1927. It states that Marcuse's August 14th broadcast would include 'a first-class orchestra and dance band to include many leading dramatic and music artists ... complete with talks and plays'. It quotes from Marcuse that residents in Australia's back blocks would be able to hear London on an ordinary two-valve receiver.

45 Four Newspaper cuttings are pasted in.

(i) The first, dated August 10th 1927 is from the Natal Mercury, Durban and is titled 'Broadcasting to the Dominions'. It states that Marcuse was prepared to do the broadcasting for a year at his own expense.

(ii) The second is a short clipping from the Daily Telegraph, in Sydney dated August 10th 1927. It mentions that programmes would be transmitted from Marcuse's studio in Caterham and could be received in New Zealand at 5.30am and in Australia at 4am.

(iii) The third is from The Press, Christchurch, N.Z., dated August 10th 1927. The content is very similar to (ii).

(iv) The final clipping is from the West Australian, Perth and is dated August 10th 1927. Marcuse is quoted as saying: 'I am prepared to carry on for a year at my own expense and to provide the data for an official scheme'.

46 Four newspaper clippings are pasted in.

(i)   The first is taken from The Friend, Bloemfontein, S.A. and is dated August 10th 1927. It states that the BBC had rejected Marcuse's offer to relay their programmes so he had 'set up a mystery of his own' and the whereabouts of his studio was a closely guarded secret. Offers of gratuitous performances by dance bands and artistes in all parts of the country were 'pouring in'.

(ii) The second is from The Courier, Brisbane, Queensland, August 10th 1927; this reports on the forthcoming broadcasts and mentions the inclusion of a first-class orchestra from 'Dance Land'. It questions how much progress the BBC had made and states the experts from the BBC blamed the difficulty in its own programmes being heard was due to 'reception in the Dominions'.

(iii) A clipping from The Cape Times, Cape Town, reports that Marcuse was the first amateur to establish regular communication with Australia.

(iv) This clipping is taken from The Argus, Melbourne, on August 16th 1927. It mentions that 'foreign programmes' were broadcast from stations PCJJ and WGY. It reports on the complete failure to broadcast addresses from Canada of the Prince of Wales and of the British Prime Minister, Mr Baldwin and states that 'Mr Marcuse does not pretend to have equipment equal to that used at PCJJ or WGY, and it is doubtful if he will employ more than about one hundredth of the power that these stations used'.

47   Four more newspaper cuttings are attached.

(i)   The first is a very interesting article from the Evening standard dated August 11th 1927. It announces Marcuse would be broadcasting three days a week using 33 metres with 23 metres as a backup and he would be getting his friends to act as artists. Marcuse states that the 'Empire settlers' had been asking for BBC programmes to be relayed to them but the BBC objected.

(ii) The second cutting is taken from The Capriconian, Rockhampton, Queensland; it is dated August 11th 1927 and includes details about the Empire Broadcasts, stating that 'domestic electricity' would be used.

(iii) The third clipping is taken from The Courier, Brisbane, Queensland, August 12th 1927. It reports that the Post Office had issued Marcuse a licence on August 10th for six months commencing September 1st. Marcuse is quoted as saying: 'The chief difficulty at the moment is the question of copyright'. The Morning Post is quoted: 'In the meantime, the BBC are maintaining a dog in the manger attitude, rendering themselves open to criticism for not showing a more active interest in the scheme'.

(iv) The fourth clipping is taken from the Daily telegraph, Sydney, dated August 12th 1927. It mentions the power restriction of one kilowatt that continuous transmissions would not take place and these would be restricted to two hours on each occasion.

48 Five newspaper cuttings are attached.

(i) The first is from the Madras Mail, August 12th 1927. It suggests that the short-wave policy conducted by the BBC at Daventry had either been abandoned, had proved a failure or was not financially viable. It suggests the Indian broadcasting Company should take note of Marcuse's operations with a view that Indian listeners could ultimately receive a wider range of programmes.

(ii) This clipping is from the Natal Mercury, Durban, Natal, August 12th 1927; it states that the official opening of Marcuse's service would be on September 1st and that 'Mr Marcuse regards South Africa as the best situated of all the Dominions as the time difference is the least'.

(iii) This clipping, from The Daily Telegraph News, August 12th 1927, repeats much of the content in the other articles.

(iv) A clipping from The Pioneer, Allahabad, August 13th 1927 confirming previous content.

(v)   The clipping is taken from the Natal Witness, Pietermaritzburg, August 13th 1927 and it repeats the content in the other clippings.

49   Three newspaper cuttings are attached.

(i)   The first is from the Paris Times, dated August 13th 1927. It mentions that Marcuse's broadcasts would not take place on more than three days a week and reflects on the failure of the BBC to provide home news to the Empire. The article comments on improvements to the telephone service for which subscribers in some London districts had their call charges doubled to 2p peremptorily for improvements in the service.

(ii) An article from the Egyptian Gazette, Alexandria, August 13th 1927. A very short clipping that mentions Marcuse's 'Imperial broadcasting venture was purely a family affair. It would last four hours on three days each week, his friends giving their services free'.

(iii) This clipping is taken from the Natal Mercury, Durban, August 16th 1927 and is titled: 'Umhlazi'. It comments on an address given by the Chairman of the Umhlazi Radio Society, Mr Claud Lancashire, in which he confirmed the improvements in communication made possible by the use short waves and that the Director General of the 'British Broadcasting Station', Sir James W. Keith (*Sir John Reith was the D.G. in 1927*), had written to the society. The address mentioned the 'Schlesinger arrangement' and went on to recognise the improvement in the signal strength of short-wave signals at night. An exhibition based on radio, was to be held in which everyone would 'have an opportunity of demonstrating their capabilities. An acknowledgement was made of the work of a well-known amateur, Mr Eric Levine.

50   Three newspaper cuttings are attached.

(i)   The first is from The Chronicle, Adelaide, S. Australia, August 16th 1927. This comments on 'how far the BBC's plan' had progressed. The BBC is quoted as saying that their difficulties were based on 'reception in the Dominions, but definite developments on this aspect are shortly expected, as a result of experiments in reception from America'.

(ii) This clipping is taken from the Hindu Madras, August 20th 1927. In an interview, Marcuse confirmed that India would benefit from his efforts and that two or three years before he had relayed programmes from London to India on a regular basis, he expressed some concern about a lack of interest in short-wave listening in India at that time and he had to close down. He mentioned copyright problems with the BBC.

(iii) The third clipping is from the Egyptian Mail dated August 19th 1927. The article covers Marcuse's broadcasting details and mentions that he had set up a studio at a secret location. The broadcast times were given as: Egypt at 6pm, New Zealand at 5.30am, Australia at 4am, India at 11pm, East Africa at 1pm and in Canada at 1pm.

51 A picture from Wireless World showing Marcuse in his shack and three other photographs taken in 1927.

(i) The Wireless World clipping dated August 24th 1927 includes a picture of Marcuse in his shack smoking his pipe. It mentions that Marcuse would be inaugurating telephony transmissions on Sept 1st 1927 for the benefit of the colonies on the 23 and 30 metre wavebands three nights a week.

(ii) The first photograph shows the front of his house (Coombe Dingle) with the aerial feeder passing out through a window.

(iii) Another photograph is a view inside the shack with QSL cards from 8AVJ and BCP visible.

(iv) The third photograph shows an impressive view of his aerial mast with stays.

52   A Post Office Telegram originating in Melbourne dated August 31st 1927 confirming clear reception: 'Heard you clearly Sunday 1645 Melbourne time later local amateur transmitting caused great interference hope rebroadcast you next trial Tremon wireless'.

53   Another Post Office Telegram originating in Victoria dated August 31st 1927: 'Every success to your new venture 2.GF.'

54   Three clippings are attached.

(i)   The first is a very detailed editorial from Radio Johannesburg dated August 1927. Once again, the 'Umlazi Radio Society' is mentioned naming a Mr C. Lancashire as president. It records the following people: Mr J. S. Streeter, FO-A4Z of Capetown, Mr Gerald Marcuse, eg, 2NM, Mr S. C. Pleass, FO-A4M who received the result of a 'big fight in America', Mr L.E. Green, technical editor to 'Radio' who was conducting experimental telephony on a crystal-controlled transmitter and a Mr P. E. Card of East London who sent a report concerning an eclipse of the sun.

(ii) The second clipping is from The Sun, New York dated September 1st 1927. It comments on Marcuse's transmission of the Transatlantic Chess match between Oxford and Harvard Universities.

(iii) The third clipping is taken from the West Australian dated August 15th 1927. It states that Mr W. E. Coxon, the manager of 6WF, confirmed that Marcuse's signal would be strong enough to relay it. The concerts being transmitted by Marcuse could be recorded at 6WF and relayed the next day. A very strong signal of a Dutch is mentioned.

55   This is a cutting from Popular Wireless Magazine dated September 3rd 1927 and shows the same picture as (51) but it is used to advertise an article written by Marcuse titled: 'My Empire Broadcasts'.

56 This is the actual Popular Wireless article and it extends over two pages (5 & 6). A picture at the top shows Marcuse with earphones on in his shack; another at the bottom is a view of the power switching and control arrangements. Marcuse sets out his plans for Empire Broadcasts and mentions the success of PCJJ, the Dutch station in Eindhoven that had just conducted short-wave transmissions. He sets out a scheme for his broadcasts that the Post Office had approved of. He could transmit for two hours on any day for six months using 1Kw input to the main valve on 23 or 33 metres. The approval was conditional that he did not 'broadcast current news or matters of an advertising nature'. This article is dated September 3rd 1927.

57 A 'Radiogramme' from Bill, OZ-4AA in Antwerp giving signal reports, dated Sept 4th 1927 via Radio station: EB4AC: 'to EG - 2NM – Rcvd fone tonite gd speaker strength det 2AF es as loud asPCJJ es much clearer modulatn vy gds peeks vy distinct usual Quick QSS hearty congrats OM es 73's sig. Bill OZ 4AA'.

58 Three clippings inserted.

(i) Part of the front page from the September 7th 1927 edition of Modern Radio and Electrics, Adelaide, volume 1, number 34. The headline is: 'Marcuse Transmissions Successful Good Reception Reported. 5CL Will Make Arrangements to Re-Broadcast". A message has been written across the top of the article" 'As yet 5CL has been unsuccessful due to local QRM. PS, 5CL's power is 5Kw & wavelength 395 metres'. It states that arrangement had been made between Marcuse and the BBC for Marcuse to rebroadcast the programme from 2LO every Sunday at 6am in the morning and evening. 5CL would be installing special equipment to pick up and relay to listeners.

(ii) An unknown clipping, most likely from an Australian newspaper dated September 1927. It states that Marcuse would be transmitting from the 'Columbia *Graphophone* Company', in London. The Australian artists named are: Miss Daisy Kennedy, Mme Evelyn Scotney, Mr John Amadio, Mr Fred Collier, Mr

Harold Williams and Mr William Murdoch. It mentions that the Australian High Commissioner, Sir Granville Ryrie would be returning to London from a League of Nations Assembly in Geneva especially to broadcast a short address. Re-broadcasting arrangements are given.

(iii) The third short clipping, dated September 11th 1927 is from the 'Daily Express' correspondent in Melbourne and it comments that Marcuse's broadcasts were disappointing owing to 'atmospherics and Morse interference'. The first three items were heard, the violin following was faint and Sir Granville Ryrie's speech was not heard.

59   A Post Office Telegraph from 2FC Sydney dated September 7th 1927. The message mention signals received at a good strength but adds that there was jamming by amateurs on the nearby 32 metre band. It suggests that Marcuse moved to 28 metres, 'which at this end is comparatively clear':
'Your transmissions yesterday received at good strength but not equal to last Sunday stop both last Sunday and yesterday we experienced trouble through jamming by amateurs whose band is around about thirty-two metres stop suggest you alter your wavelength to twenty-eight metres which at this end is comparatively clear stop would you like us rebroadcast Sundays program stop kindly reply by cable and advise when testing 2 FC Sydney'.

60   A Post Office Telegraph dated September 10th 1927 from 2FC in 'Sydney via Empiradio' stating: Marcuse Station 2NM Surrey Signals Excellent got programmes Static bad local interference bad 2FC'.

61   Three clippings of Australian origin and a Post Office Telegraph attached beneath, all dated September 11th 1927.

(i)   The first is titled 'The Great Success of 2NM' and leads with the comment: 'Mr Gerald Marcuse's voice has probably been heard in more countries than that of any other man'. It describes the room in Marcuse's Caterham home as being small and 'efficient without being in the least pretentious'. It describes a massive wooden bench running down the centre of the room upon which the transmitter is mounted. The crystal unit entirely enclosed in a screened box made from copper gauze. The author, the newspaper's 'wireless correspondent', gives a delightful description of the station. It mentions a pile of over 100 letters from all over the world including Christmas Island, Beirut and Trinidad; the latter confirmed hearing England the first time in history.

(ii) This is a very brief article titled: 'Angry with the BBC'. It comments that the BBC had shut down 2FC, a station in Sydney that was re-broadcasting a special short-wave programme. It quotes a Mr Hugh McCubbin, 'The corporation seems to be doing its best to kill all attempts to establish Empire interchange programmes on short waves. The latest move places them in an untenable position after the treatment of Mr Marcuse, and the questionable action of refusing to re-broadcast Melbourne's special programme'.

(iii) The third article was printed the day following Marcuse's first full Empire broadcast. It mentions that after the first item, the generator field coil burned out that caused the power supply to fail resulting in a one-hour delay. A Mr F. Youle of the Marconiphone Company Ltd announced the artists who were all Australians resident in Britain at that time: Miss Daisy Kennedy, Mme Evelyn Scotney, Mr John Amadio, Mr Fred. Collier, Mr Harold Williams, Mr William Murdoch and Mr Horace Stevens. Miss Ella Ivimey and Mr Victor Marmont acted as accompanists. The address given by Captain Ian Fraser MP included reference to Marcuse's achievement of being the first British amateur to communicate by wireless with Australia and obtain a reply; this was a distance of 12,000 miles. It mentions that a letter posted from Britain took four weeks to reach Australia. After the programme finished, the Sydney Sun and the Melbourne Herald entertained the artists at the Grosvenor Hotel, Victoria. An article from this newspaper's correspondent in Wellington follows stating that the broadcast was receivable but the music was faint and the speech was not clearly intelligible.

(iv) This is a Post Office Telegraph originating in Sydney but it is not clear who sent it. It states: 2FC. Rebroadcast until you disappeared at 0906 phrases speech good congratulate you deeply regret your difficulty completing programme'.

62 This is a Post Office Telegraph from someone called Barnes in Dunedin New Zealand via 'Imperial' and dated 12th September. It states: Heard every word opening remarks and Captain Fraser's address good phone strength modulation perfect Barnes Dunedin New Zealand +'.

63 This is an advertisement by the Marconiphone Company Ltd., 210-212 Tottenham Court Road, London, W.1. The title is: 'The Facts about the Empire Broadcast - read what Mr. Gerald Marcuse says. A letter follows this from Marcuse expressing appreciation for the Marconi valves used in his experiments, 28 out of the 30 used were from Marconi. It commented that the M.T.9.F. was a transmitting valve 'par excellence'. The advertisement continues with a comment about a general purpose valve, the DEL210 that had been reduced in price to 10/6.

64 This is a Post Office telegraph dated September 24th 1927. 'Tests this week excellent particularly on Thursday speak slower.' 2FC (Sydney)

65 A Post Office telegraph dated 21st September but received on the 26th from Collette Jolliffe of Horana. 'Transmission eighteenth carrier strong speech music weak few words intelligible inform Collette Jolliffe'.

66 A Post Office telegraph dated 28th September 1927 but received on the 26th. From Slingsby Mowbray of Cape Town. 'Relay Big Ben and Church service received well. Posting report good luck Slingsby Mowbray'.

67   A Post Office telegraph dated 29th September 1927 from Bombay, India. This informs Marcuse that the best broadcasting times were between 1300 & 1500, between 1600 & 1800 and between 1500 & 1600, all times GMT. '1500 and 1600 is Universal Indian dinner hour - Herring

68   This contains three newspaper clippings from 1927 all of them relate to Empire broadcasting

(i)   The first article is titled: 'Amateur to broadcast to the Dominions'. It acknowledges that for the first time since the BBC was formed in 1921, an outside party (Marcuse) had been given a licence to broadcast other than purely experimental matter. It mentions that he was preparing two studios in the London area to transmit his own programmes. Also, it mentions that the BBC would 'proceed immediately to erect short-wave transmitters'. A BBC official is quoted as saying that there was an expectation for overseas countries to erect their own receiving sets on the BBC's plan, to pick up and relay the transmissions to their local listeners.

(ii)   The second article is a clipping from the Daily Mirror, (1927). It announces that the overseas secretary of the Wireless League, incorporating the Wireless Association, a Mr H. A. Hankey was giving a talk from Marcuse's station about his projected tour to Australia and South Africa in connection with the League's interest in Empire Broadcasting. (The last part of this article is missing.)

(iii) The third article is a letter to the (English) Times from Ian Fraser of Hengistbury Head, Hants and is dated August 12th 1927. It appears that Ian Fraser used his influence, 'I said I would give him every possible assistance in securing the necessary licence and permission'. Marcuse's licence was granted from September 1st 1927. The article ends with the comment that 'All those who have for some time felt that the BBC should not have allowed a foreign station to usurp their function will regard this as eminently satisfactory'!

69 Three articles are attached to this page, one from an Irish paper and the other two from Indian papers.

(i) The Irish article gives some detail about Marcuse's transmitting station, pointing out that the studio was almost half a mile from the transmitter, but connected by a landline. It compares the great success of the two powerful stations, 2XAF of America and PCJJ of Holland with the BBC's refusal to start its own station.

(ii) The second article is from a Bombay paper dated October 6th 1927. It concerns the broadcast of a special programme to India and a request to Indian listeners that they send transmission reports to 'Messrs Jost's Engineering Company, Hararwalla Building, Ballard Estate, Bombay'.

(iii) This article is in the form of an announcement giving Marcuse's broadcast dates and times with a similar request to listeners to send transmission reports to the same company or to 6, Mangoe Lane, Calcutta.

70 A Post Office Telegraph dated October 14th 1927 from Herring in Bombay: 'reports so far Sundays transmission somewhat disappointing only two succeeded one Poona, one Madras, none Bombay writing'.

71 A Post Office Telegraph sent 12th November 1927 and received 14th November, again from Herring in Bombay: 'Many thanks informed all interested. Transmission received not strong fading bad nevertheless very enjoyable. Nobody (in) Bombay succeeded getting Chelmsford'.

72 A Post Office Telegraph dated November 12th 1927 from Collet

73 This page contains two photographs from Popular wireless dated November 26th 1927 and an article of unknown origin and date.

(i)   The first photograph shows the back of Marcuse's 'main transmitting panel'

(ii) The second photograph is also taken from the rear but shows the RF feed cables leading from the rear via isolating, standoff connectors through the windows.

(iii) The newspaper article refers to the cable sent from Bombay (71). The second part of the article gives a list of short-wave stations; the article concludes: 'I have more to follow':
  (a)   Java, ANH, 17.4, 27.32;
  (b)   Berne, EH9OC, 32;
  (c)   Johannesburg, JB, 32;
  (d)   Melbourne, 3LO, 33.4, 29.8;
  (e)   Radio Malabar, PCG, 17;
  (d)   Cincinnati, WLW, 52.02;
  (e)   Atlantic Broadcasting Corp. (New York), WABC, 64;
  (f)   Nauen (Germany), AGA, 13.5 and others;
  (g)   G. Marcuse, Caterham, 2NM, 32.4;
  (h)   BBC Experimental, 5SW, 24metres.

74   This is a page from Popular Wireless dated November 26th 1927. Under the title 'Current Topics', 'Dreadful! – The Heaviside Layer – Down-coming Waves. BY THE EDITOR.', this quite lengthy article explains the skip distance effect on radio waves. The Director general of the BBC, Sir John Reith is quoted for asking members present at a meeting not to judge the BBC's programmes by the children's hours and variety entertainments that he claimed were 'dreadful'. A photograph of 2NM's studio is also included.

75   There are three newspaper clippings on this page; the first is a very long article by Marcuse concerning his Empire Broadcasting, the second is a letter to the editor of a Singapore newspaper and the third an article form the Times of India.

(i)   The first article, dated 29th November 1927 is from the Christian Science Monitor, is headed 'Gerald Marcuse Granted New High-Powered License'. This is a very cogent and reflective look at the position of radio communications at that time. Marcuse discusses the ease with which a shortwave receiver could be constructed and how, with the invention of the dull emitter valve, receivers could be operated for months at a time with ordinary dry batteries. He explains the difficulty for listeners in Australia and New Zealand in receiving transmissions with a 12-hour time difference. In addition, he discusses reasons why the BBC appeared to be behind some other countries in broadcasting overseas by suggesting this was due to the thoroughness of their tests being conducted over many months to ensure that it provided an efficient system.

(ii) The letter to the Editor of the 'Straits Times', Singapore is dated November 21st 1927. This was written by C. P. Martinus who wrote to defend the 'British Broadcasting Commission (not Company please)' for their efforts and 'we should be extremely grateful to the BBC for this effort of theirs to entertain us'.

(iii) This undated article from 'The Times of India' is titled: ' Albert Hall Concert heard in Bombay'. It discusses the programme received by the secretary, a Mr R. H. Atkins, of the Bombay Presidency Radio Club commencing at 8pm GMT, equivalent to 1-3am Indian Standard Time. The programme contents given are:

Song:	Katie, Beautiful Katie
Song:	John Brown's Body
Speech:	Should old acquaintance.
Song:	We're here, we are, Oh here We Are.
Song:	Keep the home Fires Burning.
Song:	It's a long way to Tipperary.
Band:	Bagpipe Band and bugle calls.
Hymn:	Oh God our Help in Ages Past.
Speech:	Speech & singing of 'For He's a Jolly Good Fellow'
Speech:	Speech by H.R.H. The Prince of Wales
Hymns:	Onward Christian Soldiers & Abide with me
Finally:	God Save the King

It goes on to say that two stations were transmitting, namely the 'new Chelmsford station of the BBC and the experimental station operated by Mr Gerald Marcuse', but it was not certain which of the two stations he had tuned into. The article comments on the Indian Broadcasting Company failing to relay the BBC broadcast because nothing had been heard due to the unsuitability of the wavelength for reception in India.

76 This shows a cutting from Wireless World which is a photograph of Marcuse carrying out an adjustment to his transmitter on November 14th 1927; the photograph appears in the November 30th 1927 edition.

77 This is a Post Office Telegraph from Herring dated November 29th 1927; it reads: 'Sundays concert received fairly well much better than Melbourne heard you mention Herring Bombay but rest lost in fading = Herring'

78 This page contains five newspaper clippings, only one is dated but they all seem to have been printed in December 1927.

(i) This is an article of unknown origin that gives a preamble on the problems of fade-out when short waves are used. It discusses the BBC's plans to build two transmitters and five aerials that would be erected with a design based on a half wavelength of the actual transmitting wavelength. It suggests that the BBC would be using wavelengths around 16 metres and 31/32 metres.

(ii) The second article is a clipping from the December 7th 1927 edition of Wireless World. It suggests that the BBC's sudden decision to set up a short-wave station at Chelmsford was stimulated by articles in Wireless World, the press and 'the practical experiments of Gerald Marcuse'.

(iii) This clipping is a letter to the editor in an unknown newspaper titled 'The Wireless Champions'. It is written by Frederick Wenman of Chapel Lane, Smallfields, Surrey. This letter was written to commemorate the thirteenth birthday of the invention of wireless that was being celebrated at the Royal Albert Hall. It goes on to mention that 'Mr Gerald Marcuse of Caterham Hill, using a gramophone with a pleated diaphragm adjustment, entertained an American warship lying in New Zealand waters with songs by Caruso, violin selections by Heifetz, jazz music by Jack Hylton's orchestra, and the Savoy Orpheans and other gramophone records. Is there any country in the British Isles that can touch this? Surrey may have missed the cricket championship; at wireless she will take some beating.'

(iv) The fourth clipping is of unknown origin and is titled: 'Ocean Phone Eavesdroppers. Post Office Plan to Stop Them. Secrecy Coming.' It focuses on the £5-a-minute wireless telephone service between London and New York that was just about to be inaugurated. An amateur had received some experimental transmissions with a two-valve receiver. It explains that, with the correct equipment, the signals could be tapped but the authorities had devised means of tracking people who attempted to overhear conversations. The Post office was advising people who used the new service to avoid repeating what was said at the other end of the line and to use code names to outwit eavesdroppers.

(v) The final clipping, again of unknown origin, is titled: 'Bravo, Marcuse.' It highlights the fact that: 'If you examine a map of the world made on a great circle projection with England at the centre, this is the kind of map that gives a true idea of the distances to be covered in Empire broadcasting – you will find that New Zealand is the farthest of all countries from us...' It claims that the American stations, 2XAF and 2XAD were rated at 10 kilowatts and PCJJ used 20 kilowatts.

79 This page has three documents attached to it, two parts of the same telegraph and a list of cable stations of the Eastern Telegraph Company Ltd in London and the rest of Britain.

(i) & (ii) This Telegraph to Marcuse is dated December 23rd 1927 and is from Sydney: 'THANKS FOR YOUR CABLE LETTER FIFTEENTH NOVEMBER RECEIVED MAY WE PUBLISH THROUGH RADIO CHANNELS WE RECIPROCATE YOUR GOOD WISHES FOR XMAS AND NEW YEAR BROADCASTING EMPIRE XMAS PROGRAMME TO BBC

1630 TO 1900 GMT TWENTYFIFTH DECEMBER
DIRECTORS AND STAFF 2 FC LIMITED.'

(iii) The stations are listed along with their opening and closing times.

80   This contains a clipping from The Star, Auckland, New Zealand and is dated December 31st 1927. It shows the same photograph as page 76 of Marcuse carrying out adjustments to his transmitter. The caption reads: 'A RADIO ENTHUSIAST. – Mr Gerald Marcuse, who easily ranks with the foremost radio amateurs of the world, possesses a station at Caterham, Surrey, that has been received in practically all countries of the world. He has established two-way communication on telephony with Canada, and two-way telegraphy with the whole world, while his telephony has been heard all the world over. Mr Marcuse is seen making final adjustments at his transmitting set.'

81   Three clippings appear on this page:

(i)   A picture that is the same as on page 76 but with a caption in Spanish.

(ii) A cartoon sketch of Marcuse wearing a hat looking at a valve with the caption: 'Australia Calling Marcuse.'

(iii) A newspaper clipping titled: 'Empire Concerts – Broadcasting Plan – Inauguration this month, London Aug 9th.' The article explains the plans for the broadcasts, the times and the programme content. Marcuse is quoted as saying, 'T expect that the backblocker in Australia will hear London with an ordinary two-valve set. I want to give Britons overseas a bit of old England. I am sure it is feasible.'

82   There is one Post office Telegraph attached to this page, dated April 23rd 1928, originating in Sydney: 'MORNING TRANSMISSION R 5 6 EVENING R 5 FB OM BISCHOFT +++.'

83   On this page, there are two photos and a brief article that appear to be taken from the Pittsburgh Press, November 24th 1929. The top

photograph shows Marcuse, smoking his pipe while adjusting his equipment; the bottom photograph is the same as page 76. The caption below comments on the photographs and adds, 'The pictures were loaned to the Home Radio Club for publication by Arthur Green, short-wave expert in Klondyke, Ohio.'

84   This page contains two clippings that are likely to date from 1930.

(i)   The first one is titled: 'English Radio Fan Short Wave Veteran – Gerald Marcuse has operated Station in Surrey for years.' It records a little of the history of Marcuse's broadcasts starting in 1913 when his station was used exclusively for Morse code, changing to voice in 1923 when he built a 3⬚ Kw station to pave the way for international broadcasts. It confirms that Marcuse was the first to establish two-way communication between England and South America, Singapore and India. It mentions the Washington conference (of last November) when Marcuse was granted 31.4 metres, '... Marcuse is rebuilding the entire station to work on 20.9 metres and in a short time will be on the air, where many of his old friends all over the universe will again hear his voice.'

(ii)   The second clipping is taken from 'The People' and is titled 'It cost him £6000!' The article starts 'By the rest of the world remembered, but by Britain forgot. That, briefly is the position today of Mr Gerald Marcuse, a London seedsman, and the pioneer of Empire Broadcasting. This is a most endearing article that speaks very fondly of Marcuse's endeavours. It quotes Marcuse as saying: 'A member of an Arctic expedition who had strayed from the main party, he was lost in the North of Greenland for two years, and they (his parents) mourned him as dead. Then I picked up the signals of an Arctic Whaler. They had the young fellow on board, and were bringing him home.' Marcuse contacted the parents, an Ealing couple, and told them the good news. In another situation, a young Customs official (Brown) was lying in a Hong Kong hospital terribly ill. His parents at Guildford communicated this with Marcuse who broadcast their messages to an amateur at Hong Kong and the amateur did the rest. Daily bulletins for the parents and reassuring messages to the sick man followed and did much to bring the patient round'

85 There are four clippings on this page, two photographs from Wireless World magazine on September 24th 1930, and two short articles:

(i) The first picture gives a clearer view of Marcuse's transmitter taken when he lived at Sonning-on-Thames.

(ii) The second shows the '1930 edition of 2NM Sonning-on-Thames.

(iii) The first article is by The Associated Press, London titled: 'British Amateur Will Flash Music to U.S.' This advertises the fact that Marcuse would be broadcasting on three nights a week, Sunday from 6 to 8pm, and the other two no fixed on 23 and 24 metres.

(iv) The second article is of unknown origin and is titled: 'Test Set Rebuilt.' It claims that Marcuse 'is probably the greatest of our pioneer shortwave amateurs, has recently reconstructed his transmitting set, I understand, and is now sending out test transmissions on 20.9 metres. Although his is strictly an amateur set, it is probably the best of its kind in the country. It operates from Sonning, near Reading, under the callsign G2NM. His short telephony transmissions are picked up all over the world. He is one of the few people in this country, if not, indeed the only one, to employ a thermostatically-controlled crystal to keep his wave-length accurate.'

86 This is a single clipping that appears to be from a journal titled 'International Short Wave Radio News.' It contains a review of early broadcasting, and includes an article written by Marcuse up to the date this appeared in April 11th 1948. He starts when '2NM came into being in 1913' and continues with his activities as he worked through the higher frequencies. The article concludes with the 'firsts' he achieved; ie, two-way communication between England and Singapore, India, Canada and the American Battleship, 'N R L' that was in New Zealand waters.

87   There are three newspaper clippings on this page all of different dates.

(i)   The earliest is of unknown origin and is dated November 12th 1932. It announces a service schedule that the BBC was about to follow by broadcasting from Daventry 'after years of perfunctory experimentation through its short-wave station G5SW.' The Empire had been divided into five 'zones':

Zone 1 – Australia, New Zealand and the Pacific Islands.

Zone 2 – India, Burma and the Malay States. Signals from this zone also audible in Australasia, but at an inconvenient time.

Zone 3 – Irak (sic), Egypt, East Africa and South Africa.

Zone 4 – West Africa, including Nigeria and the Gold Coast, the Atlantic islands (Tristan da Cunha and the Falkland Islands, also South Africa.

Zone 5 – Canada, West Indies, Trinidad, British Guiana and the pacific islands. Also covers the United States.

The article continues by listing the frequencies and wavelengths to be used with the aim that every part of the Empire should be provided with a 'two-hour program between 6pm and midnight.' Seventeen aerial arrays would be arranged around the Daventry site; the transmitters would be crystal-controlled and installed by Standard Telephone and Cables Ltd, each with an output power of between 15 and 20Kw. Tests would be conducted towards the end of November and the official inauguration of the service for Christmas Day.

88   This page contains two clippings, an article from the evening Gazette, dated September 2nd 1938 and a photograph of unknown date and origin.

(i)   This clipping is titled: 'Sonning Man To Aid R.A.F. Radio Plan.' It states that Marcuse had been approached by the Air Ministry to assist in organising the Royal Air Force Civilian Wireless Reserve. Marcuse is quoted as saying 'The movement has been going on for about a year. About that time ago I was first approached by the Ministry. The navy already have a civilian wireless reserve, and now the royal Air Force want a similar auxiliary. There are about 800 amateurs working for the Navy.' A resume of Marcuse's broadcasting experience is given and the article concludes with the comment that: 'The Civilian Wireless Reserve of the R.A.F. is being formed to ensure that the Royal Air Force shall always have available a reserve of qualified radio amateurs ready immediately for service in an emergency with the signals branch.'

(ii) The photograph shows a Marcuse (sitting) on the right with G5MR in the middle, a third man is shown on the left. No date is given but the photograph could have been taken in the 1950's.

89   This page contains a long article, dated June 1942 that is taken from The T. & R. Bulletin, volume 17, No.12. The T & R Bulletin was the official Journal of the Incorporated Radio Society of Great Britain. A small clipping is also included.

(i)   The article is written by John Clarricoats (initials J.C. at end) G6CL, author of 'The World at their Fingertips.'. It discusses aspects of the formation of the T. & R. Section and pays tribute to its founders:

(ii)
Gerald Marcuse	G2NM	Pioneer of Empire Broadcasting
Cecil Goyder	G2SZ	Hero of 1st Brit.-Oceanic Contact
E. D. Simmonds	G2OD	First 'G' to work New Zealand
Jack Partridge	G2KF	A mighty 'Brasspounder'
Fred Hogg	G2SH	First contact with Iceland
Bevan Swift	G2TI	President of the T&R Section 1931
J. A. J. Cooper	G5TR	Hon. Sec. of T& R Section 1925
Sir Oliver Lodge		President of the T&R Section 1925

The article goes into some depth about the history of the T & R Section, the founding of the first T & R Bulletin and various Wireless Societies, The London Wireless Club, Wireless Society of London and the R.S.G.B.

(iii) The second clipping is a letter to the Editor from Marcuse stating that he was celebrating his 21st year as an amateur wireless investigator. As Marcuse started in 1913, this is likely to be dated around 1934; his address was given as The Ranch, Sonning-on-Thames.

90   This page contains a newspaper clipping of unknown origin and dated January 30th 1946, an insert saying that a photograph was 'borrowed' and a large group photograph.

(i)   The first article, written by Douglas Walters, is entitled: 'Hams on the air again.' When the Second World War began, all amateur stations were ordered to close down and essential parts of the equipment were removed and impounded by the Post Office. New licences were being issued at this time and around 3000 amateurs were busy preparing to transmit again. Initially, amateurs were permitted to use the 5 and 10 metre bands while others (20, 40 80 and 160 metres) were being 'derequisitioned' by the military.

(ii) The insert is a note saying 'photo borrowed by J. Ham 12.10.87 for PW article '; it is signed at the bottom but the photograph is missing.

(iii) The photograph shows a group of 28 men; Marcuse appears in the bottom right corner.

91   This page contains a letter to Marcuse from John Clarricoats, G6CL, the General Secretary of the RSGB and dated is 25th June 1946. It informs Marcuse that he has been unanimously elected as an Honorary member of the Society for his services to amateur radio and to the Society. It concludes with a few words to say that a certificate would be presented at the forthcoming AGM of the Society.

92   This page contains a clipping from an unknown, 1949, newspaper and an article from the July 1961 edition of Reader's Digest Magazine.

(i)   The newspaper clipping is an article entitled 'Round the City Cross' that is a regular 'Chichester Diary' feature, by Geoffrey White. The article discusses a special programme to be broadcast by the BBC Pacific Service the following week to commemorate the 25th anniversary of the first two-way conversation with New Zealand. The programme would include: '... a five-minute talk by Mr E. G. Marcuse, of Tidewater, Windmill Field, Bosham. My Marcuse, a radio pioneer for 36 years, established the connexion from the English end with apparatus that was entirely home-made.'

(ii)   The Reader's Digest article gives a fairly broad explanation on Amateur Radio in general and mentions Marcuse's early broadcasting experiments.

93   This page includes a letter from the Clerk to the Standing Joint Committee of the office of the Clerk of the Peace for Berkshire, in Reading. It is dated 26th June 1942 and it thanks Marcuse for his assistance in developing a wireless scheme for the Police Authority. The new scheme had been approved by the Home Office.

94   A letter from the Radio Security Service (RSS) is included on this page. It was sent by the Controller, whose rank was Colonel and it thanks Marcuse for his 'valued and devoted service which he voluntarily rendered to the organisation during the war. A Certificate was included with the letter signed by Sir Herbert Creedy, Head of the RSS Department.

95   This page contains four newspaper clippings that commemorate Marcuse's life, following his death at home on April 6th 1961 at the age of 74. His death followed several months of serious illness. He had also suffered crippling arthritis for several years. All the clippings are from unknown sources, but date shortly after his death.

(i)   The first clipping mentions Marcuse's non-amateur radio interests and achievements. He enjoyed yachting and from 1949 he represented the Parish on the County Council for 12 years. After the Second World War, he started the local fire brigade and was Station Officer for a number of years. During the First World War he had served in the Lincolnshire Regiment.

(ii) The second clipping is titled: 'Mr Marcuse Made Radio History.' It mentions: 'One of his proudest possessions was a large book of press cuttings, telegrams and letters', the basis of this chapter. Marcuse had advised and helped with the installation of special equipment in Chichester's ambulances.

(iii) A very small cutting appears to have been taken from an obituary section, this announces his death.

(iv) The final clipping is headed: 'Bosham Funeral of radio Pioneer'; it lists those in attendance.

96   This page contains three newspaper clippings; all are dated from 1961-1962; they refer to the anniversary of Marcuse's death.

(i)   The first clipping is taken from the Evening News on April 10th 1962. It mentions a commemoration plaque being fixed to the outside of his home 'Coombe Dingle', Queen's Park, Caterham, Surrey. It mentions that the Mayor and Mayoress of Caterham attended the ceremony with several others present; John Clarricoats gave the tribute. The plaque was unveiled by the Mayor who pulled aside a flag made by Marcuse's widow Irene; this had been made many years before by her and it depicted Marcuse's callsign on one side and 'Radio Society of Great Britain on the other.

(ii) The second clipping is taken from 'Electronics Weekly' and is dated April 12th 1961. It records the fact that Marcuse was a founder vice-president of the International Amateur Radio Union in 1925 and had served as President of the RSGB in both 1929 and 1930.

(iii) The third clipping is from an unknown newspaper; it is dated April 1962 and entitled: 'Memorial Plaque to Caterham's Radio Pioneer'. This article gives a brief resume of Marcuse's achievements along with some of the offices he held.

97   Two articles appear on this page, both concerning the plaque unveiling at Coombe Dingle.

(i)   The first clipping is taken from the Purley & Coulston Advertiser and is dated 13th April 1962. It shows the actual unveiling by Councillor Peter Blair. The article is very similar to 97(iii).

(ii)   The second clipping shows John Clarricoats, Irene Marcuse and Councillor Blair standing next to the plaque.

98   This page contains one clipping taken from The Observer and is dated April 13th 1962. It is titled: 'Pioneer of Empire Broadcasts Commemorated'. A large photograph shows Marcuse handing over a cup awarded for a radio competition winner at a dinner function. It gives a similar commentary to 97(iii) but adds that the High Commissioner for Australia attended Marcuse's official opening programme (to Australia) in 1922; the broadcast was received in Sydney and rebroadcast around the Australian network.

99   This page includes three newspaper clippings all unknown origin, and three photographs that appear to be dated July 1962, the time the seat was sited to commemorate Marcuse's life.

(i)   The first article mentions that an annual prize, to be known as the 'Marcuse Prize', would be awarded to the young licensed radio amateur who contributed the best article to the Radio Amateur Old Timers' Association journal.

(ii)   The second clipping is titled: 'Gift seat will Commemorate Radio Pioneer'. It mentions that the new seat would replace an old seat that had fallen to pieces.

(iii) This article mentions that the seat would cost around £85.

(iv)   The first photo shows David Marcuse and his mother Irene sitting on the new bench in its permanent position.

(v)   The second photograph is a close-up of the plaque fixed to the backrest.

(vi)   This photograph shows a group of ten people outside Marcuse's Bosham home. The lady in the middle is Marcuse's widow, Irene, immediately behind her is John Clarricoats G6CL, wearing glasses, on the far right, in the light-coloured jacket, is Ralph Royle G2WJ.

100 This page contains two newspaper clippings and a (loose) letter.

(i)   The first clipping is from an unknown source and is dated July 27th 1962. It is entitled: 'Memorial Seat at Bosham for radio pioneer.' It gives a preamble of Marcuse's achievements in amateur radio, his interests, responsibilities and describes the seat dedication ceremony and those who attended.

(ii)   The second clipping is taken from the Portsmouth Evening News and is dated 19th march 1962. It states that originally it was proposed to place the seat on Quay Meadow near a war memorial but the National Trust withdrew their support after learning that a plaque was to be fixed to the back of the seat.

(iii) This item is a letter from H.A.M. Clark to a Mr A. P. Bodily of 14 Queens Park Road, Caterham, Surrey who was the present occupier of Marcuse's house formally called 'Coombe Dingle'; the letter is dated 2nd May 1962. The letter was sent to accompany a photograph of Marcuse and his equipment, possibly by following up a request for a picture by the new owner of the house.

101 This item is a review of John Clarricoats's (G6CL) book 'World at their Fingertips.' It was published in Electronics & Power magazine and is dated December 1967. It includes a large photograph showing Marcuse with his equipment taken from the page facing page 69 in the book.

102 This page includes the RSGB tribute to Marcuse published in the May 1961 RSGB Bulletin. Also included is a delightful tribute to Marcuse, written by Kenneth Alford that is most likely from the same Bulletin because the initials 'J.C.' (John Clarricoats) appear under it.

(i) The tribute records Marcuse's life and achievements from the beginnings and it includes two photographs, both of which show him with his transmitting equipment.

(ii) The tribute by Kenneth Alford is reproduced in full:

'Marcuse could only be described as a delightful character, compelling friendship which responded in full measure the world over. I knew him for 42 years and his unbounded enthusiasm for Amateur Radio and the humility with which he acknowledged his lack of technical opportunity gave everyone the greatest pleasure in working with and for him.
He will leave a lasting memorial in his initiation of an Empire Broadcasting Service to which he devoted whole-heartedly his private resources.
He died virtually with a microphone in his hand, carrying on his Radio Circle with that delightful ease and charm we knew so well. And so he passes leaving behind a memory to all of us – one without an enemy and everyone his friend. I trust that his example, not only as a human being in normal life but also in the world of radio, may leave its mark, as I am convinced it surely will.'
VADE ATQUE VALE, MARCUSE

103 This page includes some Amateur Sound Licences renewal notices for G2NM due each year on February 7th. In 1961 the renewal fee was £2.

104 This page has two documents attached, Marcuse's invitation (ticket number 176) to the RSGB Grand Banquet to be held on 5th July 1963 and the seating plan for the banquet table. The celebration marked the 50th year since the RSGB was founded in 1913. Marcuse and his wife Irene are shown as sitting at table number 6.

105 This page has the programme attached commencing with a list of past Presidents; Marcuse's name appears as the 8th President having served two years from 1929 to 1930.

106 This page has four attachments, three newspaper clippings and one photograph.

(i) The first clipping is dated 6th January 1973 that reports on the diamond jubilee celebration of the RSGB. This was held at the Connaught Rooms at which the guest of honour was Sir John Eden, the Minister of Posts & Telecommunications. It mentions that the society had 16000 members and that it was possible to 'be a fully-fledged ham with equipment costing as little as £50.

(ii) The second clipping, dated 1972, is titled: 'Radio sets for Museum' and comments on the Science Museum housing 'the world's finest collection of telegraph, telephone, radio, radar and television equipment in Gallery 66'. The exhibition included: 'Three ships' radio cabins, of 1910, 1940 and 1970 all with their original equipment. Radio sets of the First and Second World Wars. The first telegraphs as well as the most modern telephone techniques where one line is shared by 24 callers using time division multiplexing. Communication satellites models and Arthur Clarke's historical contribution of 1945 forecasting their present-day usage. The history of radar and Sir Robert Watson Watt's first equipment. Finally the Science Museum's own amateur radio station having the well-known callsign GB2SM, has been activated again and exchanged the first calls on Tuesday with the Phillips Museum in Holland, the only other science museum which has its own radio station."

(iii) The third clipping is dated 1972 and entitled: 'Broadcasting Exhibition'. It is an appeal by Frank Atkinson, the museum director of the North of England Open-Air Museum in Beamish, Co. Durham. He was seeking early equipment for a temporary exhibition at Beamish to celebrate the fiftieth anniversary of radio Broadcasting. He was particularly interested in receiving crystal and valve radio sets, early magazines and an example of the first Baird television receiver.

(iv) This photograph, dated 1960, features Marcuse in his 'shack' surrounded by equipment at home in Tidewaters, Bosham.

107 There are three clippings on this page, two (an article and a photograph) from the Observer newspaper dated August 28th 1959 and an undated photograph that shows Marcuse's shack at Tidewaters, Bosham.

(i) The article gives an account of Marcuse's amateur radio exploits. It mentions that 'two years ago osteoarthritis crippled him'. The final paragraphs tell of his brother Walter Marcuse who died at Selsey in 1954 after living there for about 20 years. It mentions Walter's discovery of the Madagascar 'golden bean' – the butter bean that the family firm first introduced into Britain. Walter wrote a book entitled: Through Western Madagascar' which told of his experiences.

(ii) The photograph shows Marcuse, microphone in hand, in his shack at Bosham.

(iii) The second photograph shows Marcuse's shack at Bosham.

108 This page has one newspaper article, a photograph from a newspaper and another photograph attached.

(i) The article is taken from the Portsmouth Evening news, is dated August 27th, 1959 and is entitled: 'Radio Feats were reported World Over.' The article gives a resume of Marcuse's achievements and concludes by mentioning that 'the crippling effect of osteoarthritis' has compelled him to give up his other hobby, yachting, two years ago, Mr Marcuse has turned his attention towards "mobileering." He has built a small transmitting set in his car, and as he drives about West Sussex roads is able to hold direct communication with his many friends, some of them living as far away as Scotland.'

(ii) The newspaper photograph shows Marcuse holding a microphone in the passenger seat of his car with his wife Irene in the driver's seat looking on.

(iii) The photograph is taken at Longleat, Warminster, 1960 and pictured are: G5VS, Millie, Irene, and G2NM. This is likely to be the Longleat Radio Rally.

109 A certificate of membership is attached to this page; it is the First-Class Operators' Club, Certificate Number 18. Marcuse's name is printed across the top and it is dated July 1947, signed by himself (as President!) and endorsed by the Secretary A. M. Fergus. Holders of this had to satisfy the rules and all elections were notified in Short Wave Magazine.

110 This page has a certificate attached, The VHF Century Club', number 48, that Marcuse was awarded for having shown proof that he worked one hundred (two-way) amateur stations on the VHF bands from 50 MHz upwards. It is dated May 1949 and is signed by the Secretary E. J Williams, G2XC.

111 This page contains Marcuse's certificate that confirms his membership of Short Wave Magazine's 'The Five Band Club.' This was awarded in recognition for 'having undertaken to support and encourage all forms of VHF activity.' This is certificate number 70 and has been signed in endorsement by E. J. Williams, G2XC.

112 A page from the December 1980 of the RSGB publication Radio Communication is attached to this page. It includes a large photograph of 'A wartime meeting of VI group leaders at the Leatherhead regional office of the Radio Security Service. Marcuse is seated at the bottom right-hand corner. The article gives a

detailed account of how intercepted messages were handled and sent to Bletchley Park for deciphering. It also explains the duties of VI personnel.

113 This page contains a draft proposal for the memorial in the form of an oak seat outside Bosham Church and a plaque outside his former home in Caterham, Surrey. This draft was intended for inclusion in the Aug 1961 edition of the RSGB Bulletin. It includes an appeal for amateurs to contribute to the fund.

114 Included in this page is a letter dated July 20th 1961 from John Clarricoats setting out the proposals for Marcuse's memorial plaque and the oak bench. It also seeks advice from Marcuse's widow, Irene.

115 This page includes the accounts dated July 31st 1962 for the Gerald Marcuse Memorial fund. It states that the donations received totalled £149 9s 4d. This left the sum of £53 16s 9d for the Marcuse 'Memorial Prize Fund'.

116 This page names some of the attendees at the Plaque unveiling ceremony outside Marcuse's former home at Caterham.

117 Two large photographs appear on this page, one showing the Mayor and a small group, the other showing David Marcuse and his mother Irene standing in front of the plaque.

118 Two photographs appear on this page

(i) The first photograph shows Marcuse adjusting his transmitter at Caterham

(ii) The second shows Marcuse bending over a piece of equipment making an adjustment with a screwdriver. On the wall is a hand-written poster with what could be a QSL card above: 'The first radio message ever received on the pacific Coast direct from Great Britain'.

119 Blank Page

120 Blank Page

121 A small insert is attached to this page entitled 'A History of the radio Society of Great Britain' and a photograph of H.R.H. The Price of Wales is featured on the front as Patron of the Society.

122 A Programme of the 'Premier Congrès de l'Union Internationale des Amateurs de T.S.F. This is followed by "Premier Congrès Juridique du Comité International de la T.S.F. and it ends, 'Tenus à Paris Paques 1925 du 14 au 19 Avril.'

123 A three-page article by Ron Ham from Practical Wireless Magazine is attached here, dated July 1978. It gives a fairly detailed account of Marcuse's achievements, including Empire Broadcasting and includes a photograph reproduced from the November 30th 1927 edition of Wireless World Magazine. It also details the BBC's experiments conducted at the same time and describes some of the newest receiver design techniques.

124 Second part of the article continued from Page 123.
125 Third part of the article continued from Page 124.

126 A two-page article is attached entitled 'Wireless and Butter Beans', dated 26th August 1925 and taken from the London 'Star'. The article focuses on the success of the two brothers, Gerald and Walter but is mainly about Marcuse's brother and his exploits in Madagascar. Walter wrote a book entitled 'Through Western Madagascar'. See page (30).

127 Second part of the article continued from Page 126.

128 This is a letter to Marcuse from Marconi's Wireless Telegraph Company Ltd., it is dated 21st July 1925 and is signed by Norman G. Widglor (Widgas?). Two letters sent by Marcuse prompted the letter and it concerned a problem that Marcuse had with his modulation following which a Captain Round had carried out

some modifications. Marcuse was due to receive two valves from Marconi at the time this was written.

129 This is a continuation of the RadCom article found on page 112. It gives a lot more detail about the work of the deciphering operations at Bletchley Park (Station 'X' or 'BP'). It expands on the work of the VI's who were involved in covert listening and monitoring of German military communications during the war. Some of the material used for this was also used to compile material for the film 'The Secret Listeners'.

130 Page 1 of a two-page letter from a friend typed on 30th November 1928 is attached to this page. (this is from W.G.H. Miles of the Wireless Telegraphy Station, Stonecutters Island, Hong Kong who wrote the 'Admiralty handbook of Wireless Telegraphy' in 1925.) The letter describes various signal results following transmission using a transmitter that appears to have been supplied by Marcuse, 'Your set continues to prove a great success, and it certainly made the Signal School experts open their eyes when they saw it (two of the who came out in 'Carysfort') – it is about a tenth of the size they consider necessary and yet gives results at least as good as, if not better than, Cleethorpes.' Following this, is a summary of results. Miles describes his station: 'As regards the transmitter, I am feeding it off a 2.5KW silica valve, with duplicate H.T. and filament machines. I have tried all manner of aerials and it doesn't seem to matter much: I use a ½ wave vertical for 35m., full wave vertical for 25m., and a full wave Hertz for 20.5m. For receivers, I have (a) the one I told you about before. (b) a Reinartz, 1 det. 2NM, which is very good for measuring wavelengths. (c) a super regenerative Armstrong – not much good as yet. (d) a 4-valve superhet. – not yet tried out.'

131 On page 2 of the letter continued from page (130) Miles mentions that he had not succeeded in getting C.W. 'in spite of many experiments, and the use of double pulse rectification and every sort of filter circuit. It is not nearly so easy to get with the high power I am using as with low powers. Further, I don't want to go in for the complications of crystal control, master oscillator

circuits...' Miles then seeks Marcuse's advice on good C.W. for reliable daylight working.

132 This appears to be a one-page, month-by-month analysis of wireless traffic from 1st May 1926 to 30th April 1928.

133 This attachment does not appear to be related to the preceding pages although it has been fixed to page 133 and is titled: 'Separation into Groups'. It gives detailed instructions for what seems to be instructions for carrying out a chemical process of a substance.

134 The attachment is a letter dated march 11th circa 1925 from the Marconi's Wireless Telegraph Company Ltd. It is in reply to a query from Marcuse who Marconi that he had been experiencing difficulty with Marconi MT9F transmitting valves. High frequency amplifiers required 'neutrodyning' to prevent the risks of self-oscillation generated by the existence of stray capacitances among the electrodes of the active component used in the amplifier. The letter pointed out the operating characteristics of the MT9F and stated that Marconi did not have any other valve capable of satisfying the needs of Marcuse's transmitter, but suggested that two valves working in push-pull would accept a higher input power.

135 An obituary is attached to this page spanning Marcuse's life from 1913 when he was issued with his first experimental licence to 1937 when he assisted with the formation of the Civilian Wireless Reserve of the RAF. Numerous 'firsts' are recorded that represent a history of his most important radio achievements.

136 The first page of a two-page letter is attached here; it is from The General Post Office, London, E.C.1. and is dated 9th August 1927. The letter sets out the conditions that Marcuse could proceed with his 'Empire Broadcasting' confirming that the licence would be for a six-month period commencing September 1st 1927 using 23 metres and 33 metres. The transmissions could not exceed a period of two hours on each occasion for not more than three days a

week on Mondays, Thursday, Saturdays and Sundays. Two other restrictions were:

(i) No current news should be included.
(ii) Not more than 50 gramophone records could be used during the whole period.

137 The second page of the Post office letter gives three additional restrictions:

(i)   No advertisements of the gramophone company or any other body were allowed.
(ii) His transmissions should stop if he caused interference to any government service.
(iii) The Postmaster General could withdraw the authority at any time.

The letter concludes by reminding Marcuse that future broadcasting of regular programmes to the Empire or Colonies would be restricted to the BBC only.

138 A certificate is attached to this page signed by Hiram Percy Maxim, the President of the American Radio Relay League (ARRL), dated 16th October 1924; the certificate appoints Marcuse, 'Manager of the British Isles' and instructs him to co-operate with all radio amateurs in his territory in such a manner as would further the work of the ARRL.

139 Two-page article entitled 'Wireless and Butter Beans':

(i) The content is very similar to pages (126) and (127). The attachment is taken from The London Star and is dated 26th August 1925 and records the 'achievement of two brothers'.
(ii) Second page of (139).

o~o

Appendix 8. Timeline of Marcuse's Life

1886 Born in Sutton, Surrey on June 4th

1892 Caterham Primary School

1899 Caterham Secondary School

1903 Technikum, Einbeck (Engineering School)

1904 Crystal Palace School of Engineering until 1907

1908 Apprenticeship & Sales engineer for Ruston & Proctor Ltd

1909 Travelled to Odessa on the Baltic then on to Mexico by ship to install water pumping engines

1910 Marcuse's interest in Radio began

1913 Obtained his First Amateur Licence, a Post Office 'Experimental Licence'

1913 Moved to Coombe Dingle Bristol and married first wife

1914 Joined Lincolnshire Regiment

1918 Lived in Bristol

1920 Moved to Caterham, licenced as 2NM

1923 Demonstrated Loudspeaker Broadcast at a local School

1923 Joined his father's seed business at 36 Mincing Lane, London

1923 2NM's licenced extended to operate on 200m and 90m

1924 Marcuse achieves first British radio contact with California

1924 Appointed Manager of The British Isles by ARRL

1925 Vice-president of the International Amateur Radio Union

1925 2NM was the first to contact South America with Hamilton-Rice expedition on the Amazon.

1927 Post Office extended his licence to transmit speech and music to the British Empire on 32 metres

1927 British Broadcasting Corporation deplored Marcuse's Empire broadcasting as a publicity stunt

1927 Marcuse transmitted a concert to Australia. The Post Office rejected his application to re-transmit the following week

1928 Marcuse continued the Empire Broadcasts until mid-year

1929 Elected President of the Radio Society of Great Britain.

1931 Marcuse married Irene Rose at the Savoy Chapel in London

1934 Formation of Reading & District ARC, Marcuse a founder

1936 David Marcuse was born in Reading.

1937 Marcuse advised on the formation of the RAF Civilian Wireless Reserve

1937 Transmitted also from his holiday home in Clayton Road Selsey West Sussex

1939 Marcuse appointed as a Voluntary Intercept (VI) Group Leader

-45 for Berkshire & was involved in special interpretation work & translation in Morse from Germany while afloat in the Solent

1942 Mincing Lane Seed Business destroyed by air raid

1944 Marcuse & Family move to Bosham, Sussex.

1946 Honorary Member of the RSGB

1947 Bosham Fire Brigade formed with volunteers by Marcuse with appliance loaned by Chichester D C

1949 Elected as County and District Councillor for Bosham and Chidham District

1950 Marcuse experiments with mobile communications in 1950's

1961 Silent Key

1927 Preceded by the sound of Big Ben for the first time .

o~o

Appendix 9. Acknowledgements & References

1. Amberley Museum for their constant support over many years and the extensive use of their archives.
2. Wiley Global permissions for permission to use photographs from the RGS Geographical Journal, Vol. 67, No. 6, June 1926.
3. David Marcuse for his support over 10 years in providing memories, family photographs and private archives about his late father.
4. Elaine Richards (G4LFM) for use of her photograph.
5. The Diary of Gerald Marcuse (1903) (David Fry, 2022).
6. World at their Fingertips by John Clarricoats (G6CL).
7. Lyn Dougherty of the Los Gatos Library, California.
8. Claire Seymour, Curator, Amberley Museum.
9. Julia Edge, Curator, Amberley Museum.
10. Milestones in Early Radio – http://www.radio-electronics.com
11. Early experiences in Amateur Radio – G. W. Tonkin (G5RQ)
12. John Buckley G8TFO for his scrutiny of the technical content

o~o

INDEX

259, 261, 263, 264, 265, 266, 267, 268, 272, 275, 284, 287

Belles of Sutton, 12

BENZIE, 238, 240

Benzio, 142

BERU, 29

Big Ben, 10, 43, 49, 52, 106, 148, 161, 163, 175, 178, 207, 216, 262, 289

Blackstones, 135

Bletchley Park, 65, 66, 282, 285

Boa Vista, 36, 40, 99, 101

Bombay, 54, 57, 159, 162, 164, 171, 174, 249, 263, 264, 265, 266, 267

Bosham, 3, 10, 11, 61, 63, 67, 74, 75, 77, 78, 79, 103, 220, 222, 224, 228, 229, 230, 275, 276, 278, 281, 282, 289

Bosham Parish Council, 67

Bournemann, 23

Brazil, 7, 29, 36, 39, 40, 165, 172, 239, 240

British Broadcasting Company, 9, 46, 218, 219, 235

British Broadcasting Corporation, 9, 46, 56, 219, 250, 288

British Museum, 220

British Wireless Relay League, 27

Bromsgrove School, 215

Brown, 55, 126, 159, 266, 270

Burgermeisterwall, 18

C. A. Tucker, 182

C. R. Slingsby, 161, 172, 176, 191, 193

C. Runeckles, 195

C. S. Potts, 177

C. S. Taylor, 172

C. Taylor, 177

C. W. Dreyer, 184

C. Zinnecker, 190

C.E. Trott, 142

Captain Mullard, 106, 129

Cat's Whisker, 219

Caterham, 2, 13, 14, 16, 23, 24, 27, 39, 51, 52, 54, 74, 84, 103, 104, 105, 106, 107, 109, 113, 115, 116, 125, 126, 155, 165, 172, 186, 214, 215, 218, 220, 222, 224, 229, 235, 239, 243, 247, 248, 249, 250, 253, 261, 265, 267, 269, 276, 278, 283, 287, 288

Caterham & District Urban District Council, 229

Certificate of 'Valued and Devoted Service, 70

Ceylon, 57, 105, 125, 158, 159, 164, 168, 183, 241, 249

Charles Edwin Wilson, 204

Charles J. Holton, 213

Charles W. Slatham, 180

Chas. H. Mills, 215

Chichester & District Amateur Radio Club, 78, 226, 231

Christian Science Monitor, 42, 57, 238, 241, 245, 248, 265

Civilian Wireless Reserve, 61, 70, 272, 286, 288

Claire Seymour, 289

Clandestine Operations, 64

Clandestine Service, 60

Clarence E. Roach, 181

Clarence Horton, 165

Frank Brittain, 170
Frank N. Bridge, 182
Fred Lawrence, 205
Fred Miles, 120
Frederick Wenman, 245, 267
Fremain Charles Hait, 203
G. A. Jones, 202
G. B. Jolliffe, 159
G. Brooker, 163, 167, 173
G. F. Morrow, 143
G. H. Jolliffe, 168
G. J. Parris, 224
G. W. Duke, 185
Gamage, 51, 103
Garry Hooker, 201
Geddes, 220, 221, 222
Generator, 47, 100, 106, 121, 122, 126, 130, 144, 159, 261
George A. Clark, 180
George E. Moorcroft, 198
George E. Morcroft, 186
George F. Brooks, 202
George H. Atkins, 215
George H. Freeman, 184
Gerald Morrice, 189
Gilbert L. Peters, 204
Gill, 41, 229
Golden Bean, 15
Gst. J. Horan, 178
H. B. Atkins, 162, 163
H. C. Woodcock, 181
H. Collins, 199
H. F. Weber, 206
H. J. Smith, 210
H. Russell Crane, 166
H. W. Steele, 217
H.A.M. Clark, 25, 232, 278

Halifax, 29, 57, 140, 236, 244, 247
Ham and Beans, 25
Hamadie, 93, 97
Hamfest Party, 118
Hamidie, 90, 91, 93, 94, 95, 96
Hamilton Rice, 7, 34, 36, 37, 38, 40, 98, 102, 221, 239, 240
Harold J. Christmas, 206
Harold Turner, 142
Harris, 43, 142, 148, 151, 154
Harry Benn, 207
Harry Clark, 102
Harry F. Hoerner, 181
Harry W. Phair, 205
Harvard, 33, 36, 98, 104, 258
Hastings & St. Leonards & District Radio Society, 224
Haverford, 33, 140, 141, 237
Heaviside Layer, 34, 42, 246, 265
Henderlick, 118
Henri R. Griner, 177
Henry Cousin, 173, 176
Henry Gibson, 158, 159, 216
Henry Roberts, 12
Herbert Knirbl, 176
Herbert Taylor, 203
Hernandez Avenue, 31
Heywood & Tyler, 136
Hildesheim, 16
Hinks, 37, 38, 39, 100, 240, 241
Hiram Shafer, 207
Holy Trinity, 75
Honours List, 84, 209
Hugh McCubbin, 53, 261
Hugh Ryan, 130
Hydroplane, 38

Ian Fraser, 53, 57, 118, 261, 263
Ian More, 181
IARU, 28, 45, 147, 150
Ina Procter, 102, 123
India, 49, 55, 57, 108, 125, 142,
    144, 145, 146, 163, 164, 167,
    169, 171, 172, 173, 174, 176,
    194, 247, 249, 250, 257, 263,
    264, 265, 267, 270, 271, 272
International Amateur Radio
    Association, 238
International Amateur Radio
    Union, 28, 45, 146, 276, 288
International Short Wave Radio
    News, 271
Irene, 21, 71, 72, 73, 74, 75,
    103, 123, 134, 220, 224, 228,
    230, 234, 276, 277, 278, 279,
    282, 283, 288
J B Sessions, 194
J. A. Pierson, 190
J. C. Standen, 163, 172
J. E. Bowman, 140
J. F, Hall, 143
J. H. King, 217, 218
J. Hart Davis, 185
J. Hubert, 182
J. Mahoney, 194
J. P. O'Neill, 212
J. S. Riddile, 198
J. Vergouw, 185
J. W. Brauner, 194, 197
J. W. Fraser, 165
Jaap de Heer, 194
Jack Partridge, 29, 32, 140, 273
James H Webb, 207
James H. Cole, 170
James Russell, 183

Japan, 29, 41, 52, 69, 169, 190
John Borthistle, 175
John Buckley G8TFO, 289
John C. Hardy, 184
John Clarricoats, 70, 72, 74, 75,
    221, 222, 224, 225, 226, 228,
    229, 273, 274, 276, 277, 278,
    279, 283, 289
John E. Lingo, 210
John Ginocchio, 201
John P. Martin, 205
John T. C. Vigurs, 174
Jonathan Byrne, 66
Jos Rawlings, 174
Jos. P. Walsh, 204
Joseph Adams, 171
Joseph B. Sessions, 199
Joseph F. James, 163
Joseph J. Fassett, 247
Julia Edge, 289
K. L. Radburn, 215
K. N. Rastomjee, 163
K. Stewart, 180
Keith Geddes, 73, 74, 221
Ken Secretan, 123
Ken Warner, 29
Kenneth Alford, 108, 231, 279
King's Shropshire, 57
Kirchner, 16, 17
L Rijnink, 214
L. Ford Smith, 211
L. H. Pruce, 183
L. Heading, 200
L. N. Miller, 189
L.W. Norwood, 143
Leon Deloy, 27, 28
Leonard Dasler, 214
Leonard Holdrup, 211

o~o

A set of research files upon which this biography is based is available to readers. This will include photographs taken from the original files in: Marcuse's Scrapbook, the Letters, Awards & Achievements & Images most of which do not appear in either the physical or electronic versions of the book. There will be a small charge for this which will include P&P and a USB Memory Stick.

Enquiries can be made by emailing:

m a r c u s e g 2 n m @ p r o t o n m a i l . c o m

(The spaces inserted above are to assist copying the address correctly.)

o~o

BV - #0081 - 270623 - C41 - 210/148/17 - PB - 9781915972125 - Gloss Lamination